INFORMATION-LOSSLESS AUTOMATA OF FINITE ORDER

A. A. Kurmit

INFORMATION-LOSSLESS AUTOMATA OF FINITE ORDER

Translated from Russian by D. Louvish

A HALSTED PRESS BOOK

JOHN WILEY & SONS
New York · Toronto

ISRAEL PROGRAM FOR SCIENTIFIC TRANSLATIONS
Jerusalem · London

Sole distributors for the Western Hemisphere

HALSTED PRESS, a division of
JOHN WILEY & SONS, INC., NEW YORK

Library of Congress Cataloging in Publication Data

Kurmit, Avgust Avgustovich.
Information-lossless automata of finite order.

Translation of *Avtomaty bez poteri informat͡sii konechnogo pori͡adka.*
1. Sequential machine theory. 2. Automata.
I. Title.
QA267.5.S4K8413 629.8'91 74-8183
ISBN 0-470-51099-4

Distributors for the U.K., Europe, Africa and the Middle East

JOHN WILEY & SONS, LTD., CHICHESTER

Distributors for Japan, Southeast Asia and India

TOPPAN COMPANY, LTD., TOKYO AND SINGAPORE

Distributed in the rest of the world by

KETER PUBLISHING HOUSE JERUSALEM LTD.
ISBN 0 7065 1380 0
IPST 22099

This book is a translation from Russian of
AVTOMATY BEZ POTERI INFORMATSII
KONECHNOGO PORYADKA
Izdatel'stvo "Zinatne"
Riga, 1972

Printed and bound by Keterpress Enterprises, Jerusalem
Printed in Israel

PREFACE

The purpose of this book is to present the results of an investigation of a special class of finite deterministic Mealy automata, known as information-lossless automata of finite order. Type I automata of this class may be used to encode messages, by virtue of the following property: any automaton of this type has an inverse automaton, which, given the output word (response) and the initial state, reproduces the input word (some suffix of the input word may not be reproduced, but the length of this suffix is constant for each inverse automaton).

As opposed to conventional coding, in which each letter of the message is assigned a fixed code word, when information-lossless automata of finite order are used the relation between the message letters and the assigned code words (the latter being represented by letters of the output alphabet) is more complex and depends on the previous letters of the message. Neither need the assignment be one-to-one. Using the same encoding automaton, one can change the assignment by varying the initial state. Correct decoding is then achieved by suitably varying the initial state of the inverse automaton.

Type II automata differ from Type I automata in that the input word is reproduced given the final state of the automaton.

In our study of Type II automata in this book, we also require that the preceding state be recoverable. The treatment may nontheless be generalized and this additional condition relaxed.

Despite the useful properties listed above, very little consideration has been given as yet to information-lossless automata of finite order. This book, containing for the most part results of original research, is an attempt to fill this gap.

In Chapter I we discuss mainly analysis of information-lossless automata of finite order, first and foremost in regard to recognition of such automata and construction of inverse automata, and also the interrelation between an automaton and its inverse. The so-called standard inverse constructed in this book is in a certain sense universal, so that the examination of inverse automata may be confined to standard automata. In connection with the universality of these inverse automata, we consider methods for selecting their initial state and simplifying them on the basis of properties of the original automaton.

In Chapter II we consider the construction of information-lossless automata of finite order with prescribed properties, pertaining above all to the delays of the original and inverse automata. To this end we propose a new technique, based on the use of graphs whose vertices are also graphs. The above-mentioned numerical indices are well reflected in the topological properties of the "vertex-graphs," or subtrees, as we shall call them.

In addition, the topology of the subtrees provides an idea of the complexity and the different possibilities of decoding the same groups of message letters.

Graphs and subtrees are considered on three levels of abstraction, depending on the labels attached to the arcs of the graphs and of the subtrees. At the highest level no labels are assigned, at the next level the letters of one alphabet serve as labels, and at the last level the labels are pairs of letters, one from each of two alphabets. Subtrees whose arcs are labeled by letter pairs indicate which words are assigned the same code. Subtrees whose arcs are labeled by letters essentially represent groups of words over some alphabet. When the labels of arcs in subtrees representing different sets of words are deleted, the resulting graphs may be isomorphic, implying that the complexity of decoding for these sets of words is the same. We therefore use the unlabeled subtrees to introduce the concept of the type of a state, recalling the well-known concept of the type of a boolean function.

One conclusion of Chapter II is that, given arbitrary state types, one can construct information-lossless automata of finite order containing subtrees with arbitrary labels which possess the prescribed topology (or complexity of decoding). Moreover, our technique makes it possible to consider the design of information-lossless automata of finite order whose inverses are self-adjusting automata, and to determine some important numerical indices and other properties of normal automata (complete strongly connected information-lossless automata of finite order whose inverses are also complete).

The concepts of identifiable vertices of subtrees and admissible graphs, introduced and extensively employed in the book, are based on quite simple and intuitive considerations. All subtrees of an admissible graph which are ends of arcs from some fixed subtree may be obtained by the following operations: 1) draw one or more arcs from each leaf (pendant vertex) of the initial subtree; 2) delete the root of the resulting graph and the arcs issuing from it; 3) form a new system of subtrees from the resulting system of graphs, in such a way that the subgraphs have no common leaves and the root and leaves of each subgraph of the new system are the root and leaves of a graph of the initial system. It is then natural not to distinguish between identical vertices of the original subtree and the new ones (this identification procedure need not be unique).

Whereas the discussion in Chapter I is based essentially only on the definition of information-lossless automata of finite order, the methods of Chapter II penetrate more deeply into their internal logical structure.

Chapter III is devoted in the main to establishing an upper bound $O(n)$ for the delay of a normal automaton; this bound is actually attained, unlike the previously known bound $O(n^2)$ (n is the number of states). The procedure involves solution of a highly complex combinatorial problem.

It would be interesting to adapt the proposed technique to determine the interrelation between the delay, the number of states and cardinalities of the input and output alphabets for arbitrary information-lossless automata of finite order.

In Chapter IV we generalize the treatment of the first three chapters, considering mainly automata which have generalized inverse automata. The motivation for the latter is the desire to generalize the decision problem for sets of words enumerated by a finite automaton.

It is well known that for any automaton there is another automaton which accepts precisely the output words of the former. By contrast, not every automaton has a generalized inverse, but there is an algorithm which decides in a finite number of operations whether a generalized inverse exists.

Another generalization of information-lossless automata of finite order is information-lossless automata of finite order relative to a prescribed set of words; intuitively, this represents the situation when the message to be encoded belongs to a prescribed set of words. The investigation is confined to messages which are output words of some other automaton, i. e., belong to some regular event.

The Authors

CONTENTS

INTRODUCTION

An abstract finite automaton is a quintuple consisting of a finite set $I=\{i_1,\ldots, i_k\}$ of inputs, a finite set $E=\{e_1,\ldots,e_m\}$ of outputs, a finite set $Q=\{q_1,\ldots,q_n\}$ of internal states, and two functions f and g, called the output function and next-state function, respectively, both defined on (some or all) pairs (q_j, i_l) $(1\leqslant j\leqslant n, 1\leqslant l\leqslant k)$.

We denote this quintuple by M.

The value of the next-state function $g(q_j, i_l)$ is an internal state, that of the output function $f(q_j, i_l)$ an output. If $g(q_j, i_l)=q_\nu$, we say that the automaton responds to input i_l by going from state q_j to state q_ν. If $f(q_j, i_l)=e_\mu$, we say that upon application of input i_l in state q_j the automaton produces output e_μ. We shall consistently employ the abbreviated terms "automaton" and "state" instead of "abstract finite automaton" and "internal state," respectively.

If f and g are defined on all pairs (q_j, i_l), we shall say that the automaton is complete. If there is at least one pair (q_j, i_l) for which either f or g (or both) is undefined, we speak of an incomplete automaton. Throughout this book we deal only with automata such that for any pair (q_j, i_l) the next-state and output functions are either both defined or both undefined.

The functions f and g are usually displayed in tabular form. Table 1 displays the next-state function and Table 2 the output function. In any specific case, the entries $g(q_j, i_l)$ in Table 1 will be replaced by the corresponding states $q_\nu=g(q_j, i_l)$ $(j=1,\ldots,n; l=1,\ldots,k)$; similarly the values of $f(q_j, i_l)$ in Table 2 are outputs $e_\mu=f(q_j, i_l)$. It is convenient to combine the two tables; Table 3 illustrates the next-state and output functions displayed in a single table, known as the transition table.

If f or g is undefined for some pair (q_j, i_l), the corresponding values of q_ν and e_μ in Tables 1—3 are replaced by dashes (Table 4).

TABLE 1.

	i_1	...	i_k
q_1	$g(q_1, i_1)$	...	$g(q_1, i_k)$
q_2	$g(q_2, i_1)$	...	$g(q_2, i_k)$
.	.	.	.
.	.	.	.
.	.	.	.
q_n	$g(q_n, i_1)$	...	$g(q_n, i_k)$

TABLE 2.

	i_1	...	i_k
q_1	$f(q_1, i_1)$	...	$f(q_1, i_k)$
q_2	$f(q_2, i_1)$	...	$f(q_2, i_k)$
.	.	.	.
.	.	.	.
.	.	.	.
q_n	$f(q_n, i_1)$	...	$f(q_n, i_k)$

The formation table of the automaton is a table with n rows and k columns, constructed as follows: at the intersection of the l-th row and the j-th column, the table lists all pairs (q_ν, e_μ) such that $g(q_\nu, i_j)=q_l$ and $f(q_\nu, i_j)=e_\mu$.

TABLE 3.

	i_1	. . .	i_k
q_1	$g(q_1, i_1), f(q_1, i_1)$	. . .	$g(q_1, i_k), f(q_1, i_k)$
q_2	$g(q_2, i_1), f(q_2, i_1)$	. . .	$g(q_2, i_k), f(q_2, i_k)$
.	.	.	.
.	.	.	.
q_n	$g(q_n, i_1), f(q_n, i_1)$	. . .	$g(q_n, i_k), f(q_n, i_k)$

An automaton may also be defined by a labeled directed graph, whose vertices correspond to the states. The arcs are introduced by examining all possible pairs (q_j, i_l). Let $g(q_j, i_l) = q_\nu$ and $f(q_j, i_l) = e_\mu$. An arc is then drawn from the vertex q_j to the vertex q_ν and labeled (i_l, e_μ). If $g(q_j, i_l)$ and $f(q_j, i_l)$ are undefined, no arc is drawn for the pair (q_j, i_l).

TABLE 4.

	i_1	i_2	i_3
q_1	q_1, e_2	—	q_3, e_1
q_2	—	q_1, e_3	q_3, e_2
q_3	q_2, e_1	q_3, e_2	—

This graph is known as the *state diagram* (or simply diagram) of the automaton.

Thanks to the assumption adopted above, the diagram may be constructed whether the automaton is complete or not. For example, the diagram of the automaton defined by Table 4 is shown in Figure 1.

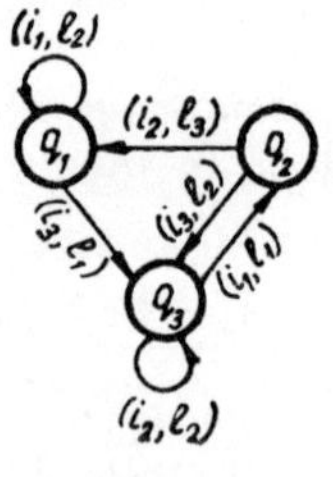

FIGURE 1.

An automaton is frequently defined in terms of its diagram. In that case the functions f and g are uniquely determined by the diagram.*

* Our definition of automaton corresponds to what is known in the literature as a *Mealy automaton*. Another important class of automata, known as *Moore automata*, will not be considered in this book.

The domain of definition of the functions f and g may be extended to include pairs of the type $(q_j, i_{l_1}i_{l_2}\ldots i_{l_r})$, by setting

$$g(q_j, i_{l_1}i_{l_2}\ldots i_{l_r}) = g(g(\ldots(g(q_j, i_{l_1}), i_{l_2}), \ldots), i_{l_r}),$$
$$f(q_j, i_{l_1}i_{l_2}\ldots i_{l_r}) = e_{k_1}e_{k_2}\ldots e_{k_r},$$

where

$$e_{k_1} = f(q_j, i_{l_1}), \; e_{k_\lambda} = f(g(q_j, i_{l_1}i_{l_2}\ldots i_{l_{\lambda-1}}), i_{l_\lambda}) \quad (\lambda = 2, \ldots, r), \tag{1}$$

on the assumption that all pairs (q_k, i_l) for which the functions f and g must be evaluated are in the domains of definition of these functions. Otherwise, the values of $g(q_j, i_{l_1}i_{l_2}\ldots i_{l_r})$ and $f(q_j, i_{l_1}i_{l_2}\ldots i_{l_r})$ (or one of them) are undefined. By virtue of the assumption adopted above, these values are either both defined or both undefined.

In what follows a sequence of inputs will be called an *input word*, a sequence of outputs an *output word*. The empty word has no letters and is denoted by Λ; $g(q_j, \Lambda) = q_j$ and $f(q_j, \Lambda) = \Lambda$.

An automaton is said to be *strongly connected* if, for any ordered pair of states (q_k, q_l), there exists a sequence of inputs $i_{j_1}, \ldots, i_{j_m}$ such that $g(q_k, i_{j_1}i_{j_2}\ldots i_{j_m}) = q_l$.

Much of the investigation of automata is concerned with the mapping of input words into output words defined by the formula

$$f(q_l, i_{j_1}i_{j_2}\ldots i_{j_m}) = e_{k_1}e_{k_2}\ldots e_{k_m}. \tag{2}$$

It is clear that, depending on the first argument of the function (the state), the automaton may map the same input word into different output words. If the mapping (2) is being considered for a fixed state $q_l = q_{l_0}$, the automaton is said to be *initialized*. If one is interested in these mappings for all states $q_l \in Q$, the automaton is *noninitialized*.

It is also possible to consider the mapping of input words into output words for $q_l \in \{q_{i_1}, q_{i_2}, \ldots, q_{i_\lambda}\}$, where $\{q_{i_1}, q_{i_2}, \ldots, q_{i_\lambda}\}$ is a proper subset of the set of all states, containing more than one state. In such cases we shall say that the automaton is partially initialized.

Whether the automaton is initialized, partially initialized or noninitialized, any state of the automaton for which the mapping (2) is being examined will be called an *initial state*.

Let M_1 and M_2 be automata with the same input and output sets, state sets $q_{11}, \ldots, q_{1n_1}$ and $q_{21}, \ldots, q_{2n_2}$, respectively, next-state functions g_1, g_2 and output functions f_1, f_2. We shall say that the automaton M_2 is an *equivalent extension* of M_1 if, for any initial state q_{1l_0} of M_1, there is a state q_{2j_0} such that for all input words $i_{j_1}i_{j_2}\ldots i_{j_m}$ for which $f_1(q_{1l_0}, i_{j_1}i_{j_2}\ldots i_{j_m})$ is defined we have

$$f_2(q_{2j_0}, i_{j_1}i_{j_2}\ldots i_{j_m}) = f_1(q_{1l_0}, i_{j_1}i_{j_2}\ldots i_{j_m}).$$

An important problem of automata theory is to determine whether a given automaton has an equivalent extension with fewer states, and if so to construct it. This procedure is known as *simplification* of the original automaton. The procedure generally involves the concepts of compatible states and systems of invariant classes.

States q_j and q_k of an automaton M are said to be compatible if, for any input word $i_{l_1}i_{l_2}\ldots i_{l_m}$ for which both $f(q_j, i_{l_1}i_{l_2}\ldots i_{l_m})$ and $f(q_k, i_{l_1}i_{l_2}\ldots i_{l_m})$ are defined,

$$f(q_j, i_{l_1}i_{l_2}\ldots i_{l_m}) = f(q_k, i_{l_1}i_{l_2}\ldots i_{l_m}).$$

If the automaton is complete the term "equivalent" is used instead of "compatible."

A system of invariant classes is a system of sets of states $K_1, \ldots, K_m$ satisfying the following conditions: 1) any state of the automaton is in at least one of the sets $K_1, \ldots, K_m$; 2) any two states in the same class $K_\varkappa$ are compatible; 3) for any input i_j and any set $K_\varkappa$, there exists a set K_λ such that for any $q_m \in K_\varkappa$ either $g(q_m, i_j) \in K_\lambda$ or $g(q_m, i_j)$ is undefined.

To simplify an automaton M using a system of invariant classes $K_1, \ldots, K_m$, one defines a new automaton M_1 whose input and output sets coincide with those of M, with states $\{K_1, \ldots, K_m\}$. The functions f_1 and g_1 are defined as follows: $f_1(K_\varkappa, i_j) = f(q_l, i_j)$, where $q_l \in K_\varkappa$ is a state of M such that $f(q_l, i_j)$ is defined. If there is no such state, $f_1(K_\varkappa, i_j)$ is undefined. $g_1(K_\varkappa, i_j) = K_\lambda$, where K_λ is the set satisfying the third condition in the definition of a system of invariant classes.

A finite graph G is a finite set $V = \{v_1, \ldots, v_m\}$ whose elements are called vertices, and a list of ordered pairs (v_j, v_k) known as arcs. If the list contains an arc (v_i, v_k), we shall say that the vertices v_i and v_k are adjacent. An arc (v_j, v_j) is called a loop. Throughout this book we shall encounter only finite graphs, and so we shall omit the adjective "finite" for the sake of brevity. No restrictions are imposed on the nature of the vertices of a graph.*

Graphs are conveniently represented as plane figures. The vertices are drawn as dots or small circles, and for every arc (v_j, v_k) the vertices v_j and v_k are joined by an arbitrary curve, which is then assigned the direction from v_j to v_k. This directed curve is also called an arc. We shall say that there is an arc from v_j to v_k if the graph contains an arc (v_j, v_k).

If the list of arcs contains at most one pair (v_j, v_k) for any fixed v_j and v_k, we shall say that the graph is simple. If the list may contain several pairs (v_j, v_k) for the same v_j and v_k, the graph is known as a multigraph. In the planar representation of a simple graph there may be only one curve between any two vertices v_j and v_k which is assigned the direction from v_j to v_k. In a multigraph, on the other hand, there is at least one pair of vertices v_j and v_k joined by more than one curve pointing from v_j to v_k. Note that in this case any two arcs (v_j, v_k) in the list are treated as distinct.

We shall usually say "graph" instead of "simple graph" or "multigraph," provided it is clear from the context (or immaterial) which type of graph is meant.

* We shall use only directed graphs. We therefore omit the adjective "directed" throughout, and all concepts will be defined in such a way that there is no need to refer to undirected graphs.

Two graphs G' and G'' are said to be isomorphic if there is a one-to-one mapping of the vertices of G' onto those of G'' such that for any ordered pair v'_i, v'_j of vertices of G', mapped respectively onto vertices v''_k, v''_l of G'', there are as many arcs (v'_i, v'_j) as there are arcs (v''_k, v''_l).

A graph is labeled if an element from some set, called a label, is attached to each arc. In the planar representation of a graph the label is usually written alongside the arc.

Example. Let G be a graph with set of vertices $V=\{\Box, 0, A, B\}$ and list of arcs $\{(\Box, 0), (\Box, A), (\Box, A), (\Box, A), (0, \Box), (0, 0)\}$. The graph G is illustrated in Figure 2, a.

Now let $X=\{(x, -), (0, c), d\}$. We can now form a labeled graph G' from G by attaching to each arc an element of X as follows:

$$\{((\Box, 0), d), ((\Box, A), (x, -)), ((\Box, A), (x, -)), ((\Box, A), (0, c)), ((0, \Box), d), ((0, 0), d)\}.$$

The labeled graph G' is illustrated in Figure 2, b.

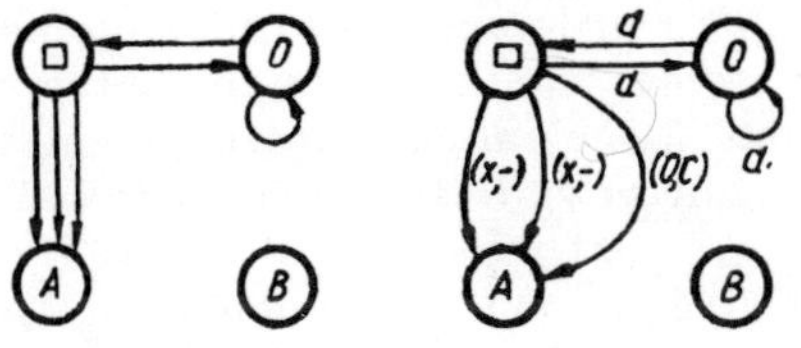

a b

FIGURE 2.

The following definitions will be more easily understood if the planar representation of the graph is kept in mind.

A path in a graph G is a sequence of arcs $(v_{k_0}, v_{k_1}), (v_{k_1}, v_{k_2}), \ldots, (v_{k_{n-1}}, v_{k_n})$. If there is such a path in G, we shall say that there is a path in G from v_{k_0} to v_{k_n}. The path is said to be proper if all the vertices v_{k_j} $(j=0, 1, \ldots, n)$ are distinct. If $v_j = v_k$ a path from v_j to v_k will be called a cycle. A cycle is said to be proper if all its arcs are distinct. The length of a path $(v_{i_1}, v_{i_2}), (v_{i_2}, v_{i_3}), \ldots, (v_{i_{n-1}}, v_{i_n})$ is the number $n-1$.

A graph G' is a subgraph of a graph G if the vertex set V' of G' is a subset of the vertex set of G, and for any arc of G joining vertices of V' there is an arc joining the same vertices in G'.

A graph G' is called a partial graph of G if it may be obtained from G by deleting certain arcs.

A graph G is said to be strongly connected if any two of its vertices v_i, v_j may be joined by a path from v_i to v_j.

Let $\overline{G}$ be a graph formed from G by adjoining new arcs, in such a way that for each arc (v_i, v_j) of G the graph $\overline{G}$ contains an arc (v_j, v_i). We shall say that G is connected if $\overline{G}$ is strongly connected.

A graph G is called a tree if it is connected and the number of arcs is one less than the number of vertices.

Any tree has at least one vertex which is not the end of any arc; a vertex of this type is called a root, and a tree having only one root is said to be rooted. A vertex from which no arcs emanate will be called a leaf [see /17/; Berge /13/ calls a leaf a pendant vertex].

Paths in a labeled graph determine sequences of labels in a natural manner: if the path is $(v_{j_0}, v_{j_1}), (v_{j_1}, v_{j_2}), \ldots, (v_{j_{n-1}}, v_{j_n})$ and each arc in the path has a label x_{k_l} $(l=0, 1, \ldots, n-1)$ from some set X, we shall say that the path defines the sequence $x_{k_0}x_{k_1}\ldots x_{k_{n-1}}$.

Any set of such sequences is called an event. It is clear that the set of paths of a labeled graph defines an event. An event is said to be regular if there exists a labeled graph with two subsets V_1 and V_2 of the vertex set such that the event in question is defined precisely by all paths in the graph going from a vertex in V_1 to a vertex in V_2. A graph whose paths define a regular event in this way is known as a source.*

Our interest in regular events in this book is motivated by the fact that for any automaton the set of all output words produced in response to input words, when the automaton is in states from some given subset of the whole state set, is a regular event (here one considers only pairs $(q_l, i_{j_1}i_{j_2}\ldots i_{j_\lambda})$ for which $f(q_l, i_{j_1}i_{j_2}\ldots i_{j_\lambda})$ is defined).

If we restrict the input words applied to the automaton in the last paragraph to belong to some regular event, the automaton will again produce a regular event. (One can also introduce an additional restriction, requiring that for each initial state the input word belong to a specific regular event.**)

For the subsequent discussion, it is important to fix certain notational conventions once and for all. Throughout this book we shall consider two classes of automata. The automata of one class will be denoted by A, those of the other by B. We shall consider two sets, $\mathfrak{A}=\{a_1,\ldots,a_k\}$ and $\mathfrak{B}=\{b_1,\ldots,b_n\}$. The set $\mathfrak{A}$ is the input set for automata of the first class and $\mathfrak{B}$ is their output set; and conversely for automata of the second class. The sets $\mathfrak{A}$ and $\mathfrak{B}$ will be called alphabets.

The state set of an automaton of the first class will be denoted by $\mathfrak{S}$, and the states themselves by s. The state set of an automaton of the second class will be denoted by $\mathfrak{T}$, and its states by t (other notation may also be employed). The next-state functions will be denoted by δ and ε, respectively, and the output functions by λ and μ. We shall of course distinguish between automata of the same class by using indices (both superscripts and subscripts). For example, if we are discussing automata A_1 and A'_2, their state sets will be denoted by $\mathfrak{S}_1=\{s_{11}, s_{12},\ldots,s_{1n}\}$ and $\mathfrak{S}'_2=\{s'_{21}, s'_{22},\ldots,s'_{2m}\}$, respectively, and their next-state and output functions by $\delta_1, \delta'_2, \lambda_1, \lambda'_2$.

* [There is apparently no direct equivalent to this term in the Western literature. The closest concept is the "sequence generator" of A.W. Burks and J.B. Wright (Information and Control 5 (1963), 204–212).]

** The above definition of regular event differs somewhat, both in form and in content, from the generally accepted definition, which uses the concept of regular expressions. The essential difference is that according to our definition no regular event contains the empty sequence. This restriction is immaterial because in the sequel regular events containing the empty sequence are of no interest. For sets of sequences not containing empty sequences, the two definitions are equivalent. Our definition may nevertheless be completed in such a way as to make it equivalent to the definition of regular events using regular expressions. To this end, it is sufficient to stipulate that the empty sequence is an element of any regular event defined by a source, provided the sets V_1 and V_2 have at least one vertex in common.

Sequences of the type $a_{j_1}a_{j_2}\ldots a_{j_n}$ will be called *words over the alphabet* $\mathfrak{A}$, and sequences $b_{k_1}b_{k_2}\ldots b_{k_m}$ *words over the alphabet* $\mathfrak{B}$. Words over $\mathfrak{A}$ will be denoted by α, words over $\mathfrak{B}$ by β. Again, different words α and β will be differentiated by the use of indices. Note, however, that two words with different indices need not be graphically distinct when written out in terms of their letters. Notation of type $\alpha_1\alpha_2$ and the like will stand for concatentation of the corresponding words: if $\alpha_1=a_{j_1}a_{j_2}\ldots a_{j_n}$ and $\alpha_2=a_{k_1}a_{k_2}\ldots a_{k_m}$, then $\alpha_1\alpha_2=a_{j_1}a_{j_2}\ldots a_{j_n}a_{k_1}a_{k_2}\ldots a_{k_m}$.

Apart from words consisting of at least one letter, the symbols α and β (with or without indices) may also stand for the empty word. If $\alpha_1=\Lambda$, then $\alpha_1\alpha_2=\alpha_2\alpha_1=\alpha_2$ for any α_2. The symbol $|\alpha|$ will denote the number of letters in the word α (its *length*), i. e., if $\alpha=a_{j_1}a_{j_2}\ldots a_{j_n}$, then $|\alpha|=n$.

The symbol $^{-1}$ indicates inversion of the order of letters in a word: if $\alpha=a_{i_1}a_{i_2}\ldots a_{i_M}$, then $\alpha^{-1}=a_{i_M}a_{i_{M-1}}\ldots a_{i_1}$.

By a *set* we shall always mean a collection of arbitrary elements. Together with sets consisting of at least one element, we shall also need the *empty set*, containing no elements at all. The usual notation for the empty set is $\varnothing$. The number of elements in a set $\mathfrak{N}$ (its *cardinality*) will be denoted by $|\mathfrak{N}|$.

Let $\mathfrak{N}$ and $\mathfrak{M}$ be sets. Then $x\in\mathfrak{N}$ means that x is an element of $\mathfrak{N}$, and $x\overline{\in}\mathfrak{N}$ that $\mathfrak{N}$ does not contain the element x. $\mathfrak{N}\cup\mathfrak{M}$ denotes the set consisting of all elements that belong to at least one of the sets $\mathfrak{N}$ or $\mathfrak{M}$ (their *union*). $\mathfrak{N}\cap\mathfrak{M}$ denotes the set of all common elements of $\mathfrak{N}$ and $\mathfrak{M}$ (their *intersection*). $\mathfrak{N}\setminus\mathfrak{M}$ denotes the set of all elements of $\mathfrak{N}$ which are not elements of $\mathfrak{M}$. The notation $\mathfrak{N}\subset\mathfrak{M}$ means that each element of $\mathfrak{N}$ is also an element of $\mathfrak{M}$, and $\mathfrak{N}\neq\mathfrak{M}$ ($\mathfrak{M}$ is then said to be a (proper) *subset* of $\mathfrak{N}$). The notation $\mathfrak{N}\subseteq\mathfrak{M}$ means that either $\mathfrak{N}\subset\mathfrak{M}$ or $\mathfrak{N}=\mathfrak{M}$.

A collection of subsets $\{\mathfrak{N}_1, \ldots, \mathfrak{N}_n\}$ of a set $\mathfrak{N}$ such that $\mathfrak{N}_i\cap\mathfrak{N}_j=\varnothing$ for $i\neq j$ and $\mathfrak{N}_1\cup\ldots\cup\mathfrak{N}_n=\mathfrak{N}$ will be called a *partition* of $\mathfrak{N}$ and the subsets $\mathfrak{N}_i$ will be called the *classes* of the partition. Let $\mathfrak{M}_1$ and $\mathfrak{M}_2$ be two partitions of a set $\mathfrak{N}$. Then $\mathfrak{M}_1\times\mathfrak{M}_2$ will denote the partition $\mathfrak{M}_3$ of $\mathfrak{N}$ with the largest classes satisfying the condition: each class of $\mathfrak{M}_3$ has elements in common with exactly one class of each of $\mathfrak{M}_1$ and $\mathfrak{M}_2$.

Square brackets will be used in this book only to denote the integral part of a number: $[a]=n$, where n is the integer such that $a-1<n\leqslant a$.

Chapter I

INFORMATION-LOSSLESS AUTOMATA OF FINITE ORDER AND THEIR BASIC PROPERTIES

§ 1. DEFINITION OF INFORMATION-LOSSLESS AUTOMATA OF FINITE ORDER AND THEIR MOST IMPORTANT PROPERTY

The concept of an information-lossless automaton of finite order arises in connection with the question as to when one can recover, albeit incompletely, the input word in response to which an automaton in a given state will produce a prescribed output word.

An alternative formulation of the problem is to require that one be able to recover (at least in part) the input word, from knowledge of the output word and the state of the automaton immediately after producing the prescribed output.

Both questions were first considered by Huffman /1, 2/. The latter, however, concentrates his attention on complete recovery of the input word. If complete recovery of the input requires knowledge of the initial state, Huffman calls the automaton an information-lossless automaton of class I. If knowledge of the next state is required, he speaks of an information-lossless automaton of class II.

Huffman also considered a generalization of his information-lossless automata of class I, allowing the input word to be recovered only after a certain delay; in other words, to recover an input word containing N letters one needs an output word containing more than N letters. These he calls information-lossless automata of finite order.

Huffman gives no systematic consideration to the question of deciding whether a given automaton belongs to one of these classes. A more systematic study has been undertaken by Even /3, 4/, although his work involves a number of inaccuracies and there are some important questions which are not discussed at all.

The concepts to be defined here generalize those of Huffman.

Definition 1. An automaton A is called a type I information-lossless automaton of finite order N (IL-I-N) if

$$\lambda(s_i, a_k\alpha_1) \neq \lambda(s_i, a_l\alpha_2) \quad (1)$$

for any triple $(s_i, a_k\alpha_1, a_l\alpha_2)$, where s_i is an arbitrary state of A, $a_k \neq a_l$ and $|\alpha_1| = |\alpha_2| = N$.

An automaton A is called a type I information-lossless automaton of strict order N (ILS-I-N) if A is IL-I-N but not IL-I-$N-1$.

Definition 2. An automaton A is called a type II information-lossless automaton of finite order N (IL-II-N) if

$$\lambda(s_i, \alpha_1 a_k) \neq \lambda(s_j, \alpha_2 a_l) \tag{2}$$

for any state s_n and any states s_i, s_j and words $\alpha_1 a_k$ and $\alpha_2 a_l$ such that $|\alpha_1| = |\alpha_2| = N$ and $\delta(s_i, \alpha_1 a_k) = \delta(s_j, \alpha_2 a_l) = s_n$, provided that either

$$\delta(s_i, \alpha_1) \neq \delta(s_j, \alpha_2) \tag{3}$$

or

$$a_k \neq a_l. \tag{4}$$

An automaton A is a type II information-lossless automaton of strict order N (ILS-II-N) if it is IL-II-N but not IL-II-$N-1$.

When considering IL-II-N automata, we shall confine ourselves to automata with the property that for every state s_i there exist a state s_j and a letter a_l such that $\delta(s_j, a_l) = s_i$.

We shall abbreviate the statement that A is an IL-I-N automaton by A(I, N), while the statement that A is an ILS-I-N will be symbolized by A(SI, N); similar conventions will hold for automata of type II. [The same symbol will sometimes be used to designate the automaton itself and not only the statement that it has the desired property.]

The motivation for Definition 1 is readily understood: if A(I, N), then knowledge of the present state of A and an output word of length $N+1$ produced by A in this state is sufficient to recover the first letter of the corresponding input word. If A(SI, N), the automaton A has a state and an output word of length $N+1$ produced in this state such that these data alone are insufficient to recover more than the first letter of the input word.

Similarly, it follows from Definition 2 that if A(II, N), then knowledge of an output word of length $N+1$ and the state of the automaton immediately after emission of the word is sufficient to recover the last letter of the corresponding input word and to determine the state the automaton is in when it produces the last output letter.

If A(SII, N), there exist a state of A and an output word of length $N+1$ such that knowledge of this output word and of the state of the automaton immediately after its emission is insufficient either to recover more than the last letter of the corresponding input word, or to establish the state of the automaton preceding the state in which it produces the last output letter.

We shall now prove this rigorously, and also establish a stronger property of IL-I-N and IL-II-N automata.

Theorem 1_{I}.* *If $A(I, N)$, and the automaton responds to application of an unknown input word α_x in a known state s_i by producing an output word*

* From now on we shall frequently be dealing with theorems, lemmas, etc. which have two versions — for IL-I-N and IL-II-N automata. Propositions referring only to IL-I-N automata will be indexed "I" and those referring to IL-II-N automata "II." No index will be provided if the proposition does not refer to a specific type of automaton.

β, then one can recover in finitely many steps a prefix of α_x of length at least $|\alpha_x|-N$.

Proof. Construct sets B_{k_i} as follows. The set B_{k_i} will consist of all words β satisfying the condition: there exists a word $a_k\alpha$, $|\alpha|=N$, such that $\lambda(s_i, a_k\alpha)=\beta$. By Definition 1, $B_{k_i}\cap B_{l_i}=\varnothing$ for all i if $k\neq l$. The sets B_{k_i} are finite, and therefore, for any word β of length $N+1$, $\lambda(s_i, \alpha)=\beta$, finitely many steps suffice to establish the unique class $B_{k_{i_0}}$ that contains β. In other words, we can determine the first letter of α_x.

Thus the theorem is true for all input words α_x of length $N+1$.

Now suppose the theorem true for all input words of length $N+L$. Consider an arbitrary state s_i and a word β_0 of length $N+L+1$, such that for some word $\alpha_x, \lambda(s_i, \alpha_x)=\beta_0$. We may write $\alpha_x=\alpha_1\alpha_2$, $\beta_0=\beta_1\beta_2\beta_3$, where $|\alpha_1|=|\beta_1|=L$, $|\beta_2|=N$. By the induction hypothesis, the word $\beta_1\beta_2$ produced by the automaton in state s_i suffices to recover the word α_1 in finitely many steps. But this means that in finitely many steps we can find the state entered by A from s_i after producing the first L letters of α_x — this is simply the state $\delta(s_i, \alpha_1)$. We also know that in state $\delta(s_i, \alpha_1)$ the automaton produces the word $\beta_2\beta_3$ of length $N+1$. It follows from what we have proved that these data alone enable us in finitely many steps to recover the first letter of α_2.

Thus the assumption that the theorem is true for input words of length $N+L$ implies its truth for input words of length $N+L+1$, and so by induction it is true for all input words of length exceeding N.

Theorem 1_{II}. If $A(II, N)$ and the automaton responds to application of some input word α_x by producing a known output word β and entering a known state α_x, then one can recover in finitely many steps a suffix of α_x of length at least $|\alpha_x|-N$.

Proof. Define sets B_{kji} as follows. The set B_{kji} will consist of all words β satisfying the condition: there exist a word αa_k, $|\alpha|=N$, and states s_l, s_j such that $\delta(s_l, \alpha a_k)=s_i$, $\delta(s_l, \alpha)=s_j$, $\lambda(s_l, \alpha a_k)=\beta$. By Definition 2, we have $B_{kji}\cap B_{lri}=\varnothing$ for all i if either $k\neq l$ or $j\neq r$.

Let $|\beta|=N+1$. If $\delta(s_l, \alpha_x)=s_{i_0}$ and $\lambda(s_l, \alpha_x)=\beta$, then, examining the sets B_{kji_0}, one can determine in finitely many steps the unique set $B_{k_0j_0i_0}$ that contains β. But this means that in finitely many steps we can find the last letter a_{k_0} of α_x. Moreover, again in finitely many steps, we can determine the state s_{j_0} the automaton is in when it produces the last output word.

Suppose the theorem true for all output words β of length $N+L$ and that we can determine in finitely many steps the state s_{r_0} the automaton is in when it produces the last L output letters.

Consider an arbitrary state s_i and a word β_0 of length $N+L+1$ such that for some state s_l we have $\delta(s_l, \alpha_x)=s_i$ and $\lambda(s_l, \alpha_x)=\beta_0$. We may write $\alpha_x=\alpha_2\alpha_1$ and $\beta_0=\beta_3\beta_2\beta_1$, where $|\alpha_1|=|\beta_1|=L$, $|\beta_2|=N$. By the induction hypothesis, if we know the output word $\beta_2\beta_1$ of length $N+L$ and the state s_{i_0} of the automaton immediately after producing this word, we can determine in finitely many steps the suffix of α_x of length L, i. e., the word α_1; we can also establish the state s_{r_0} in which A produces the word β_1. But then we have at our disposal the word $\beta_3\beta_2$ of length $N+1$ and the state s_{r_0} of the automaton immediately after producing this word. In view of what we have proved, we can recover in finitely many steps the last letter of the word α_2 and also establish the state of the automaton when it produces the last letter of β_2. Again using the induction hypothesis, we see that knowledge of an output word of length $N+L+1$ and of the state of the automaton directly after producing the word is sufficient to recover in finitely many steps a suffix of the corresponding input word, of length at least $L+1$, and also to determine the state the automaton is in when it produces the last $L+1$ output letters.

The theorem now follows by induction.

§2. DECISION PROBLEMS FOR INFORMATION-LOSSLESS AUTOMATA OF FINITE ORDER

In connection with Definitions 1 and 2, we have the following problems.

1) Is it possible to decide in finitely many steps, for any given automaton, whether it is IL-I-N or IL-II-N for some natural number N?

2) If it is known that an automaton is IL-I-N or IL-II-N for some natural N, is it possible to determine in finitely many steps a natural number N_1 for which the automaton is ILS-I-N_1 or ILS-II-N_1?

For type I automata both problems may be solved by a method due to Even /3, 4/, which carries over readily to type II automata.

We first consider IL-I-N automata. Even's method is to construct a certain graph and check it for the existence of cycles. The same graph enables one to determine N_1.

Definition 3. An unordered* pair of states (s_i, s_j) (s_i and s_j need not be distinct) is said to be I-indistinguishable if at least one of the following conditions is satisfied:

(1) there exist a state s_k and letters a_l, a_m ($a_l \neq a_m$) such that $\lambda(s_k, a_l) = \lambda(s_k, a_m)$ and $\delta(s_k, a_l) = s_i$, $\delta(s_k, a_m) = s_j$;

(2) there exist an I-indistinguishable pair of states (s_k, s_l) ($s_k \neq s_l$) and letters a_m, a_n (not necessarily distinct) such that $\lambda(s_k, a_m) = \lambda(s_l, a_n)$ and $\delta(s_k, a_m) = s_i$, $\delta(s_l, a_n) = s_j$.

All I-indistinguishable pairs may be determined by the following procedure.

Algorithm 1_{I}.

Step 1. Find all pairs of states satisfying condition 1 of Definition 3.

Step $n+1$. Assuming that Step n has produced all pairs of I-indistinguishable states not determined at previous steps, take each of these pairs as the pair (s_k, s_l) of condition 2 in Definition 3 and find the new pairs (s_i, s_j).

Since there are only finitely many unordered pairs of states for any given automaton, there exists an integer n_1 such that Step n_1 produces no new I-indistinguishable pairs. In particular, if the number of states of the automaton is N, then $n_1 \leqslant N(N-1)/2+1$, since the number of unordered pairs of distinct states is $N(N-1)/2$ and at each step there must be at least one new pair unless the process breaks off.

Given an automaton A, we construct a special graph which will henceforth be denoted by $G_{\text{I}}(A)$. The vertices of $G_{\text{I}}(A)$ are the pairs of I-indistinguishable states of A. For any two vertices (s_k, s_l) and (s_i, s_j) of $G_{\text{I}}(A)$, there is an

* I.e., no distinction is made between the pairs (s_i, s_j) and (s_j, s_i).

arc from (s_k, s_l) to (s_i, s_j) if and only if these two pairs satisfy condition 2 of Definition 3. The graph $G_{\mathrm{I}}(A)$ solves the problems stated at the beginning of the section; this is shown by the following theorems and lemmas.

Theorem 2_{I}. *An automaton A is IL-I-N if and only if the graph $G_{\mathrm{I}}(A)$ contains no vertices of the form (s_i, s_i) and no cycles. An automaton $A(I, N)$ is ILS-I-N_1, where N_1 is the maximum length of a path in $G_{\mathrm{I}}(A)$.*

Proof. Suppose there are words $a_k\alpha$, $a_l\alpha_1$ $(a_k \neq a_l)$ and a state s_i such that $\lambda(s_i, a_k\alpha) = \lambda(s_i, a_l\alpha_1)$. Then $\lambda(s_i, a_k) = \lambda(s_i, a_l)$ and the pair of states $(\delta(s_i, a_k), \delta(s_i, a_l))$ is I-indistinguishable by condition 1 of Definition 3. Let α_i and α'_i denote the prefixes of the words $a_k\alpha$ and $a_l\alpha_1$ of length i. Let $(\delta(s_i, \alpha_j), \delta(s_i, \alpha'_j))$ $(j < |a_k\alpha|)$ be a pair of I-indistinguishable states, $\delta(s_i, \alpha_j) \neq \delta(s_i, \alpha'_j)$ and $\lambda(s_i, \alpha_j) = \lambda(s_i, \alpha'_j)$. Then $\lambda(s_i, \alpha_{j+1}) = \lambda(s_i, \alpha'_{j+1})$, or $\lambda(\delta(s_i, \alpha_j), a_{l_j}) = \lambda(\delta(s_i, \alpha'_j), a_{k_j})$ where $\alpha_{j+1} = \alpha_j a_{l_j}$ and $\alpha'_{j+1} = \alpha'_j a_{k_j}$, and the pair of states $(\delta(\delta(s_i, \alpha_j), a_{l_j}), \delta(\delta(s_i, \alpha'_j), a_{k_j}))$ is I-indistinguishable by condition 2 of Definition 3. We may write this pair as $(\delta(s_i, \alpha_{j+1}), \delta(s_i, \alpha'_{j+1}))$. Consequently, the graph $G_{\mathrm{I}}(A)$ contains vertices $(\delta(s_i, \alpha_j), \delta(s_i, \alpha'_j))$ for all $j = 1, \ldots, J \leqslant |a_k\alpha|$ such that $\delta(s_i, \alpha_{J-1}) \neq \delta(s_i, \alpha'_{J-1})$ and there is an arc from the vertex $(\delta(s_i, \alpha_{j-1}), \delta(s_i, \alpha'_{j-1}))$ to the vertex $(\delta(s_i, \alpha_j), \delta(s_i, \alpha'_j))$. Thus, for any pair of words $a_k\alpha$ and $a_l\alpha_1$ as specified at the beginning of the proof, either the graph $G_{\mathrm{I}}(A)$ contains a path of length $|a_k\alpha| - 1$, or there is no such path but there is a shorter path terminating at a vertex of the type (s_r, s_r).

Suppose now that the automaton is not IL-I-N for any N; in other words, for arbitrarily large N' there exist a state s_i and words $a_k\alpha$, $a_l\alpha'$ $(a_k \neq a_l,$ $|\alpha| = |\alpha'| = N' - 1)$ such that $\lambda(s_i, a_k\alpha) = \lambda(s_i, a_l\alpha')$.

As we have just proved, this implies that $G_{\mathrm{I}}(A)$ contains either a vertex of type (s_r, s_r) or an arbitrarily long path. But the latter alternative cannot hold unless $G_{\mathrm{I}}(A)$ contains cycles, for the graph has at most $n_1(n_1 - 1)/2$ vertices from which arcs emanate, where n_1 is the number of states of A.

Now let the automaton be ILS-I-N_1 for some N_1. Then there exist words $a_k\alpha$, $a_l\alpha'$ $(a_k \neq a_l$, $|\alpha| = |\alpha'| = N_1 - 1)$ and a state s_i such that $\lambda(s_i, a_k\alpha) = \lambda(s_i, a_l\alpha)$, and the graph $G_1(A)$ contains a path of length $N_1 - 1$.

Suppose that $G_{\mathrm{I}}(A)$ has a path passing through vertices (s_{i_1}, s_{j_1}), (s_{i_2}, s_{j_2}), $\ldots$, (s_{i_N}, s_{j_N}). We claim that there exist a state s_i and words $a_k\alpha$, $a_l\alpha'$, where $|a_k\alpha| = |a_l\alpha'| \geqslant N$ and $a_k \neq a_l$, such that $\lambda(s_i, a_k\alpha) = \lambda(s_i, a_l\alpha')$.

Case 1. The pair (s_{i_1}, s_{j_1}) first appeared at Step 1 of Algorithm 1_{I}. Then there exist s_i, a_k and a_l $(a_k \neq a_l)$ such that $\lambda(s_i, a_k) = \lambda(s_i, a_l)$ and $\delta(s_i, a_k) = s_{i_1}$, $\delta(s_i, a_l) = s_{j_1}$.

Suppose there exist words α_n and α'_n of length n such that $\lambda(s_i, \alpha_n) = \lambda(s_i, \alpha'_n)$ and $\delta(s_i, \alpha_n) = s_{i_n}$, $\delta(s_i, \alpha'_n) = s_{j_n}$ $(n = 1, \ldots, N-1)$. Since there is an arc going from the vertex (s_{i_n}, s_{j_n}) to $(s_{i_{n+1}}, s_{j_{n+1}})$, there exist letters a_{m_n} and a_{r_n} such that

$$\lambda(s_{i_n}, a_{m_n}) = \lambda(s_{j_n}, a_{r_n}), \delta(s_{i_n}, a_{m_n}) = s_{i_{n+1}}, \ \delta(s_{j_n}, a_{r_n}) = s_{j_{n+1}}.$$

Hence it follows that $\lambda(s_i, \alpha_n a_{m_n}) = \lambda(s_i, \alpha'_n a_{r_n})$ and $\delta(s_i, \alpha_n a_{m_n}) = s_{i_{n+1}}$, $\delta(s_i, \alpha'_n a_{r_n}) = s_{j_{n+1}}$ or $\lambda(s_i, \alpha_{n+1}) = \lambda(s_i, \alpha'_{n+1})$ and $\delta(s_i, \alpha_{n+1}) = s_{i_{n+1}}$, $\delta(s_i, \alpha'_{n+1}) = s_{j_{n+1}}$. Setting $n = N - 1$, we get the proof of our assertion and $|a_k\alpha| = N$.

Case 2. The vertex (s_{i_1}, s_{j_1}) did not appear at Step 1 of Algorithm 1_{I}. Then there exist a pair of I-indistinguishable states (s_{f_1}, s_{g_1}), produced at Step 1, and a sequence of pairs of I-indistinguishable states $(s_{f_2}, s_{g_2}), \ldots, (s_{f_M}, s_{g_M})$, satisfying the following conditions:

(1) There exist letters a_{k_ν} and a_{l_ν} such that $\lambda(s_{f_\nu}, a_{k_\nu}) = \lambda(s_{g_\nu}, a_{l_\nu})$ and $\delta(s_{f_\nu}, a_{k_\nu}) = s_{f_{\nu+1}}$, $\delta(s_{g_\nu}, a_{l_\nu}) = s_{g_{\nu+1}}$ $(\nu = 1, \ldots, M-1)$.

(2) $(s_{f_M}, s_{g_M}) = (s_{i_1}, s_{j_1})$.

But then the graph $G_{\mathrm{I}}(A)$ contains a path passing through the vertices $(s_{f_1}, s_{g_1}), \ldots, (s_{f_{M-1}}, s_{g_{M-1}}), (s_{i_1}, s_{j_1}), \ldots, (s_{i_N}, s_{j_N})$, for which Case 1 applies. We thus obtain $|a_k\alpha| > N$.

Now let the graph $G_{\mathrm{I}}(A)$ contain a vertex (s_j, s_j). Then there exist a state s_i and words $a_k\alpha$, $a_l\alpha'$ $(a_k \neq a_l, |\alpha| = |\alpha'|)$ such that $\lambda(s_i, a_k\alpha) = \lambda(s_i, a_l\alpha')$ and $\delta(s_i, a_k\alpha) = \delta(s_i, a_l\alpha) = s_j$. For any word α'' for which $\lambda(s_j, \alpha'')$ is defined, we have $\lambda(s_i, a_k\alpha\alpha'') = \lambda(s_i, a_l\alpha'\alpha'')$. Since the length of α'' is unbounded, the automaton A is not IL-I-N for any natural number N.

Let $G_{\mathrm{I}}(A)$ contain a cycle. Then there are arbitrarily long paths in the graph and by what we have just proved there exist a state s_i and arbitrarily long input words $a_k\alpha$, $a_l\alpha'$ $(a_k \neq a_l, |\alpha| = |\alpha'|)$ such that $\lambda(s_i, a_k\alpha) = \lambda(s_i, a_l\alpha')$. Thus the automaton cannot be IL-I-N for any natural number N.

Now suppose that $G_{\mathrm{I}}(A)$ contains a path of length $N_1 - 1$. Then there exist a state s_i and words $a_k\alpha$, $a_l\alpha'$ $(a_k \neq a_l, |\alpha| = |\alpha'| = N_1 - 1)$ such that $\lambda(s_i, a_k\alpha) = \lambda(s_i, a_l\alpha')$. In view of the length of α, it follows that the automaton is not IL-I-$N_1 - 1$.

This completes the proof of the theorem.

According to Theorem 2_{I}, in order to check whether a given automaton is IL-I-N and to determine the number N_1 for which $A\,(\mathrm{SI}, N_1)$, we need only construct the graph $G_{\mathrm{I}}(A)$, check it for cycles or vertices of type (s_j, s_j) and, if there are no cycles or vertices of this type, find the length of the longest path. This may be done in finitely many steps. Vertices of the type (s_j, s_j) are detected by Algorithm 1_{I}.

To check for the existence of cycles, one can use Algorithm 2, described below. If $G_{\mathrm{I}}(A)$ is a multigraph, one first forms the corresponding simple graph by deleting all but one arc joining any two vertices. We may therefore assume that both $G_{\mathrm{I}}(A)$ and the graph $G_{\mathrm{II}}(A)$ to be defined later are simple graphs. The algorithm also determines the maximum length of a path. It is applied to the connection matrix of the graph.

We recall the definition of the connection matrix of a simple graph G. Suppose that G has N vertices, numbered from 1 to N. Then the connection matrix is an $N \times N$ matrix with entry 1 at the (i, j)-th position and only if there is an arc in G from the i-th vertex to the j-th, and 0 otherwise.

Algorithm 2.

Step 1. Find the indices of all rows of the relevant matrix that contain only zeros, and proceed to the next step. If there are no such rows, stop. At the first application of Step 1, the "relevant matrix" is the matrix being checked for cycles.

Step 2. Suppose that Step 1 has produced a sequence of indices $i_1, i_2, \ldots, i_k$. Delete the corresponding rows and columns from the relevant matrix, and return to Step 1 (the "relevant matrix" will now be the new matrix produced by deleting the appropriate rows and columns).

It is obvious that for any connection matrix Algorithm 2 will indeed stop after finitely many alternating applications of Steps 1 and 2.

We have to justify our assertion that Algorithm 2 indeed establishes the existence of cycles. We shall need two lemmas.

Lemma 1. If each row of the connection matrix contains a one, the graph contains a cycle.

Proof. Let v_{i_1} be an arbitrary vertex of the graph. The i_1-th row of the connection matrix contains a one, say in the i_2-th column. Thus the graph contains a path (in this case, an arc) going from v_{i_1} to v_{i_2}.

Suppose we have already found a path in the graph passing through vertices $v_{i_1}, v_{i_2}, \ldots, v_{i_n}$ and ending at v_{i_n}. By assumption, the i_n-th row of the connection matrix contains a one, say in the i_{n+1}-th column. This means that there is an arc from v_{i_n} to $v_{i_{n+1}}$ or, in view of the induction hypothesis, a path passing through the vertices $v_{i_1}, v_{i_2}, v_{i_3}, \ldots, v_{i_{n+1}}$ and ending at $v_{i_{n+1}}$.

It follows that the graph contains arbitrarily long paths. But since the graph contains only finitely many vertices, this is possible only if there are cycles.

Lemma 2. If a graph contains no cycles, its connection matrix contains a row all of whose entries are zeros.

Proof. If the connection matrix contains no row all of whose entries are zeros, it must contain a cycle, by Lemma 1 — contradiction.

Theorem 3. If the application of Algorithm 2 to the connection matrix of a graph produces an empty matrix (i.e., all rows and columns are deleted), the graph contains no cycles. If the outcome is not empty, the graph contains cycles.

Proof. Suppose the graph has no cycles. By Lemma 2, its connection matrix contains a row all of whose entries are zeros — this will be ascertained at the first application of Step 1 in Algorithm 2. Step 2 will then produce the connection matrix of some subgraph of the original graph. It is clear that there are no cycles in this subgraph. Repeating the argument, we see that at some step Algorithm 2 must produce a matrix all of whose entries are zeros. Step 2 applied to this matrix yields the empty matrix.

Now suppose conversely that the algorithm produces a nonempty matrix. This means that at some step a matrix is produced all of whose rows contain a one. This matrix is the connection matrix of a subgraph of the original graph. By Lemma 2, the subgraph must contain a cycle, and hence so does the original graph.

That Algorithm 2 also yields the maximum length of a path in the graph follows from the next theorem.

Theorem 4. If Algorithm 2 applied to the connection matrix of a graph produces an empty matrix, the maximum length of a path in the graph is one less than the number of iterations of Step 2 in the algorithm.

Proof. Each application of Step 2 is equivalent to forming the connection matrix of a graph whose longest path contains one less arc than the preceding graph, since it essentially involves deletion of vertices (and of the arcs converging on them) from which no arcs emanate.

Now suppose that some application of Step 2 yields an empty matrix. This means that the relevant matrix has only zero entries, so that the corresponding subgraph has no arcs and the maximum length of a path is 0.

Suppose the theorem true for all connection matrices for which Step 2 is iterated n times. Consider some matrix for which Step 2 is iterated $n+1$ times. By assumption, the maximum length of a path in the graph corresponding to the connection graph produced by the first application of Step 2 is $n-1$. Consider any longest path in the original graph. Since this path contains a vertex from which no arcs emanate, the length of a longest path in the newly formed subgraph is exactly one less. The conclusion now follows by induction.

A few examples will illustrate the theory.

Example 1. Let A_1 be the automaton defined by Table 5. We wish to check whether A_1 is IL-I-N for some N and, if A_1(I, N), to find the number N_1 such that A_1 (SI, N_1). We first use Algorithm 1_I to find all pairs of I-indistinguishable states.

TABLE 5.

	a_1	a_2		a_1	a_2
s_{11}	s_{13}, b_1	s_{14}, b_1	s_{14}	s_{12}, b_1	s_{16}, b_2
s_{12}	s_{15}, b_2	s_{16}, b_2	s_{15}	s_{11}, b_1	s_{12}, b_2
s_{13}	s_{11}, b_1	s_{15}, b_2	s_{16}	s_{11}, b_2	s_{12}, b_1

Step 1. We find the pairs (s_{13}, s_{14}) and (s_{15}, s_{16}).

Step 2. Using the pair (s_{15}, s_{16}), we find a new pair (s_{11}, s_{12}).

Using the pair (s_{13}, s_{14}), we find the same pair (s_{11}, s_{12}) and the pair (s_{15}, s_{16}) already found at Step 1.

Step 3. Starting from the only new pair produced by Step 2, namely (s_{11}, s_{12}), one can find no new pairs of I-indistinguishable states.

Consequently, we have $n_1 = 3 < 6(6-1)/2+1 = 16$.

We now construct the graph $G_I(A_1)$ (Figure 3). It is immediately clear from the extremely simple structure of this graph that it contains no cycles. Neither is there any state which is I-indistinguishable from itself. Thus A_1 is an IL-I-N automaton. The longest path in the graph $G_I(A_1)$ is of length 2, and so A_1 is ILS-I-3.

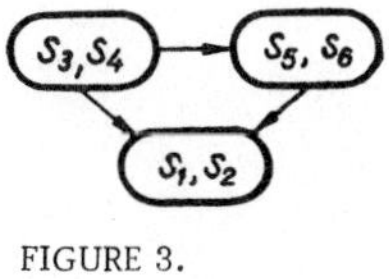

FIGURE 3.

Alternatively, application of Algorithm 2 to check the graph $G_I(A_1)$ for cycles produces the following sequences of matrices:

	1	2	3
1	0	1	1
2	0	0	1
3	0	0	0

	1	2
1	0	1
2	0	0

	1
1	0

The first matrix in this sequence is the connection matrix of $G_I(A_1)$ (the vertices are numbered in accordance with the order in which the pairs of I-indistinguishable state are detected by Algorithm 1_I). The last matrix in the sequence (*) is empty.

Example 2. Solve the same problem as in Example 1 for the automaton A_2 of Table 6.

TABLE 6.

	a_1	a_2
s_{21}	s_{22}, b_2	s_{23}, b_2
s_{22}	s_{21}, b_1	s_{21}, b_2
s_{23}	s_{22}, b_1	s_{23}, b_2

Application of Algorithm 1_I. Step 1 yields the pair (s_{22}, s_{23}). Step 2: (s_{21}, s_{22}), (s_{21}, s_{23}). Step 3: (s_{23}, s_{23}). Since we have an I-indistinguishable pair (s_{23}, s_{23}), it follows from Theorem 3 that the automaton is not IL-I-N for any N.

Example 3. The same problem for the automaton of Table 7.

TABLE 7.

	a_1	a_2		a_1	a_2
s_1	s_1, b_2	s_3, b_2	s_4	s_3, b_1	s_2, b_1
s_2	s_5, b_1	s_2, b_2	s_5	s_2, b_2	s_1, b_1
s_3	s_4, b_1	s_1, b_1			

Application of Algorithm 1_I. Step 1: (s_1, s_3), (s_1, s_4), (s_2, s_3). Step 2: (s_1, s_5), (s_4, s_5). Step 3: (s_1, s_2). The graph $G_I(A)$ is illustrated in Figure 4. It clearly contains a cycle, and so the automaton is not IL-I-N.

Algorithm 2 for this example produces the sequence of matrices

```
000000        0110
000000        1001
000110        0001
001001        1001
100001
001001
```

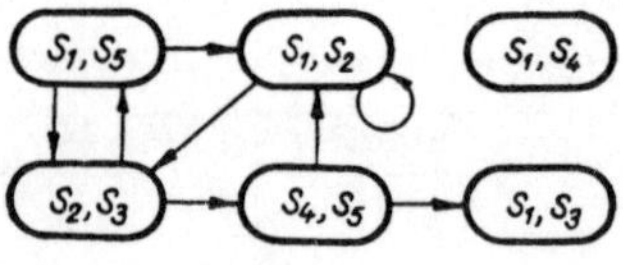

FIGURE 4.

We now proceed to an investigation of IL-II-N automata.

Definition 4. An unordered pair of (not necessarily distinct) states (s_i, s_j) is said to be II-indistinguishable if at least one of the following conditions is satisfied:

(1) there exist a state s_k and letters a_l, a_n, $(a_l \neq a_n)$ such that

$$\lambda(s_i, a_l) = \lambda(s_j, a_n), \quad \delta(s_i, a_l) = \delta(s_j, a_n) = s_k;$$

(2) $s_i \neq s_j$ and there exist a state s_k and a letter a_m such that

$$\lambda(s_i, a_m) = \lambda(s_j, a_m), \ \delta(s_i, a_m) = \delta(s_j, a_m) = s_k;$$

(3) there exist a II-indistinguishable pair (s_k, s_l) $(s_k \neq s_l)$ and letters a_m, a_n (not necessarily distinct) such that

$$\lambda(s_i, a_m) = \lambda(s_j, a_n), \ \delta(s_i, a_m) = s_k, \ \delta(s_j, a_n) = s_l.$$

To determine the II-indistinguishable states of an automaton, we use the following algorithm.

Algorithm 1_{II}.

Step 1. Find all pairs of states satisfying condition 1 or 2 of Definition 4.

Step 2. Suppose that Step n produces all pairs of II-indistinguishable states not detected at previous steps. Taking each such pair as the pair (s_k, s_l), find all pairs (s_i, s_j) satisfying condition 3 of Definition 4.

The fact that Algorithm 1_{II} indeed terminates after, say, n_1 steps is established in the same way as for Algorithm 1_{I}.

We now construct a special graph $G_{\text{II}}(A)$. The vertices are all pairs of II-indistinguishable states of the automaton A. The arcs are introduced in accordance with condition 3 of Definition 4 (compare the construction of $G_{\text{I}}(A)$).

Theorem 2_{II}. *An automaton A is IL-II-N if and only if the graph* $G_{\text{II}}(A)$ *contains no vertices* (s_i, s_i) *and no cycles. An automaton A(II, N) is ILS-II-*N_1, *where* $N_1 - 1$ *is the maximum length of a path in* $G_{\text{II}}(A)$.

Proof. Suppose there exist words $\alpha_1 a_k$, $\alpha_2 a_l$ and states s_{i_1}, s_{i_2} and s_j such that $\delta(s_{i_1}, \alpha_1 a_k) = \delta(s_{i_2}, \alpha_2 a_l) = s_j$ and $\lambda(s_{i_1}, \alpha_1 a_k) = \lambda(s_{i_2}, \alpha_2 a_l)$. We consider two cases.

Case 1. $a_k \neq a_l$. Then it is readily verified, using condition 1 of Definition 4, that there is a pair of II-indistinguishable states $(\delta(s_{i_1}, \alpha_1), \delta(s_{i_2}, \alpha_2))$.

Case 2. $a_k = a_l$ and $\delta(s_{i_1}, \alpha_1) \neq \delta(s_{i_2}, \alpha_2)$. By condition 2 of Definition 4, we have a pair of II-indistinguishable states $(\delta(s_{i_1}, \alpha_1), \delta(s_{i_2}, \alpha_2))$.

Let α_i and α'_i denote the prefixes of the words $\alpha_1 a_k$ and $\alpha_2 a_l$, respectively, of length $(0 \leqslant i \leqslant |\alpha_1 a_k|)$.

Let $(\delta(s_{i_1}, \alpha_i), \delta(s_{i_2}, \alpha'_i))$ $(i \geqslant 1)$ be some pair of II-indistinguishable states, $\delta(s_{i_1}, \alpha_i) \neq \delta(s_{i_2}, \alpha'_i)$ and $\alpha_i = \alpha_{i-1} a_{k_i}, \alpha'_i = \alpha'_{i-1} a_{l_i}$. Then $\lambda(\delta(s_{i_1}, \alpha_{i-1}), a_{k_i}) = \lambda(\delta(s_{i_2}, \alpha'_{i-1}), a_{l_i})$, the pair $(\delta(s_{i_1}, \alpha_{i-1}), \ \delta(s_{i_2}, \alpha'_{i-1}))$ is II-indistinguishable by condition 3 of Definition 4, and there is an arc in $G_{\text{II}}(A)$ from the vertex $(\delta(s_{i_1}, \alpha_i), \delta(s_{i_2}, \alpha'_i))$ to the vertex $(\delta(s_{i_1}, \alpha_{i-1}), \ \delta(s_{i_2}, \alpha'_{i-1}))$. Thus the graph $G_{\text{II}}(A)$ contains vertices $(\delta(s_{i_1}, \alpha_j), \ \delta(s_{i_1}, \alpha'_j))$ for all $j = J, \ldots, |\alpha_1 a_k| - 1$ such that $\delta(s_{i_2}, \alpha_J) \neq \delta(s_{i_2}, \alpha'_J)$ and by the construction of $G_{\text{II}}(A)$ there is an arc from the vertex $(\delta(s_{i_1}, \alpha_{j+1}), \ \delta(s_{i_2}, \alpha'_{j+1}))$ to the vertex $(\delta(s_{i_1}, \alpha_j), \ \delta(s_{i_2}, \alpha'_j))$.

Consequently, for every pair of words $\alpha_1 a_k$, $\alpha_2 a_l$ and any triple of states s_{i_1}, s_{i_2}, s_j with the indicated properties, either the graph $G_{\mathrm{II}}(A)$ contains a path of length $|\alpha_1|$, or there is no such path but there is a shorter path ending at a vertex of type (s_r, s_r).

If A is not an IL-II-N automaton, for any N, there exist states s_j, s_{i_1}, s_{i_2} and words $\alpha_1 a_k$, $\alpha_2 a_l$ of the same arbitrarily large length such that $\delta(s_{i_1}, \alpha_1 a_k) = \delta(s_{i_2}, \alpha_2 a_l) = s_j$, $\lambda(s_{i_1}, \alpha_1 a_k) = \lambda(s_{i_2}, \alpha_2 a_l)$ and either $a_k \neq a_l$ or $\delta(s_{i_1}, \alpha_1) \neq \delta(s_{i_2}, \alpha_2)$.

Then, by what we have just proved, $G_{\mathrm{II}}(A)$ contains either a vertex (s_r, s_r) or arbitrarily long paths. Since the number of vertices in $G_{\mathrm{II}}(A)$ is finite, the second alternative cannot hold unless the graph contains cycles.

Suppose that $G_{\mathrm{II}}(A)$ contains a path through the vertices $(s_{i_1}, s_{j_1}), \ldots, (s_{i_N}, s_{j_N})$. Then, as in the proof of Theorem 2_{I}, we can show that there exist a pair of words αa_k, $\alpha' a_l$, $|\alpha a_k| \geqslant N$, and a triple of states s_{i_1}, s_{i_2}, s_j such that $\delta(s_{i_1}, \alpha a_k) = \delta(s_{i_2}, \alpha' a_l) = s_j$, $\lambda(s_{i_1}, \alpha a_k) = \lambda(s_{i_2}, \alpha' a_l)$ and either $a_k \neq a_l$ or $\delta(s_{i_1}, \alpha) \neq \delta(s_{i_2}, \alpha')$.

Suppose now that $G_{\mathrm{II}}(A)$ contains a vertex (s_r, s_r). By the preceding arguments, this means that for some words αa_k and $\alpha' a_l$ of the same length there exists a state s_p such that $\delta(s_r, \alpha a_k) = \delta(s_r, \alpha' a_l) = s_p$, $\lambda(s_r, \alpha a_k) = \lambda(s_r, \alpha' a_l)$ and either $a_k \neq a_l$ or $\delta(s_r, \alpha) \neq \delta(s_r, \alpha')$. But then it is clear that, for any state s_j and word α_1 such that $\delta(s_j, \alpha_1) = s_r$, we have

$$\delta(s_j, \alpha_1 \alpha a_k) = \delta(s_j, \alpha_1 \alpha' a_l) = s_p, \quad \lambda(s_j, \alpha_1 \alpha a_k) = \lambda(s_j, \alpha_1 \alpha' a_l),$$

and either $a_k \neq a_l$ or $\delta(s_j, \alpha_1 \alpha) \neq \delta(s_j, \alpha_1 \alpha')$. Since there is no restriction on the length of α_1, it follows that the automaton cannot be IL-II-N for any N.

The proof in the case that $G_{\mathrm{II}}(A)$ contains cycles is similar (see the proof of Theorem 2_{I}).

To check for the existence of cycles in the graph $G_{\mathrm{II}}(A)$ and to determine the length of the longest paths, one can again use Algorithm 2.

Example 2. Given the automaton of Table 8, find all pairs of II-indistinguishable states and check whether it is IL-II-N.

TABLE 8.

	a_1	a_2
s_1	s_3, b_1	s_4, b_2
s_2	s_4, b_1	s_3, b_2
s_3	s_1, b_1	s_2, b_1
s_4	s_3, b_2	s_4, b_2

TABLE 9.

	a_1	a_2
s_1	s_3, b_1	—
s_2	—	s_3, b_1
s_3	s_1, b_1; s_4, b_2	s_2, b_2
s_4	s_2, b_1	s_1, b_2; s_4, b_2

To facilitate the application of Algorithm 1_{II} in this case, it is convenient to appeal to the formation table of the automaton, (Table 9).

Step 1. Find all the pairs $((s_i, b_j), (s_r, b_l))$ such that $b_j = b_l$ and the pairs (s_i, b_j) and (s_i, b_l) lie in the same row but different columns of the formation table. It is evident from the construction of this table that the pair (s_i, s_r) is II-indistinguishable by condition 1 of Definition 4. In the present example, this yields the pair (s_2, s_4).

Now find all pairs $((s_i, b_j), (s_r, b_l))$ such that $b_j = b_l$ and the pairs (s_i, b_j) and (s_r, b_l) lie in the same row and the same column of the formation table. The pair (s_i, s_r) is II-indistinguishable by condition 2 of Definition 4. In the example, this gives the pair (s_1, s_4).

Step $n+1$. Let (s_i, s_j) be a pair produced at Step n. Find all pairs $((s_r, b_m), (s_p, b_t))$ such that $b_m = b_t$, the pair (s_r, b_m) is in the i-th row and the pair (s_p, b_t) in the j-th row of the formation table.

The pair (s_r, s_p) is II-indistinguishable by virtue of condition 3 of Definition 4.

Thus, Step 2 produces (s_2, s_3), and Step 3 (s_1, s_3). Step 4 introduces no new pairs, and Algorithm 1_{II} stops. It is clear from the graph $G_{\text{II}}(A)$ (Figure 5) that the automaton is not IL-II-N, since it contains a cycle (the loop at (s_1, s_3)). For comparison, we also illustrate the graph $G_{\text{I}}(A)$ (Figure 6), from which it is clear that the automaton is ILS-I-2.

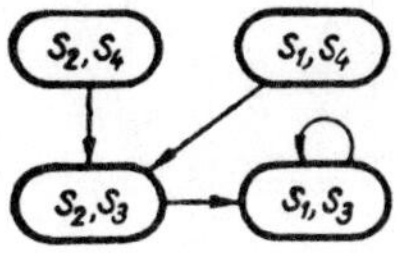

FIGURE 5.

FIGURE 6.

Example 5. The same problem for the automaton given in Table 10.

TABLE 10.

	a_1	a_2		a_1	a_2
s_1	s_5, b_2	s_8, b_2	s_5	s_3, b_1	s_3, b_2
s_2	s_7, b_1	s_5, b_2	s_6	s_7, b_1	s_4, b_1
s_3	s_1, b_1	s_2, b_2	s_7	s_6, b_1	s_3, b_2
s_4	s_2, b_2	s_1, b_1	s_8	s_8, b_2	s_6, b_1

Using the formation table (Table 11), we construct the graph $G_{\text{II}}(A)$ (Figure 7), from which it is apparent that the automaton is ILS-II-2. Since the graph $G_{\text{I}}(A)$ has a cycle through the vertices (s_5, s_8), (s_3, s_8) and (s_2, s_8), the automaton is not IL-I-N.

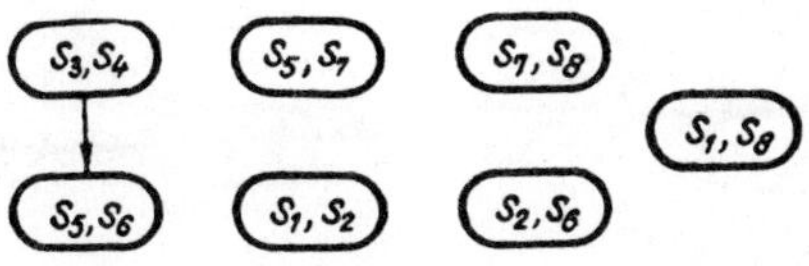

FIGURE 7.

TABLE 11.

	a_1	a_2		a_1	a_2
s_1	s_3, b_1	s_4, b_1	s_5	s_1, b_2	s_2, b_2
s_2	s_4, b_2	s_3, b_2	s_6	s_7, b_1	s_8, b_1
s_3	s_5, b_1	s_5, b_2; s_7, b_2	s_7	s_2, b_1; s_6, b_1	—
s_4	—	s_6, b_1	s_8	s_8, b_2	s_1, b_2

Example 6. The same problem for the automaton of Table 12 (Table 13 is the formation table).

TABLE 12.

	a_1	a_2		a_1	a_2
s_1	s_5, b_1	s_6, b_2	s_6	s_7, b_2	s_8, b_2
s_2	s_5, b_2	s_6, b_1	s_7	s_1, b_1	s_2, b_1
s_3	s_6, b_1	s_5, b_1	s_8	s_2, b_2	s_1, b_2
s_4	s_6, b_2	s_5, b_2	s_9	s_3, b_1	s_4, b_1
s_5	s_9, b_1	s_{10}, b_1	s_{10}	s_4, b_2	s_3, b_2

Examination of the graphs $G_{\text{I}}(A)$ and $G_{\text{II}}(A)$ (Figures 8 and 9) shows that the automaton is both ILS-I-2 and ILS-II-2.

TABLE 13.

	a_1	a_2		a_1	a_2
s_1	s_7, b_1	s_8, b_2	s_6	s_3, b_1; s_4, b_2	s_1, b_2; s_2, b_1
s_2	s_8, b_2	s_7, b_1	s_7	s_6, b_2	—
s_3	s_9, b_1	s_{10}, b_2	s_8	—	s_6, b_2
s_4	s_{10}, b_2	s_9, b_1	s_9	s_5, b_1	—
s_5	s_1, b_1; s_2, b_2	s_3, b_1; s_4, b_2	s_{10}	—	s_5, b_1

It is clear from Examples 4—6 that there are automata which are both IL-I-N and IL-II-N, as well as automata which are only IL-I-N or only IL-II-N. The existence of automata which are neither IL-I-N nor IL-II-N is obvious.

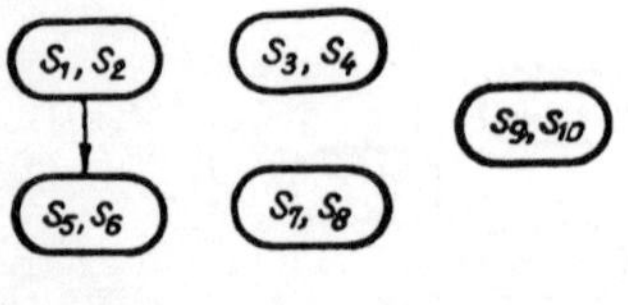

FIGURE 8.

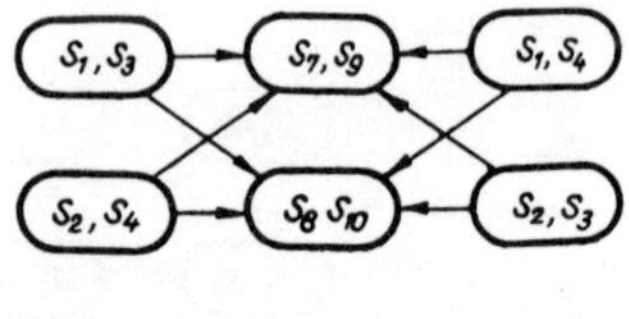

FIGURE 9.

The results of this section may be summarized as follows.

Theorem 5. There exists an algorithm which, in finitely many steps, decides whether any given automaton is IL-I-N (or IL-II-N) and, if it is, determines a number N_1 such that the automaton is ILS-I-N_1 (ILS-II-N_1).

§3. THE INVERSE AUTOMATON AND ITS CONSTRUCTION

Let A be an ILS-I-N automaton. By Theorem 1_{I}, it has the following property. Suppose that upon application of an unknown input word the automaton A, when in state s_{i_0}, produces an output word β. Then the input word may be recovered in finitely many steps, with the possible exception of its last N letters.

If A is an ILS-II-N automaton, Theorem 1_{II} implies the following property. Suppose that upon application of some unknown input word the automaton produces a word β and passes into state s_{i_0}. Then the input word may be recovered in finitely many steps, with the possible exception of its first N letters.

It turns out that the recovery procedure may be entrusted to another automaton.

In this section and the next we shall study two families of automata. Those of the first will be denoted by the letter A (with various subscripts). Those of the second family will be denoted by the letter B and will generally be viewed as inverses of the automata in the first family, though in some cases this standpoint will be reversed.

Definition 5. An automaton B will be called a *type I inverse with delay* N for an automaton A if, for any state s_i, there is a state t_j such that for any word $\alpha\alpha_1$ ($|\alpha_1|=N$) for which $\lambda(s_i, \alpha\alpha_1)$ is defined

$$\mu(t_j, \lambda(s_i, \alpha\alpha_1)) = \alpha_2\alpha, \tag{5}$$

where α_2 is an arbitrary word of length N.

Definition 6. An automaton B will be called a *type II inverse with delay* N for an automaton A if, for any state s_i, there exists a state t_j with the property: for any state s_m and any word $\alpha_1\alpha$ ($|\alpha_1|=N$) such that $\delta(s_m, \alpha_1\alpha) = s_i$,

$$\mu(t_j, (\lambda(s_m, \alpha_1\alpha))^{-1}) = \alpha_2\alpha^{-1}, \tag{6}$$

where α_2 is an arbitrary word of length N.

The relationship between IL-I-N automata and their inverses is established in the following

Theorem 6. If an automaton A has a type I inverse with delay N, then A is ILS-I-N_1 with $N_1 \leqslant N$.

Proof. We first show that $N_1 > N$ cannot hold. If A (SI, N_1), there exist a state s_i and words $a_k\alpha$, $a_l\alpha_1$ ($a_k \neq a_l$, $|\alpha_k\alpha| = N_1$), such that $\lambda(s_i, a_k\alpha) = \lambda(s_i, a_l\alpha_1)$. Then, for any automaton B and any state t_i, it is clear that $\mu(t_i, \lambda(s_i, a_k\alpha))$ may take only one value and so, regardless of the strcuture of B, one can always find a word of length N_1 for which (5) fails to hold. Thus an automaton A (SI, N_1) cannot have a type I inverse with delay $N_2 \leqslant N_1 - 1$.

Suppose that A is not IL-I-N for any N. Then the graph $G_I(A)$ contains either a vertex of type (s_i, s_i) or a cycle. In the first case, there exist a state s_j and words $a_k\alpha$, $a_l\alpha_1$ such that $\lambda(s_j, a_k\alpha) = \lambda(s_j, a_l\alpha_1)$, $\delta(s_j, a_k\alpha) = \delta(s_j, a_l\alpha_1)$. But then, for any word α_2 such that $\lambda(\delta(s_j, a_k\alpha), \alpha_2)$ is defined, we have $\lambda(s_j, a_k\alpha\alpha_2) = \lambda(s_j, a_l\alpha_1\alpha_2)$. Since there is no bound on the length of α_2, it follows as before that for no finite N does the automaton A have a type I inverse with delay N.

Similar reasoning disposes of the second case.

An analogous theorem may be proved, subject to certain modifications, for type II automata.

By Theorem 6, an automaton A may have a type I inverse with delay N only if A(SI, N_1), where $N \geqslant N_1$.

We shall now show that any ILS-I-N_1 (or ILS-II-N_1) automaton has a type I (type II) inverse with delay N for any $N \geqslant N_1$. This will be done by actually constructing the inverse.

We first consider the case A(SI, N_1).

Algorithm 3_{I}.

Taking any number $N \geqslant N_1$, we construct an automaton B whose state set is the union of two disjoint sets $\mathfrak{T}_1$ and $\mathfrak{T}_2$, as follows.

$\mathfrak{T}_1$ is the set of all pairs (s_i, β), where $s_i \in \mathfrak{S}$ and β ($|\beta| = N$) is a word such that $\lambda(s_i, \alpha) = \beta$ for some word α.

For states in $\mathfrak{T}_1$, the next-state and output functions are defined as follows. Let $(s_i, b_r\beta) \in \mathfrak{T}_1$. Given any letter b_p for which there exists a word α_p with $\lambda(s_i, \alpha_p) = b_r\beta b_p$, we set $\mu((s_i, b_r\beta), b_p) = a_k$, where a_k is the first letter of α_p. Since $|\alpha_p| \geqslant N_1 + 1$, it follows from Definition 1 that $\lambda(s_i, \alpha) \neq \lambda(s_i, \alpha_p)$ for any word α whose first letter differs from that of α_p. We now define

$$\varepsilon((s_i, b_r\beta), b_p) = (\delta(s_i, \mu((s_i, b_r\beta), b_p)), \beta b_p).$$

We have thus defined a certain automaton, referred to henceforth as the principal part of B and denoted by B_1.

We complete the definition of the automaton B as follows.

Let $\mathfrak{T}_2$ be the set of all pairs (s_i, β), where $s_i \in \mathfrak{S}$ and β ($0 \leqslant |\beta| \leqslant N-1$) is a word such that $\lambda(s_i, \alpha) = \beta$ for some word α. For all states in $\mathfrak{T}_2$, we set $\varepsilon((s_i, \beta), b_p) = (s_i, \beta b_p)$, * provided that $\lambda(s_i, \alpha) = \beta b_p$ for some word α. The value of $\mu((s_i, \beta), b_p)$ is assigned arbitrarily.**

In the case A (SII, N_1), the construction of B is as follows.

Algorithm 3_{II}.

As before, we choose $N \geqslant N_1$ arbitrarily and construct an automaton whose state set is again the union of two disjoint sets $\mathfrak{T}_1$ and $\mathfrak{T}_2$.

$\mathfrak{T}_1$ is the set of all pairs (s_i, β), where β ($|\beta| = N$) is a word such that there exist a state s_j and a word α with $\delta(s_j, \alpha) = s_i$, $(\lambda(s_j, \alpha))^{-1} = \beta$.

The output and next-state functions are defined as follows. Let $(s_i, b_r\beta) \in \mathfrak{T}_1$ and let b_p be a letter such that there exist a state s_k and a word α_p with $\delta(s_k, \alpha_p) = s_i$, $(\lambda(s_k, \alpha_p))^{-1} = b_r\beta b_p$. Then $\mu((s_i, b_r\beta), b_p) = a_l$, where a_l is the last letter of α_p, and $\varepsilon((s_i, b_r\beta), b_p) = (\delta(s_k, \alpha'), \beta b_p)$, where α' is the prefix of α_p of length N. Since $|\alpha_p| \geqslant N_1 + 1$, it follows from condition 2 of Definition 2 that for any pair (s_{i_1}, α_1) such that $|\alpha_1| = |\alpha_p|$, $\delta(s_{i_1}, \alpha_1) = s_i$ and

* If $|\beta| = N-1$, then $\varepsilon((s_i, \beta), b_p) \in \mathfrak{T}_1$.

** In other words, the values $\mu((s_i, \beta), b_p)$ for $(s_i, \beta) \in \mathfrak{T}_2$ may be defined subject to any desired rule.

the last letters of the words α_p and α_l are distinct, we have $\lambda(s_{i_1}, \alpha_l) \neq \lambda(s_k, \alpha_p)$. Thus the output function is well defined.

Now let s_{i_1} and s_{i_2} be states and $\alpha_1 a_l$, $\alpha_2 a_l$ ($|\alpha_1 a_l| = |\alpha_2 a_l| \geqslant N_1 + 1$) words such that

$$\delta(s_{i_1}, \alpha_1 a_l) = \delta(s_{i_2}, \alpha_2 a_l) = s_i$$

and

$$(\lambda(s_{i_1}, \alpha_1 a_l))^{-1} = (\lambda(s_{i_2}, \alpha_2 a_l))^{-1} = b_n \beta b_p .$$

Then by condition 3 of Definition 2 we have $\delta(s_{i_1}, \alpha_1) = \delta(s_{i_2}, \alpha_2)$ and the next-state function is also well-defined.

As before, the automaton thus constructed will be called the principal part of B and denoted by B_1.

We now continue our description of the automaton B.

$\mathfrak{T}_2$ will be the set of all pairs (s_i, β), where $s_i \in \mathfrak{S}$ and β ($|\beta| < N$) is a word satisfying the condition: there exist a state s_j and a word α such that $\delta(s_j, \alpha) = s_i$ and $(\lambda(s_j, \alpha))^{-1} = \beta$. For states in the set $\mathfrak{T}_2$, we set $\varepsilon((s_i, \beta), b_p) = (s_i, \beta b_p)$ where b_p is a letter for which there exist a state s_j and a word α with $\delta(s_j, \alpha) = s_i$, $(\lambda(s_j, \alpha))^{-1} = \beta b_p$. The value of $\mu((s_i, \beta), b_p)$ is again assigned arbitrarily.

We shall say that the automata produced by Algorithms 3_{I} and 3_{II} are constructed with delay N.

The relationship between an automaton A (SI, N_1) (or A (SII, N_1)) and the automaton B produced by Algorithm 3_{I} (3_{II}) is established by the following

Theorem 7. The automaton B constructed with delay N by Algorithm 3_{I} (or 3_{II}) for an automaton A(SI, N_1) (or A (SII, N_1)) for $N \geqslant N_1$ is a type I (type II) inverse with delay A for the automaton N.

Proof. We first consider the case A (SI, N_1). Let B be the automaton produced by Algorithm 3_{I}. It follows from the definition of the functions ε and μ that $\mu((s_i, \Lambda), \lambda(s_i, a_{i_1} \alpha a_{i_2})) = \alpha_2 a_{i_1}$ for any word $a_{i_1} \alpha a_{i_2}$ of length $N+1$ such that $\lambda(s_i, a_{i_1} \alpha a_{i_2})$ is defined (α_2 is a certain word of length N, depending on how the function μ is defined for states in $\mathfrak{T}_2$). It is also clear that

$$\varepsilon((s_i, \Lambda), \lambda(s_i, a_{i_1} \alpha a_{i_2})) = (\delta(s_i, a_{i_1}), \lambda(\delta(s_i, a_{i_1}), \alpha a_{i_2})).$$

Suppose that

$$\varepsilon((s_\nu, \Lambda), \lambda(s_\nu, \alpha_1 a_{i_1} \alpha_2)) = (\delta(s_\nu, \alpha_1), \lambda(\delta(s_\nu, \alpha_1), a_{i_1} \alpha_2))$$

and

$$\mu((s_\nu, \Lambda), \lambda(s_\nu, \alpha_1 a_{i_1} \alpha_2)) = \alpha_3 \alpha_1$$

for any state s_ν and word $\alpha_1 a_{i_1} \alpha_2$ of length $N+M$ or less such that $\lambda(s_\nu, \alpha_1 a_{i_1} \alpha_2)$ is defined ($|\alpha_2| = N-1$, $|\alpha_3| = N$). For any letter a_{i_2} such that $\lambda(\delta(s_\nu, \alpha_1), a_{i_1} \alpha_2 a_{i_2})$ is defined, it follows from the definition of μ that

$$\mu((\delta(s_\nu, \alpha_1), \lambda(\delta(s_\nu, \alpha_1), a_{i_1} \alpha_2)), \lambda(\delta(s_\nu, \alpha_1 a_{i_1} \alpha_2), a_{i_2})) = a_{i_1}$$

or

$$\mu((s_v, \Lambda),\ \alpha_1 a_{i_1}\alpha_2 a_{i_2}) = \alpha_3\alpha_1 a_{i_1}.$$

By the definition of ε,

$$\varepsilon((\delta(s_v, \alpha_1), \lambda(\delta(s_v, \alpha_1), a_{i_1}\alpha_2)), \lambda(\delta(s_v, \alpha_1 a_{i_1}\alpha_2), a_{i_2})) =$$
$$= (\delta(s_v, \alpha_1 a_{i_1}), \lambda(\delta(s_v, \alpha_1 a_{i_1}), \alpha_2 a_{i_2})).$$

Hence it follows by induction that the conclusion of the theorem is valid for Algorithm 3_{I}.

We now consider an automaton $A(\mathrm{SII}, N_1)$ and the automaton B constructed with delay N by Algorithm 3_{II}.

As before, given any state s_v and word αa_{i_1} of length $N+1$, for which there exists a state s_i with $\delta(s_i, \alpha a_{i_1}) = s_v$, it follows from the definitions of ε and μ that

$$\mu((s_v, \Lambda), (\lambda(s_i, \alpha a_{i_1}))^{-1}) = \alpha_2 a_{i_1}$$

and

$$\varepsilon((s_v, \Lambda), (\lambda(s_i, \alpha a_{i_1}))^{-1}) = (\delta(s_i, \alpha), (\lambda(s_i, \alpha))^{-1})$$

(the word α_2, of length N, depends on the definition of μ for states of $\mathfrak{T}_2$). Suppose that for some state s_v and any word $\alpha_2\alpha_1$ of length $N+M$ or less, such that there exists a state s_i with $\delta(s_i, \alpha_2\alpha_1) = s_v$, we have

$$\mu((s_v, \Lambda), (\lambda(s_i, \alpha_2\alpha_1))^{-1}) = \alpha_3\alpha_1^{-1}$$

and

$$\varepsilon((s_v, \Lambda),\ (\lambda(s_i, \alpha_2\alpha_1))^{-1}) = (\delta(s_i, \alpha_2), (\lambda(s_i, \alpha_2))^{-1})$$

$(|\alpha_2| = |\alpha_3| = N)$.

Let s_v be an arbitrary state and $a_{i_2}\alpha_2 a_{i_1}\alpha_1$ a word of length $N+M+1$, $|\alpha_2| = N-1$, such that there exists a state s_i for which $\delta(s_i, a_{i_2}\alpha_2 a_{i_1}\alpha_1) = s_v$. By assumption,

$$\mu((s_v, \Lambda),\ (\lambda(\delta(s_i, a_{i_2}), \alpha_2 a_{i_1}\alpha_1))^{-1}) = \alpha_3\alpha_1^{-1}$$

and

$$\varepsilon((s_v, \Lambda),\ (\lambda(\delta(s_i, a_{i_2}), \alpha_2 a_{i_1}\alpha_1))^{-1}) =$$
$$= (\delta(\delta(s_i, a_{i_2}), \alpha_2 a_{i_1}),\ (\lambda(\delta(s_i, a_{i_2}), \alpha_2 a_{i_1}))^{-1}).$$

Since $|a_{i_2}\alpha_2 a_{i_1}| = N+1$, it follows from the definitions of ε and μ that

$$\mu((\delta(s_i, a_{i_2}\alpha_2 a_{i_1}),\ (\lambda(\delta(s_i, a_{i_2}), \alpha_2 a_{i_1}))^{-1}), \lambda(s_i, a_{i_2})) = a_{i_1}$$

and

$$\varepsilon((\delta(s_i, a_{i_2}\alpha_2 a_{i_1}), (\lambda(\delta(s_i, a_{i_2}), \alpha_2 a_{i_1}))^{-1}), \lambda(s_i, a_{i_2}))$$
$$= (\delta(s_i, a_{i_2}\alpha_2), (\lambda(s_i, a_{i_2}\alpha_2))^{-1}).$$

We thus obtain

$$\mu((s_v, \Lambda), (\lambda(s_i, a_{i_2}\alpha_2 a_{i_1}\alpha_1))^{-1}) = \alpha_3\alpha_1{}^{-1}a_{i_1} = \alpha_3(a_{i_1}\alpha_1)^{-1},$$
$$\varepsilon((s_v, \Lambda), (\lambda(s_i, a_{i_2}\alpha_2 a_{i_1}\alpha_1))^{-1}) = (\delta(s_i, a_{i_2}\alpha_2), (\lambda(s_i, a_{i_2}\alpha_2))^{-1}).$$

The conclusion now follows by induction.

According to Theorem 7, if Algorithm 3_{I} (Algorithm 3_{II}) is applied to an automaton A (SI, N_1) (A (SII, N_1) to produce an algorithm B with delay N ($N \geqslant N_1$), the automaton B is indeed an inverse of A with delay N.

Note that an automaton A may have more than one inverse with delay N. For this reason, the specific inverse automata produced by Algorithms 3_{I} and 3_{II} will be referred to as standard inverses.

§4. UNIVERSALITY OF STANDARD INVERSE AUTOMATA

The first question arising naturally in the context of Theorem 7 is to ascertain the relation between standard inverses and other inverses, if such exist. That there may indeed be other inverses is clear: the standard inverses may frequently be simplified, by using systems of invariant classes. The answer to our question is implicit in the following theorem.

Theorem 8. Let B_2 be a type I (type II) inverse with delay N for an automaton (A(SI, N_1) (A(SII, N_1)). Then one can construct from B_2 an automaton B_3 with the same number of states, defining $\mu_3(t_{3i}, b_p) = \mu_2(t_{2i}, b_p)$ and $\varepsilon_3(t_{3i}, b_p) = t_{3k}$ if $\varepsilon_2(t_{2i}, b_p) = t_{2k}$, for all pairs (t_{3i}, b_p) for which $\mu_2(t_{2i}, b_p)$ is defined except for some (possibly empty) set of pairs $\{(t_{3i_1}, b_{p_1}), \ldots, (t_{3i_n}, b_{p_n})\}$ for which $\mu_3(t_{3i_j}, b_{p_j})$ and $\varepsilon_3(t_{3i_j}, b_{p_j})$ $(j = 1, \ldots, n)$ are left undefined, such that the following conditions are satisfied:

(1) B_3 is a type I (type II) inverse with delay N for A;

(2) A has a type I (type II) standard inverse B' with delay N such that B' and B_3 possess isomorphic simplifications (see Definition 62).

Proof. We consider type I inverses with delay N. For any standard inverse B, we shall construct a graph $\Gamma(B_2, B)$ whose vertices are all ordered pairs $(t_{2j}, (s_i, \beta))$, where (s_i, β) ranges all states of B.

For each state s_i, choose a state t_{2j} satisfying (5). Any vertex $(t_{2j}, (s_i, \Lambda))$, where $s_i \in \mathfrak{S}$ and t_{2j} is chosen in this way, will be called an initial vertex.

For each initial vertex $(t_{2j}, (s_i, \Lambda))$ and each letter b_k such that $\varepsilon((s_i, \Lambda), b_k)$ is defined (and then $\varepsilon_2(t_{2j}, b_k)$ must also be defined, since for some letter a_l we have $\lambda(s_i, a_l) = b_k$, the graph will contain an arc going to the vertex $(\varepsilon_2(t_{2j}, b_k), (s_i, b_k))$. We label this arc by the pair of letters $(\mu_2(t_{2j}, b_k), b_k)$. For any vertex $(t_{2k}, (s_j, \beta))$, $|\beta| < N$, which is the end of a path from some initial vertex, and any letter b_l such that $\mu((s_j, \beta), b_l)$ is defined, the graph will contain an arc going to the vertex $(\varepsilon_2(t_{2k}, b_l), (s_i, \beta b_l))$, labeled $(\mu_2(t_{2k}, b_l), b_l)$. This construction continues until there remain no vertices from which a new arc may emanate subject to these rules. We now consider all vertices

$(t_{2j}, (s_i, \beta))$, $|\beta| = N$, which (at the present stage of the construction) are ends of paths from initial vertices. The set of all such vertices will be called the set of rank 1.

Suppose we have already constructed the (nonempty) set Γ_i of rank i. The set Γ_{i+1} of rank $i+1$ is then defined as follows. For each vertex $(t_{2j}, (s_i, \beta)) \in \Gamma_i$ and each letter b_l such that $\varepsilon((s_i, \beta), b_l)$ is defined, an arc goes to the vertex $(\varepsilon_2(t_{2j}, b_l), \varepsilon((s_i, \beta), b_l))$ and is labeled $(\mu((s_i, \beta), b_l), b_l)$. Let Γ'_{i+1} be the set of all vertices which are ends of arcs emanating in this way from vertices in Γ_i, and set $\Gamma_{i+1} = \Gamma'_{i+1} \setminus \Gamma_1 \cup \ldots \cup \Gamma_i$.

Since the total number of vertices in the graph is finite, there is some $i = I$ for which $\Gamma'_{I+1} \setminus \Gamma_1 \cup \ldots \cup \Gamma_I = \varnothing$. The procedure then terminates.

Henceforth we shall consider only vertices which are the ends of paths from some initial vertex.

We now define a new automaton B_3. For any pair (t_{3j}, b_l), we stipulate that $\varepsilon_3(t_{3j}, b_l)$ and $\mu_3(t_{3j}, b_l)$ are defined if and only if the graph $\Gamma(B_2, B)$ contains a vertex $(t_{2j}, (s_i, \beta))$ from which emanates an arc labeled (a_i, b_l). There is only one such arc, going, say, to the vertex $(t_{2k}, (s_r, \beta'))$. We then define $\mu_3(t_{3j}, b_l) = a_i$, $\varepsilon_3(t_{3j}, b_l) = t_{3k}$. Since any pair (t_{3j}, b_l) is in the domain of definition of μ_3 only if $\mu_2(t_{2j}, b_l)$ is defined, the automaton B_3 is as stipulated in the statement of the theorem.

For each state (s_i, β) of the standard inverse we now define a set $M(s_i, \beta)$ of states of B_3: this set will contain all, and only those, states t_{3j} for which the graph $\Gamma(B_2, B)$ contains a vertex $(t_{2j}, (s_i, \beta))$. We claim that the collection of all sets $M(s_i, \beta)$ is a system of invariant classes. Indeed, any two states t_{3j} and t_{3k} such that the graph $\Gamma(B_2, B)$ contains vertices $(t_{2j}, (s_i, \beta))$ and $(t_{2k}, (s_i, \beta))$ with the same state (s_i, β) are compatible by construction. Let t_{3r} and t_{3j} be two states in the same set $M(s_i, \beta)$, i. e., the graph $\Gamma(B_2, B)$ contains vertices $(t_{2r}, (s_i, \beta))$ and $(t_{2j}, (s_i, \beta))$ for some (s_i, β). Let b_l be any letter such that $\varepsilon((s_i, \beta), b_l)$ is defined. Then the graph must contain arcs from the vertex $(t_{2r}, (s_i, \beta))$ to the vertex $(\varepsilon_2(t_{2r}, b_l), \varepsilon((s_i, \beta), b_l))$, and from the vertex $(t_{2j}, (s_i, \beta))$ to the vertex $(\varepsilon_2(t_{2j}, b_l), \varepsilon((s_i, \beta), b_l))$. But then the states $\varepsilon_3(t_{3r}, b_l)$ and $\varepsilon_3(t_{3j}, b_l)$ belong to the same class $M(\varepsilon((s_i, \beta), b_l))$.

Let B_4 denote the automaton obtained by simplifying the automaton B_3 with respect to the system of invariant classes $\{M(s_i, \beta)\}$.

Construct a graph $\Gamma(B_4, B)$ for the automata B_4 and B, applying the same rules as in the construction of $\Gamma(B_2, B)$.

The difference between the graphs $\Gamma(B_4, B)$ and $\Gamma(B_2, B)$ is that the former cannot contain two vertices $(t_{4j}, (s_i, \beta))$ and $(t_{4k}, (s_i, \beta))$ with the same state (s_i, β) and $t_{4j} \neq t_{4k}$. For each state t_{4j} of B_4, let $M(t_{4j})$ be the set of all states (s_i, β) of the standard inverse for which the graph $\Gamma(B_4, B)$ contains a vertex $(t_{4j}, (s_i, \beta))$.

It is clear that all states $(s_i, \beta) \in \mathfrak{T}_1$ in the same class $M(t_{4j})$ are compatible. States $(s_i, \beta) \in \mathfrak{T}_2$ of the original automaton B may be incompatible with other states of the class to which they belong, but for such states the function $\mu((s_i, \beta), b_p)$ may be defined arbitrarily. We set $\mu'((s_i, \beta), b_p) = \mu_4(t_{4j}, b_p)$ for all $(s_i, \beta) \in M(t_{4j})$. We have thus defined a new standard inverse B' for which all states (s_i, β) in the same class are compatible. Proceeding as above, we can show that the set of classes $\{M(t_{4j})\}$ satisfies the second condition in the definition of an invariant system. Simplifying the standard inverse B' with respect to the system of invariant classes $\{M(t_{4j})\}$, we obtain an automaton isomorphic to B_4.

The proof for type II inverses is analogous.

§5. CHOICE OF INITIAL STATES IN STANDARD INVERSE AUTOMATA

Theorem 8 shows that the class of standard inverse automata essentially exhausts all inverse automata. A closer study of this class is therefore in order.

The first question is to what degree introduction of the set of states $\mathfrak{T}_2$ is actually necessary, since it is quite possible that the equality $\mu(t_i, \lambda(s_j, \alpha_1\alpha_2)) = \alpha_3\alpha_1$ may remain valid if $t_i \in \mathfrak{T}_2$ is replaced by some state $(s_k, \beta) \in \mathfrak{T}_1$. Put differently, we may phrase the question thus. Can we define the output function for states of $\mathfrak{T}_2$ in such a way that the standard inverse has a system of invariant classes with the following properties:

(1) any two states in $\mathfrak{T}_1$ lie in distinct classes;

(2) for some set of states $s_{i_1}, \ldots, s_{i_L}$, all states $(s_{i_l}, \beta) \in \mathfrak{T}_2$, $1 \leqslant l \leqslant L$, are in the same class as a certain state $(s_j, \beta_j) \in \mathfrak{T}_1$ with the property: if $\mu((s_{i_l}, \beta), \beta_1)$ is defined for some word β_1, then so is $\mu((s_j, \beta_j), \beta_1)$.

We define an ordering of states by setting $q_i \geqslant q_j$ if and only if, for any word $i_{j_1} \ldots i_{jn}$ such that $f(q_j, i_{j_1} \ldots i_{jn})$ is defined,

$$f(q_i, i_{j_1} \ldots i_{jn}) = f(q_j, i_{j_1} \ldots i_{jn}).$$

We shall write $q_i \geqq q_j$ for states q_i and q_j if the following holds: let $i_{j_1} \ldots i_{jn}$ be a word for which there exists a state q_ν such that $g(q_\nu, i_{j_1} \ldots i_{jn}) = q_j$; then there exists a state q_μ such that $g(q_\mu, i_{j_1} \ldots i_{jn}) = q_i$ and $f(q_\nu, i_{j_1} \ldots i_{jn}) = f(q_\mu, i_{j_1} \ldots i_{jn})$.

Let $\mathfrak{M}_\mathrm{I}(s_i, \beta)$ denote the set of all words α such that $\lambda(s_i, \alpha) = \beta$.

To simplify the discussion, we shall say that a state $(s_i, \beta_i) \in \mathfrak{T}_2$ is replaceable by a state $(s_j, \beta_j) \in \mathfrak{T}_1$ if $(s_j, \beta_j) \geqslant (s_i, \beta_i)$.

Theorem 9_I. *An automaton $A(\mathrm{I}, N)$ has a type I standard inverse B with delay N such that the state $(s_i, \beta_i) \in \mathfrak{T}_2$ is replaceable by a state $(s_j, \beta_j) \in \mathfrak{T}_1$ if and only if, for any word $\alpha \in \mathfrak{M}_\mathrm{I}(s_i, \beta_i)$, any nonempty word α' and any word α'' of length N, there exist a word $\alpha_{\alpha\alpha'\alpha''} \in \mathfrak{M}_\mathrm{I}(s_j, \beta_j)$ of the form $\alpha_{\alpha\alpha'\alpha''} = \alpha'''\alpha$ and a word α^{IV} of length N such that*

$$\lambda(\delta(s_j, \alpha_{\alpha\alpha'\alpha''}), \alpha'\alpha^{\mathrm{IV}}) = \lambda(\delta(s_i, \alpha), \alpha'\alpha'').$$

Proof. Suppose the condition is satisfied. It follows from the construction of the standard inverse that

$$\mu((s_j, \lambda(s_j, \alpha_{\alpha\alpha'\alpha''})), \lambda(\delta(s_j, \alpha_{\alpha\alpha'\alpha''}), \alpha'\alpha^{\mathrm{IV}})) = \alpha_{\alpha\alpha'\alpha''}\alpha' = \alpha'''\alpha\alpha'$$

and

$$\mu((s_i, \lambda(s_i, \alpha)), \lambda(\delta(s_i, \alpha), \alpha'\alpha'')) = \alpha_x\alpha\alpha',$$

where $|\alpha_x|=N-|\alpha|$, or $\mu((s_j,\beta_j),\beta)=\alpha'''\alpha\alpha'$ and $\mu((s_i,\beta_i),\beta)=\alpha_x\alpha\alpha'$, where $\lambda(\delta(s_i,\alpha),\alpha'\alpha'')=\beta$. The states (s_j,β_j) and (s_i,β_i) may be compatible only if $\alpha_x=\alpha'''$. But $\mu((s_i,\beta_i),\beta_1)$, where $|\beta_1|=N-|\alpha|$, $\beta=\beta_1\beta_2$, may be defined arbitrarily; in particular, we may set $\mu((s_i,\beta_i),\beta_1)=\alpha'''$. Suppose that for $\alpha_1\in\mathfrak{M}_{\mathrm{I}}(s_i,\beta_i)$, a nonempty word α'_1 and a word α''_1 of length N the corresponding word $\alpha_{\alpha,\alpha'_1,\alpha''_1}\in\mathfrak{M}_{\mathrm{I}}(s_j,\beta_j)$ has the form $\alpha_{\alpha,\alpha'_1,\alpha''_1}=\alpha^{\mathrm{V}}\alpha_1$ and $\alpha^{\mathrm{V}}\alpha_1\neq\alpha'''\alpha$. By assumption,

$$\lambda(\delta(s_j,\alpha^{\mathrm{V}}\alpha_1),\alpha'_1\alpha_1^{\mathrm{IV}})=\lambda(\delta(s_i,\alpha_1),\alpha'_1\alpha''_1)$$

for some word α_1^{IV}. Suppose that the words $\alpha^{\mathrm{V}}\alpha_1$ and $\alpha'''\alpha$ first differ at the i-th letter (counting from the beginning of each word). Since $A(\mathrm{I},\ N)$, the words $\lambda(\delta(s_j,\alpha'''\alpha),\alpha'\alpha^{\mathrm{IV}})$ and $\lambda(\delta(s_j,\alpha^{\mathrm{V}}\alpha_1),\alpha'_1\alpha_1^{\mathrm{IV}})$ are different, and their first different letter is the j-th, $1\leqslant j\leqslant i$. But then the words $\lambda(\delta(s_i,\alpha),\alpha'\alpha'')$ and $\lambda(\delta(s_i,\alpha_1),\alpha'_1\alpha''_1)$ are also different, the first different letter again being the j-th $(1\leqslant j\leqslant i)$. Hence it follows that when the values of $\mu((s_i,\beta),\beta_1)$ for $(s_i,\beta)\in\mathfrak{T}_2$ and $|\beta_1|=N-|\beta|$ are defined by the above method they cannot take different values.

This proves sufficiency.

Now suppose that the condition fails to hold for states $(s_i,\beta_i)\in\mathfrak{T}_2$ and $(s_j,\beta_j)\in\mathfrak{T}_1$.

Only the following cases may occur.

Case I. There exists a word $\alpha\in\mathfrak{M}_{\mathrm{I}}(s_i,\beta_i)$ such that no word $\alpha_1\in\mathfrak{M}_{\mathrm{I}}(s_j,\beta_j)$ can be expressed as $\alpha_1=\alpha'''\alpha$. Let β $(|\beta|>N)$ be a word for which $\mu((s_i,\beta_i),\beta)$ is defined. If $\mu((s_j,\beta_j),\beta)$ is undefined, the proof is complete. Otherwise, we must have $\mu((s_i,\beta_i),\beta)=\alpha'''\alpha_2\alpha_3$, where $|\alpha'''|=N-|\alpha|$ and $\alpha_2\neq\alpha$. Since $\mu((s_i,\beta_i),\beta)=\alpha_x\alpha\alpha_4$, where $|\alpha_x|=|\alpha'''|$, it is clear that no modification of the definition of μ for states in $\mathfrak{T}_2$ can possibly yield the desired property of the states (s_i,β_i) and (s_j,β_j).

Case II. There exist a word $\alpha\in\mathfrak{M}_{\mathrm{I}}(s_i,\beta_i)$, a nonempty word α' and a word α'' of length N, such that for any word $\alpha_1\in\mathfrak{M}_{\mathrm{I}}(s_j,\beta_j)$ expressible as $\alpha_1=\alpha'''\alpha$ and any word α^{IV} of length N we have $\lambda(\delta(s_j,\alpha_1),\alpha'\alpha^{\mathrm{IV}})\neq$ $\neq\lambda(\delta(s_i,\alpha),\alpha'\alpha'')$.

We now distinguish three subcases.

Subcase 1. There exists a word $\alpha_1\in\mathfrak{M}_{\mathrm{I}}(s_j,\beta_j)$ which cannot be expressed as $\alpha_1=\alpha'''\alpha$, and $\lambda(\delta(s_j,\alpha_1),\alpha'\alpha^{\mathrm{IV}})=\lambda(\delta(s_i,\alpha),\alpha'\alpha'')=\beta$. Then $\mu((s_i,\beta_i),\beta)=$ $=\alpha_x\alpha\alpha'$, $\mu((s_j,\beta_j),\beta)=\alpha_1\alpha'$. Since $\alpha_1\neq\alpha'''\alpha$ for every α''', these words differ at some letter of their suffixes of length $|\alpha|$. But then no modification of the word α_x will make the states (s_i,β_i) and (s_j,β_j) compatible.

Subcase 2. For any word $\alpha_1\in\mathfrak{M}_{\mathrm{I}}(s_j,\beta_j)$ and any word α^{IV} of length N,

$$\lambda(\delta(s_j,\alpha_1),\alpha'\alpha^{\mathrm{IV}})\neq\lambda(\delta(s_i,\alpha),\alpha'\alpha'')=\beta.$$

Then the value of $\mu((s_j,\beta_j),\beta)$ is undefined whereas that of $\mu((s_i,\beta_i),\beta)$ is defined.

Subcase 3. For any word $\alpha_1\in\mathfrak{M}_{\mathrm{I}}(s_j,\beta_j)$ of the form $\alpha_1=\alpha'''\alpha$, where $\alpha\in\mathfrak{M}_{\mathrm{I}}(s_i,\beta_i)$, there exist a nonempty word α'_1 and a word α''_1 of length N such that $\lambda(\delta(s_i,\alpha),\alpha'\alpha'')=\lambda(\delta(s_j,\alpha_1),\alpha'_1\alpha''_1)=\beta$, $\alpha'_1\neq\alpha'$ and $|\alpha'_1|=|\alpha'|$. Then, by the construction of the standard inverse, we have $\mu((s_i,\beta_i),\beta)=\alpha_x\alpha\alpha'$ and

$\mu((s_j, \beta_j), \beta) = \alpha'''\alpha\alpha'_1$ and the states (s_i, β_i) and (s_j, β_j) cannot be rendered compatible by any choice of α_x.

This completes the proof.

The analog of this theorem for type II inverse automata may be formulated as follows.

Let $\mathfrak{M}_{\mathrm{II}}(s_i, \beta)$ denote the set of all words α for which there is a state s_j such that $\delta(s_j, \alpha) = s_i$ and $(\lambda(s_j, \alpha))^{-1} = \beta$.

Theorem 9_{II}. *An automaton $A(II, N)$ has a type II standard inverse B with delay N such that the state $(s_i, \beta_i) \in \mathfrak{T}_2$ is replaceable by a state $(s_j, \beta_j) \in \mathfrak{T}_1$ if and only if, for any word $\alpha \in \mathfrak{M}_{\mathrm{II}}(s_i, \beta_i)$, any nonempty word α' and any word α'' of length N, if there is a state s_{i_1} with the property $\delta(s_{i_1}, (\alpha'\alpha'')^{-1}\alpha) = s_i$, $(\lambda(\delta(s_{i_1}, (\alpha'\alpha'')^{-1}), \alpha))^{-1} = \beta_i$, then there exist a word $\alpha_{\alpha\alpha'\alpha''} \in \mathfrak{M}_{\mathrm{II}}(s_j, \beta_j)$ of the form $\alpha_{\alpha\alpha'\alpha''} = \alpha\alpha'''$, a word α^{IV} of length N and a state s_{j_1}, such that $\delta(s_{j_1}, (\alpha'\alpha^{\mathrm{IV}})^{-1}\alpha\alpha''') = s_j$,*

$$(\lambda(\delta(s_{j_1}, (\alpha'\alpha^{\mathrm{IV}})^{-1}), \alpha\alpha'''))^{-1} = \beta_j$$

and

$$\lambda(s_{j_1}, (\alpha'\alpha^{\mathrm{IV}})^{-1}) = \lambda(s_{i_1}, (\alpha'\alpha'')^{-1}).$$

Proof. Suppose that the condition holds. We have

$$\mu((s_j, (\lambda(\delta(s_{j_1}, (\alpha'\alpha^{\mathrm{IV}})^{-1}), \alpha\alpha'''))^{-1}), (\lambda(s_{j_1}, (\alpha'\alpha^{\mathrm{IV}})^{-1}))^{-1}) = (\alpha\alpha''')^{-1}\alpha'$$

and

$$\mu((s_i, (\lambda(\delta(s_{i_1}, (\alpha'\alpha'')^{-1}), \alpha))^{-1}), (\lambda(s_{i_1}, (\alpha'\alpha'')^{-1}))^{-1}) = (\alpha\alpha_x)^{-1}\alpha'.$$

Let β_1 be the prefix of the word $(\lambda(s_{i_1}, (\alpha'\alpha'')^{-1}))^{-1}$ of length $N - |\alpha|$; the value of $\mu((s_i, \beta_i), \beta_1)$ may be defined arbitrarily. In particular, we may let this word be $(\alpha''')^{-1}$, i. e., $\alpha_x^{-1} = (\alpha''')^{-1}$.

It remains to show that in no case will similar arguments dictate the choice of a value $\mu((s_i, \beta_i), \beta_2)$ for some word β_2 which contradicts the previous definition. This situation may arise only if there exist a word $\alpha_1 \in \mathfrak{M}_{\mathrm{II}}(s_i, \beta_i)$, a nonempty word α'_1, a word α''_1 of length N and a state s_{i_2} such that

$$\delta(s_{i_2}, (\alpha'_1\alpha''_1)^{-1}\alpha_1) = s_i,$$
$$(\lambda(\delta(s_{i_2}, (\alpha'_1\alpha''_1)^{-1}), \alpha_1))^{-1} = \beta_i,$$

a word $\alpha_{\alpha_1\alpha'_1\alpha''_1} \in \mathfrak{M}_{\mathrm{II}}(s_j, \beta_j)$ of the form $\alpha_{\alpha_1\alpha'_1\alpha''_1} = \alpha_1\alpha'''_1 \neq \alpha\alpha'''$, a word α^{IV} of length N and a state s_{j_2} such that $\delta(s_{j_2}, (\alpha'_1\alpha_1^{\mathrm{IV}})^{-1}\alpha_1\alpha'''_1) = s_j$ and $(\lambda(\delta(s_{j_2}, (\alpha'_1\alpha_1^{\mathrm{IV}})^{-1}), \alpha_1\alpha'''_1))^{-1} = \beta_j$. Suppose that the last different letter of the words $\alpha_1\alpha'''_1$ and $\alpha\alpha'''$ is the i-th, counting from the end of each word $(1 \leqslant i \leqslant N)$. Since $A(\mathrm{II}, N)$, the words $(\lambda(s_{j_2}, (\alpha'_1\alpha_1^{\mathrm{IV}})^{-1}))^{-1}$ and $(\lambda(s_{j_1}, (\alpha'\alpha^{\mathrm{IV}})^{-1}))^{-1}$ are different, and in both of them the first different letter is the j-th, counting from the beginning of each word $(1 \leqslant j \leqslant i)$. Consequently, if the need arises to define $\mu((s_i, \beta_i), \beta_2) \neq \mu((s_i, \beta_i), \beta_1)$ for some word β_2, the latter will differ from β_1 so that the function μ remains single-valued.

Now suppose that the conditions of the theorem fail to hold for two states (s_i, β_i) and (s_j, β_j).

Case I. There is a word $\alpha \in \mathfrak{M}_{II}(s_i, \beta_i)$ such that no word $\alpha_1 \in \mathfrak{M}_{II}(s_j, \beta_j)$ is expressible as $\alpha_1 = \alpha\alpha'''$. This case is treated as in the proof of Theorem 9_I.

Case II. There exist a word $\alpha \in \mathfrak{M}_{II}(s_i, \beta_i)$, a nonempty word α', a word α'' of length N and a state s_{i_1} such that $\delta(s_{i_1}, (\alpha'\alpha'')^{-1}\alpha) = s_i$ and $(\lambda(\delta(s_{i_1}, (\alpha'\alpha'')^{-1}), \alpha))^{-1} = \beta_i$, and for any word $\alpha_1 \in \mathfrak{M}_{II}(s_j, \beta_j)$ of the form $\alpha_1 = \alpha\alpha'''$ and any word α^{IV} of length N there is no state s_{j_1} such that

$$\delta(s_{j_1}, (\alpha'\alpha^{IV})^{-1}\alpha_1) = s_j,$$

$$(\lambda(\delta(s_{j_1}, (\alpha'\alpha^{IV})^{-1}), \alpha_1))^{-1} = \beta_j$$

and

$$\lambda(s_{j_1}, (\alpha'\alpha^{IV})^{-1}) = \lambda(s_{i_1}, (\alpha'\alpha'')^{-1}).$$

Subcase 1. There is a word $\alpha_1 \in \mathfrak{M}_{II}(s_j, \beta_j)$, not expressible as $\alpha_1 = \alpha\alpha'''$, such that there exist a state s_{j_1} and a word α^{IV} satisfying the conditions

$$\delta(s_{j_1}, (\alpha'\alpha^{IV})^{-1}\alpha_1) = s_j,$$
$$(\lambda(\delta(s_{j_1}, (\alpha'\alpha^{IV})^{-1}), \alpha_1))^{-1} = \beta_j$$

and

$$\lambda(s_{j_1}, (\alpha'\alpha^{IV})^{-1}) = \lambda(s_{i_1}, (\alpha'\alpha'')^{-1}).$$

Subcase 2. For any word $\alpha_1 \in \mathfrak{M}_{II}(s_j, \beta_j)$ expressible as $\alpha_1 = \alpha\alpha'''$, there do not exist a word α^{IV} of length N and a state s_{j_1} such that

$$\delta(s_{j_1}, (\alpha'\alpha^{IV})^{-1}\alpha_1) = s_j,$$

$$(\lambda(\delta(s_{j_1}, (\alpha'\alpha^{IV})^{-1}), \alpha_1))^{-1} = \beta_j$$

and

$$\lambda(s_{j_1}, (\alpha'\alpha^{IV})^{-1}) = \lambda(s_{i_1}, (\alpha'\alpha'')^{-1}).$$

Subcase 3. For any word $\alpha_1 \in \mathfrak{M}_{II}(s_j, \beta_j)$ expressible as $\alpha_1 = \alpha\alpha'''$, there exist a word α^{IV} of length N, a nonempty word α'_1 and a state s_{j_1} such that

$$\delta(s_{j_1}, (\alpha'_1\alpha^{IV})^{-1}\alpha_1) = s_j,$$

$$(\lambda(\delta(s_{j_1}, (\alpha'_1\alpha^{IV})^{-1}), \alpha_1))^{-1} = \beta_j,$$

$$\lambda(s_{j_1}, (\alpha'_1\alpha^{IV})^{-1}) = \lambda(s_{i_1}, (\alpha'\alpha'')^{-1}),$$

$$\alpha'_1 \neq \alpha' \text{ and } |\alpha'_1| = |\alpha'|.$$

For each of these subcases one can employ reasoning analogous to that used in the corresponding subcases in the proof of Theorem 9_{I}.

This completes the proof of the theorem.

Theorems 9_{I} and 9_{II} have several corollaries.

Corollary 1_{I}. If a state $(s_i, \beta_i)\in\mathfrak{T}_2$ of a type I standard inverse automaton is replaceable by a state $(s_j, \beta_j)\in\mathfrak{T}_1$, then for every state of the form $(s_i, \beta_i\beta'_i)\in\mathfrak{T}_1$ there exists a word $\alpha\in\mathfrak{M}_{\mathrm{I}}(s_j, \beta_j)$ of the form $\alpha=\alpha_1\alpha_2$, $|\alpha_1|=N-|\beta_i|$, such that $(s_i, \beta_i\beta'_i)\leqslant(\delta(s_j,\alpha_1), \beta'_j\beta'_i)$ (where β'_j is the suffix of β_j of length $|\beta_i|$).

This follows from the following arguments. If $(s_i, \beta_i\beta'_i)\in\mathfrak{T}_1$ for some word β'_i, then $\mu((s_i, \beta_i)\cdot\beta'_i)$ is defined and

$$\mu((s_i, \beta_i), \beta'_i)=\mu((s_j, \beta_j), \beta'_i)\,.$$

Since $(s_i, \beta_i)\leqslant(s_j, \beta_j)$, it follows that also

$$\varepsilon((s_i, \beta_i), \beta'_i)\leqslant\varepsilon((s_j, \beta_j), \beta'_i)\,.$$

Using the equalities

$$\varepsilon((s_i, \beta_i), \beta'_i)=(s_i, \beta_i\beta'_i),$$
$$\varepsilon((s_j, \beta_j), \beta'_i)=(\delta(s_j, \alpha_1), \beta'_j\beta'_i)\,,$$

where $\alpha_1=\mu((s_j, \beta_j), \beta'_i)$, we obtain the desired conclusion.

Corollary 1_{II}. If a state $(s_i, \beta_i)\in\mathfrak{T}_2$ of a type II standard inverse automaton is replaceable by a state $(s_j, \beta_j)\in\mathfrak{T}_1$, then for every state $(s_i, \beta_i\beta'_i)\in\mathfrak{T}_1$ there exist a word $\alpha\in\mathfrak{M}_{\mathrm{II}}(s_j, \beta_j)$ of the form $\alpha=\alpha_2\alpha_1$, $|\alpha_1|=N-|\beta_i|$, and states s_{j_1}, s_{j_2} such that $\delta(s_{j_1}, \alpha_1)=s_j$, $\delta(s_{j_2}, \alpha_2)=s_{j_1}$ and $(s_i, \beta_i\beta'_i)\leqslant(s_{j_1}, \beta'_j\beta'_i)$ (where β'_j is the suffix of β_j of length $|\beta_i|$).

The proof is analogous to that of Corollary 1_{I}.

Corollary 2_{I}. Let $(s_i, \beta_i)\in\mathfrak{T}_2$ and $(s_j, \beta_j)\in\mathfrak{T}_1$ be states of a type I standard inverse automaton such that for every word $\alpha\in\mathfrak{M}_{\mathrm{I}}(s_i, \beta_i)$ there is a word $\alpha_1\in\mathfrak{M}_{\mathrm{I}}(s_j, \beta_j)$ of the form $\alpha_1=\alpha_2\alpha$, such that $\delta(s_i, \alpha)\leqslant\delta(s_j, \alpha_2\alpha)$; then (s_i, β_i) is replaceable by (s_j, β_j).

Corollary 2_{II}. Let $(s_i, \beta_i)\in\mathfrak{T}_2$ and $(s_j, \beta_j)\in\mathfrak{T}_1$ be states of a type II standard inverse automaton such that for every word $\alpha\in\mathfrak{M}_{\mathrm{II}}(s_i, \beta_i)$ and state s_{i_1}, where $(\lambda(s_{i_1}, \alpha))^{-1}=\beta_i$ and $\delta(s_{i_1}, \alpha)=s_i$, there exist a word $\alpha_1\in\mathfrak{M}_{\mathrm{II}}(s_j, \beta_j)$ of the form $\alpha_1=\alpha\alpha_2$ and a state s_{j_1}, where $\delta(s_{j_1}, \alpha\alpha_2)=s_j$, $(\lambda(s_{j_1}, \alpha\alpha_2))^{-1}=\beta_j$ and $s_{j_1}\geqq s_{i_1}$; then (s_i, β_i) is replaceable by (s_j, β_j).

Corollary 2 is essentially a rephrased version of Theorem 9. Thus, for example, it follows from the condition $\delta(s_i, \alpha)\leqslant\delta(s_j, \alpha_2\alpha)$ that $\lambda(\delta(s_i, \alpha), \alpha'\alpha'')=\lambda(\delta(s_j, \alpha_2\alpha), \alpha'\alpha'')$.

The simplest case to consider is replacement of states (s_i, Λ). In this special case, we have the following results.

Corollary 3_{I}. Let $A(\mathrm{I}, N)$, and suppose that for any word α' such that $\lambda(s_i, \alpha')$ is defined there is a word $\alpha_{\alpha'}\in\mathfrak{M}_{\mathrm{I}}(s_j, \beta)$ with $\lambda(\delta(s_j, \alpha_{\alpha'}), \alpha')=\lambda(s_i, \alpha')$. Then A has a type I standard inverse with delay N in which the state (s_i, Λ) is replaceable by (s_j, β).

Corollary 3_{II}. Let $A(\text{II}, N)$, and suppose that for every word α' and state s_{i_1} such that $\delta(s_{i_1}, \alpha') = s_i$ there exist a word $\alpha_{\alpha'} \in \mathfrak{M}_{II}(s_j, \beta)$ and a state s_{j_1} with $\delta(s_{j_1}, \alpha') = s_{j_2}$, $\delta(s_{j_2}, \alpha_{\alpha'}) = s_j$, $(\lambda(s_{j_2}, \alpha_{\alpha'}))^{-1} = \beta$ and $\lambda(s_{j_1}, \alpha') = \lambda(s_{i_1}, \alpha')$. Then A has a type II standard inverse with delay N in which the state (s_i, Λ) is replaceable by (s_j, β).

Essentially, the fact that a state $(s_i, \Lambda) \in \mathfrak{T}_2$ is replaceable by a state $(s_j, \beta) \in \mathfrak{T}_1$ means that $\mu((s_j, \beta), \lambda(s_i, \alpha\alpha')) = \alpha''\alpha$ for any nonempty word α and any word α' of length N.

The most easily visualized instance of the situation described in Corollary 3 occurs when there exist a state s_j and a word α of length N such that either $\delta(s_j, \alpha) = s_i$ (for type I inverses) or $\delta(s_i, \alpha) = s_j$ (for type II). Remember that we are considering only automata with the property that, for any state s_i and any number M, there is a word α of length M for which $\delta(s_i, \alpha)$ is defined; hence it follows that for type II inverses the set $\mathfrak{T}_2$ is in effect superfluous, since the principal part of B already has, for every state s_i, a state t_j satisfying condition (6). Similarly, the set $\mathfrak{T}_2$ is superfluous for type II inverses provided the original automaton is strongly connected.

In such cases, the state t_j of a type II inverse for a state s_i may be any pair (s_j, β) for which there is a word α of length N such that $\delta(s_i, \alpha) = s_j$, $(\lambda(s_i, \alpha))^{-1} = \beta$. For a type I inverse, t_j may be any state (s_j, β) for which there is a word α of length N with $\delta(s_j, \alpha) = s_i$, $\lambda(s_j, \alpha) = \beta$. The following examples will show, however, that this by no means exhausts the possible correlations between the states of an automaton and its standard inverse.

Example 7. An automaton A is defined by Table 14 ($a_1 = b_1 = 0$, $a_2 = b_2 = 1$) It can be shown that A (SI, 2). The principal part of a type I standard inverse B with delay 2 is given by Table 15. (The automaton A is strongly connected, and so the set of states $\mathfrak{T}_2$ is not specified — we have already stated that it is superfluous.) With the state s_1 we may correlate any of the states $(s_1, 10)$, $(s_4, 10)$, $(s_5, 11)$ or $(s_6, 00)$, since

$$\delta(s_1, 00) = s_1,\ \lambda(s_1, 00) = 10,\ \delta(s_4, 00) = s_1,\ \lambda(s_4, 00) = 10,$$
$$\delta(s_5, 01) = s_1,\ \lambda(s_5, 01) = 11,\ \delta(s_6, 10) = s_1,\ \lambda(s_6, 10) = 00.$$

If we choose one of these states to be (s_j, β_j), we always obtain $\mu((s_j, \beta_j), \lambda(s_1, \alpha'\alpha'')) = \alpha'''\alpha'$, with the same word α''' for all α' and α'' (α'' and α''' are of length 2). If the state (s_1, Λ) is replaceable by any other states of the principal part of the inverse, it follows from Corollary 1_I that the latter are necessarily states (s_j, β_j) with the property: for every word β_i such that the inverse has a state (s_1, β_i), there is a word α_i ($|\alpha_i| = 2$) satisfying the condition $(\delta(s_j, \alpha_i), \beta_i) \geqslant (s_1, \beta_i)$. We have $(s_1, 01) \leqslant (s_5, 01)$ and $(s_1, 10) \leqslant (s_4, 10)$. Thus (s_j, β_j) may be any state such that for some words α_1 and α_2 of length 2 we have $\delta(s_j, \alpha_1) = s_5$, $\delta(s_j, \alpha_2) = s_4$ and $\lambda(s_j, \alpha_1) = \lambda(s_j, \alpha_2) = \beta_j$. The first two conditions are valid for the states s_1, s_4, s_5 and s_6. It is readily seen, however, that these states also satisfy the last condition. In particular:

$$\delta(s_1, 10) = s_4,\ \delta(s_1, 11) = s_5,\ \lambda(s_1, 10) = \lambda(s_1, 11) = 01;$$
$$\delta(s_4, 10) = s_5,\ \delta(s_4, 11) = s_4,\ \lambda(s_4, 10) = \lambda(s_4, 11) = 00;$$
$$\delta(s_5, 10) = s_4,\ \delta(s_5, 11) = s_5,\ \lambda(s_5, 10) = \lambda(s_5, 11) = 01;$$
$$\delta(s_6, 00) = s_4,\ \delta(s_6, 01) = s_5,\ \lambda(s_6, 00) = \lambda(s_6, 01) = 11.$$

TABLE 14.

	0	1		0	1
s_1	s_2, 1	s_3, 0	s_5	s_8, 1	s_3, 0
s_2	s_1, 0	s_6, 0	s_6	s_3, 1	s_2, 0
s_3	s_4, 1	s_5, 1	s_7	s_5, 0	s_4, 0
s_4	s_2, 1	s_7, 0	s_8	s_6, 1	s_1, 1

TABLE 15.

	0	1		0	1
(s_1, 01)	(s_3, 10), 1	(s_3, 11), 1	(s_5, 01)	(s_3, 10), 1	(s_3, 11), 1
(s_1, 10)	(s_2, 00), 0	(s_2, 01), 0	(s_5, 11)	(s_8, 10), 0	(s_8, 11), 0
(s_2, 00)	(s_6, 00), 1	(s_1, 01), 0	(s_6, 00)	(s_2, 00), 1	(s_2, 01), 1
(s_2, 01)	(s_1, 10), 0	(s_6, 11), 1	(s_6, 11)	(s_3, 10), 0	(s_3, 11), 0
(s_3, 10)	(s_4, 00), 0	(s_5, 01), 1	(s_7, 00)	(s_4, 00), 1	(s_5, 01), 0
(s_3, 11)	(s_4, 10), 0	(s_5, 11), 1	(s_7, 01)	(s_4, 10), 1	(s_5, 11), 0
(s_4, 00)	(s_7, 00), 1	(s_7, 01), 1	(s_8, 10)	(s_6, 00), 0	(s_1, 01), 1
(s_4, 10)	(s_2, 00), 0	(s_2, 01), 0	(s_8, 11)	(s_1, 10), 1	(s_6, 11), 0

TABLE 16.

	0	1		0	1
s_1	s_2, 0	s_3, 0	s_5	s_6, 0	s_8, 0
s_2	s_3, 0	s_1, 1	s_6	s_7, 0	s_5, 1
s_3	—	s_6, 0	s_7	s_4, 1	—
s_4	—	s_7, 1	s_8	s_7, 1	s_4, 1

TABLE 17.

	0	1		0	1
s_1	—	s_2, 1	s_5	—	s_6, 1
s_2	s_1, 0	—	s_6	s_5, 0	s_3, 0
s_3	s_2, 0	s_1, 0	s_7	s_6, 0; s_8, 1	s_4, 1
s_4	s_7, 1	s_8, 1	s_8	—	s_5, 0

TABLE 18.

	0	1		0	1
(s_1, 10)	—	(s_2, 01), 1	(s_6, 00)	(s_3, 00), 1	(s_3, 01), 1
(s_2, 01)	(s_1, 10), 0	—	(s_6, 01)	(s_5, 10), 0	—
(s_3, 00)	—	(s_2, 01), 0	(s_7, 00)	(s_6, 00), 0	(s_6, 01), 0
(s_3, 01)	(s_1, 10), 1	—	(s_7 10)	—	(s_8, 01), 0
(s_4, 10)	(s_7, 00), 0	(s_8, 01), 1	(s_7, 11)	(s_4, 10), 1	(s_4, 11), 1
(s_4, 11)	(s_7, 10), 0	(s_7, 11), 0	(s_8, 01)	(s_5, 10), 1	—
(s_5, 10)	(s_6, 00), 1	(s_6, 01), 1			

Alternatively, the state (s_j, β_j) may be chosen as any one of $(s_1, 01)$, $(s_4, 00)$, $(s_5, 01)$ or $(s_6, 11)$. This choice of (s_j, β_j) has the result that the word α''' in the equality $\mu((s_j, \beta_j),\ \lambda(s_1, \alpha'\alpha'')) = \alpha'''\alpha'$ takes two values, depending on the word $\alpha'\alpha''$.

Example 8. An automaton A is defined by Table 16. It may be verified that A is not IL-I-N for any N, but it is ILS-II-2. Its formation table is Table 17.

To construct a type II inverse automaton, we can use the formation table in the same way as the transition table is used to construct a type I inverse. Table 18 exhibits the type II standard inverse for this case.

With the state s_3 we may correlate either of the states $(s_7, 00)$ or $(s_5, 10)$, since $\delta(s_3, 10) = s_7$, $\delta(s_3, 11) = s_5$, $\lambda(s_3, 10) = 00$ and $\lambda(s_3, 11) = 01$. It is clear from Table 17 that the set of all words $\{\alpha\}$ for which there is a state s_i with $\delta(s_i, \alpha) = s_3$ may be partitioned into two subsets $\{\alpha_1\}$ and $\{\alpha_2\}$ so that for every word α_1 there is a state s_j with $\delta(s_j, \alpha_1) = s_7$ and $\lambda(s_j, \alpha_1) = \lambda(s_i, \alpha_1)$, provided that $\delta(s_i, \alpha_1) = s_3$. For every word α_2, there is a state s_k such that $\delta(s_k, \alpha_2) = s_8$ and $\lambda(s_k, \alpha_2) = \lambda(s_i, \alpha_2)$, provided that $\delta(s_i, \alpha_2) = s_3$. Since

$$\delta(s_7, 01) = s_7,\ \lambda(s_7, 01) = 11,\ \delta(s_8, 11) = s_7,\ \lambda(s_8, 11) = 11,$$

the state (s_3, Λ) is also replaceable by the state $(s_7, 11)$.

Some of the results of this section were published previously in /5, 6/.

§6. DETECTION OF COMPATIBLE STATES OF STANDARD INVERSE AUTOMATA. GENERAL CASE

The next important problem to be considered in regard to the construction of inverse automata is simplification of standard inverses.

Essentially, Theorem 8 indicates that any minimal inverse automaton may be constructed by minimization of some standard inverse. The only exceptions occur when the functions $\mu(t_j, \beta)$ and $\varepsilon(t_j, \beta)$ of the inverse are defined for pairs which can never appear if the set of input words of the inverse coincides with the set of output words of the original IL-I-N or IL-II-N automaton. We may therefore look upon the standard inverses as prototypes of all inverse automata.

It is important to note that the question whether two states of the standard inverse are compatible or equivalent may be solved on the sole basis of the properties of the original (direct) automaton. In this connection, it will be convenient to introduce a few new concepts.

Definition 7. States s_i and s_j are said to be disjoint of order M if $\lambda(s_i, \alpha') \neq \lambda(s_j, \alpha'')$ for any words α' and α'' of length M.

Definition 8. States s_i and s_j are said to be consistent with delay N if $\lambda(s_i, \alpha') \neq \lambda(s_j, \alpha'')$ for any two different words α' and α'' of equal length whose first different letters, counting from the end of each word, are their $(N+1)$-th letters.

Definition 9. States s_i and s_j are said to be inversely disjoint of order M if

$$\lambda(s_{i_1}, \alpha') \neq \lambda(s_{j_1}, \alpha'')$$

for any two states s_{i_1}, s_{j_1} and any two words α', α'' of length M such that $\delta(s_{i_1}, \alpha') = s_i$ and $\delta(s_{j_1}, \alpha'') = s_j$.

Definition 10. States s_i and s_j are said to be inversely consistent with delay N if

$$\lambda(s_{i_1}, \alpha') \neq \lambda(s_{j_1}, \alpha'')$$

for any two states s_{i_1}, s_{j_1} and any two words α', α'' of equal length, whose last distinct letters are their $(N+1)$-th letters (counting from the beginning of each word), such that $\delta(s_{i_1}, \alpha') = s_i$ and $\delta(s_{j_1}, \alpha'') = s_j$.

Theorem 10$_{\mathrm{I}}$. States $(s_i, \beta_i) \in \mathfrak{T}_1$ and $(s_j, \beta_j) \in \mathfrak{T}_1$ of a standard inverse automaton for an automaton A are compatible if and only if:

(1) *for any $\alpha_i \in \mathfrak{M}_{\mathrm{I}}(s_i, \beta_i)$ and $\alpha_j \in \mathfrak{M}_{\mathrm{I}}(s_j, \beta_j)$ which first differ in their M-th letters, the states $\delta(s_i, \alpha_i)$ and $\delta(s_j, \alpha_j)$ are disjoint of order M;*

(2) *for any identical words $\alpha_i \in \mathfrak{M}_{\mathrm{I}}(s_i, \beta_i)$ and $\alpha_j \in \mathfrak{M}_{\mathrm{I}}(s_j, \beta_j)$ the states $\delta(s_i, \alpha_i)$ and $\delta(s_j, \alpha_j)$ are consistent with delay N.*

Proof. Suppose the conditions fail to hold.

Case I (condition 2 fails). Let α be a word such that $\lambda(s_i, \alpha) = \beta_i$ and $\lambda(s_j, \alpha) = \beta_j$ and the states $\delta(s_i, \alpha)$ and $\delta(s_j, \alpha)$ are not consistent with delay N; in other words, there exist words $\alpha_i a_k \alpha'_i$ and $\alpha_i a_l \alpha'_j$, $a_k \neq a_l$, $|\alpha'_i| = |\alpha'_j| = N$, such that

$$\lambda(\delta(s_i, \alpha), \alpha_i a_k \alpha'_i) = \lambda(\delta(s_j, \alpha), \alpha_i a_l \alpha'_j) = \beta.$$

In the standard inverse, we have $\mu((s_i, \beta_i), \beta) = \alpha\alpha_i a_k$ and $\mu((s_j, \beta_j), \beta) = \alpha\alpha_i a_l$. Since $a_k \neq a_l$, the states (s_i, β_i) and (s_j, β_j) are incompatible.

Case II (condition 1 fails). Consider words $\alpha_i a_k \alpha'_i \in \mathfrak{M}_{\mathrm{I}}(s_i, \beta_i)$, $\alpha_i a_l \alpha'_j \in \mathfrak{M}_{\mathrm{I}}(s_j, \beta_j)$, where $a_k \neq a_l$, $|\alpha_i| = M-1$. Suppose that the states $\delta(s_i, \alpha_i a_k \alpha'_i)$ and $\delta(s_j, \alpha_i a_l \alpha'_j)$ are not disjoint of order M; in other words, there exist words α_m and α_n of length M such that

$$\lambda(\delta(s_i, \alpha_i a_k \alpha'_i), \alpha_m) = \lambda(\delta(s_j, \alpha_i a_l \alpha'_j), \alpha_n) = \beta.$$

In the inverse automaton, we have

$$\mu((s_i, \beta_i), \beta) = \alpha_i a_k, \quad \mu((s_j, \beta_j), \beta) = \alpha_i a_l,$$

and the states (s_i, β_i) and (s_j, β_j) are incompatible.

This proves necessity. We now proceed to prove sufficiency.

Suppose that the states (s_i, β_i) and (s_j, β_j) are incompatible, i. e., there is a word β such that $\mu((s_i, \beta_i), \beta) = \alpha_i a_k$, $\mu((s_j, \beta_j), \beta) = \alpha_i a_l$, $a_k \neq a_l$.

Case I. $|\beta| = M \leqslant N$. Take arbitrary words α'_i, α''_i, α'_j and α''_j such that

$$\lambda(s_i, \alpha_i a_k \alpha'_i) = \beta_i, \quad \lambda(s_j, \alpha_i a_l \alpha'_j) = \beta_j,$$
$$\lambda(\delta(s_i, \alpha_i a_k \alpha'_i), \alpha''_i) = \beta, \quad \lambda(\delta(s_j, \alpha_i a_l \alpha'_j), \alpha''_j) = \beta.$$

Such words exist because $\mu((s_i, \beta_i), \beta)$ and $\mu((s_j, \beta_j), \beta)$ are defined. (If $|\beta| = N$, the words α'_i and α'_j are empty.) It follows from the first two equalities that $\alpha_i a_k \alpha'_i \in \mathfrak{M}_{\mathrm{I}}(s_i, \beta_i)$, $\alpha_i a_l \alpha'_j \in \mathfrak{M}_{\mathrm{I}}(s_j, \beta_j)$. The other two equalities imply that the states $\delta(s_i, \alpha_i a_k \alpha'_i)$ and $\delta(s_j, \alpha_i a_l \alpha'_j)$ are not disjoint of order M, so that condition 1 fails to hold.

Case II. $|\beta| > N$. Set $\beta = \beta'\beta''$, where $|\beta'| = N$, $\mu((s_i, \beta_i), \beta') = \mu((s_j, \beta_j), \beta') = \alpha'$. By the construction of the inverse, we have $\lambda(s_i, \alpha') = \beta_i$, $\lambda(s_j, \alpha') = \beta_j$, i. e., $\alpha' \in \mathfrak{M}_{\mathrm{I}}(s_i, \beta_i)$, $\alpha' \in \mathfrak{M}_{\mathrm{I}}(s_j, \beta_j)$. Set $\alpha_i = \alpha'\alpha'_i$ (if $|\beta| = N+1$, the word α'_i is empty). Since $\mu((s_i, \beta_i), \beta)$ and $\mu((s_j, \beta_j), \beta)$ are defined, there exist words α'''_i and α'''_j of length N such that

$$\lambda(s_i, \alpha'\alpha'_i a_k \alpha'''_i) = \beta_i \beta,$$

$$\lambda(s_j, \alpha'\alpha'_i a_l \alpha'''_j) = \beta_j \beta$$

or

$$\lambda(\delta(s_i, \alpha'), \alpha'_i a_k \alpha'''_i) = \lambda(\delta(s_j, \alpha'), \alpha'_i a_l \alpha'''_j) = \beta.$$

Thus the states $\delta(s_i, \alpha')$ and $\delta(s_j, \alpha')$ are not consistent with delay N, so that condition 1 is not satisfied.

This completes the proof.

For type II inverse automata, we have the following

Theorem 10$_{\mathrm{II}}$. *States $(s_i, \beta_i) \in \mathfrak{T}_1$ and $(s_j, \beta_j) \in \mathfrak{T}_1$ of a type II standard inverse automaton are compatible if and only if:*

(1) *any two states s_k and s_l such that there exist words α_i, α_j ($\alpha_i \neq \alpha_j$) with the properties*

$$\delta(s_k, \alpha_i) = s_i, \delta(s_l, \alpha_j) = s_j, (\lambda(s_k, \alpha_i))^{-1} = \beta_i, \quad (\lambda(s_l, \alpha_j))^{-1} = \beta_j$$

are inversely disjoint of order M, provided the last different letters of α_i and α_j, counting from the end of each word, are their M-th letters;

(2) *any two states s_k and s_l such that there exists a word α with the property*

$$\delta(s_k, \alpha) = s_i, \quad \delta(s_l, \alpha) = s_j, \quad (\lambda(s_k, \alpha))^{-1} = \beta_i, \quad (\lambda(s_l, \alpha))^{-1} = \beta_j$$

are inversely consistent with delay N.

Proof. Suppose that conditions 1 and 2 are not satisfied.

Case I (condition 2 fails). Let s_k and s_l be states which are not inversely consistent with delay N, and α_i a word such that

$$\delta(s_k, \alpha_i) = s_i, \ \delta(s_l, \alpha_i) = s_j, \ (\lambda(s_k, \alpha_i))^{-1} = \beta_i, \ (\lambda(s_l, \alpha_i))^{-1} = \beta_j.$$

Then there exist words $\alpha'_i a_k \alpha_j$ and $\alpha'_j a_l \alpha_j$, $a_k \neq a_l$, $|\alpha'_i| = |\alpha'_j| = N$, such that for suitable states s_ν and s_μ we have

$$\delta(s_\nu, \alpha'_i a_k \alpha_j) = s_k, \quad \delta(s_\mu, \alpha'_j a_l \alpha_j) = s_l, \quad \lambda(s_\nu, \alpha'_i a_k \alpha_j) = \lambda(s_\mu, \alpha'_j a_l \alpha_j) = \beta.$$

In a type II standard inverse we have

$$\mu((s_i, \beta_i), \beta^{-1}) = (\alpha_j\alpha_i)^{-1}a_k,$$
$$\mu((s_j, \beta_j), \beta^{-1}) = (\alpha_j\alpha_i)^{-1}a_l,$$

so that the states (s_i, β_i) and (s_j, β_j) are incompatible.

Case II (condition 1 fails). Consider states s_k, s_l and words $\alpha'_i a_k \alpha_i$, $\alpha'_j a_l \alpha_i$ such that

$$a_k \neq a_l, \ |\alpha_i| = M-1, \ \delta(s_k, \alpha'_i a_k \alpha_i) = s_i, \ \delta(s_l, \alpha'_j a_l \alpha_i) = s_j,$$
$$(\lambda(s_k, \alpha'_i a_k \alpha_i))^{-1} = \beta_i, \ (\lambda(s_l, \alpha'_j a_l \alpha_i))^{-1} = \beta_j.$$

Suppose that the states s_k and s_l are not inversely disjoint of order M, i. e., there exist states s_ν, s_μ and words α_m, α_n of length M such that

$$\delta(s_\nu, \alpha_m) = s_k, \delta(s_\mu, \alpha_n) = s_l, \ \lambda(s_\nu, \alpha_m) = \lambda(s_\mu, \alpha_n) = \beta.$$

For a type II standard inverse, we have

$$\mu((s_i, \beta_i), \beta^{-1}) = \alpha_i^{-1}a_k,$$
$$\mu((s_j, \beta_j), \beta^{-1}) = \alpha_i^{-1}a_l,$$

so that the states (s_i, β_i) and (s_j, β_j) are incompatible.

Conversely, let (s_i, β_i) and (s_j, β_j) be incompatible states, i. e., there exists a word β such that

$$\mu((s_i, \beta_i), \beta^{-1}) = \alpha_i^{-1}a_k, \ \mu((s_j, \beta_j), \beta^{-1}) = \alpha_i^{-1}a_l, a_k \neq a_l.$$

Case I. $|\beta| = M \leqslant N$. Consider arbitrary words α'_i, α''_i, α'_j and α''_j and states s_k, s_l and s_ν, s_μ such that

$$\delta(s_k, \alpha'_i a_k \alpha_i) = s_i, \ \delta(s_l, \alpha'_j a_l \alpha_i) = s_j, \ (\lambda(s_k, \alpha'_i a_k \alpha_i))^{-1} = \beta_i, \ (\lambda(s_l, \alpha'_j a_l \alpha_i))^{-1} =$$
$$= \beta_j, \ \delta(s_\nu, \alpha''_i) = s_k, \ \delta(s_\mu, \alpha''_j) = s_l; \ \lambda(s_\nu, \alpha''_i) = \lambda(s_\mu, \alpha''_j) = \beta.$$

Words and states satisfying these requirements exist, since otherwise both $\mu((s_i, \beta_i), \beta^{-1})$ and $\mu((s_j, \beta_j), \beta^{-1})$ would be undefined. It follows from the last four equalities that the states s_k and s_l are not inversely disjoint of order M. The first four equalities imply that the states s_k and satisfy the premise of condition 1. Thus condition 1 indeed fails to hold.

Case II. $|\beta| > N$. Set $\beta = \beta_2\beta_1$, where $|\beta_1| = N$ and $\mu((s_i, \beta_i), \beta_1^{-1}) = \mu((s_j, \beta_j), \beta_1^{-1}) = \alpha_1$. It follows that there exist states s_k and s_l for which

$$\delta(s_k, \alpha_1^{-1}) = s_i, \delta(s_l, \alpha_1^{-1}) = s_j, (\lambda(s_k, \alpha_1^{-1}))^{-1} = \beta_i, (\lambda(s_l, \alpha_1^{-1}))^{-1} = \beta_j.$$

Set $\alpha = \alpha_1\alpha_2$ Since $\mu((s_i, \beta_i), \beta^{-1})$ and $\mu((s_j, \beta_j), \beta^{-1})$ are defined, there exist words α'''_i and α'''_j of length N and states s_ν and s_μ such that

$$\delta(s_\nu, \alpha'''_i a_k \alpha_2^{-1}) = s_k,$$
$$\delta(s_\mu, \alpha'''_j a_l \alpha_2^{-1}) = s_l,$$
$$\lambda(s_\nu, \alpha'''_i a_k \alpha_2^{-1}) = \lambda(s_\mu, \alpha'''_j a_l \alpha_2^{-1}) = \beta.$$

It follows from these equalities that the states s_k and s_l are not inversely consistent with delay N, so that condition 2 fails to hold.

In some cases, the application of Theorems 10_{I} and 10_{II} makes it easier to find compatible states of standard inverse automata. Their principal import, however, is that they ultimately yield certain general information concerning the properties of standard inverse automata and hence, via Theorem 8, of inverse automata in general.

§7. DETECTION OF COMPATIBLE STATES OF STANDARD INVERSE AUTOMATA. SPECIAL CASES

We shall now derive a few corollaries of Theorems 10_{I} and 10_{II} in cases that the direct automaton or its standard inverse obeys certain restrictions.

Theorem 11_{I}. Given a complete type I standard inverse automaton, let (s_i, β_i), (s_j, β_j) be equivalent states. Then $\mathfrak{M}_{\mathrm{I}}(s_i, \beta_i) = \mathfrak{M}_{\mathrm{I}}(s_j, \beta_j)$ and the states $\delta(s_i, \alpha)$ and $\delta(s_j, \alpha)$ are compatible for every word $\alpha \in \mathfrak{M}_{\mathrm{I}}(s_i, \beta_i)$.

Proof. We first show that the sets $\mathfrak{M}_{\mathrm{I}}(s_i, \beta_i)$ and $\mathfrak{M}_{\mathrm{I}}(s_j, \beta_j)$ are identical. Suppose there is a word α such that $\lambda(s_i, \alpha) = \beta_i$ but $\lambda(s_j, \alpha) \neq \beta_j$. It follows from Theorem 10_{I} that for any word $\alpha_j \in \mathfrak{M}_{\mathrm{I}}(s_j, \beta_j)$ the states $\delta(s_i, \alpha)$ and $\delta(s_j, \alpha_j)$ are disjoint of order M, $M \leqslant N$. But then for any words α_k and α_l of length N we have $\lambda(\delta(s_i, \alpha), \alpha_k) \neq \lambda(\delta(s_j, \alpha_j), \alpha_l)$. Since $\mu((s_j, \beta_j), \beta)$ is defined for any β, there must exist words $\alpha'_j \in \mathfrak{M}_{\mathrm{I}}(s_j, \beta_j)$ and α' such that $\lambda(s_j, \alpha'_j\alpha') = \beta_j\beta$, or $\lambda(\delta(s_j, \alpha'_j), \alpha') = \beta$. Let β be the word $\lambda(\delta(s_i, \alpha), \alpha_k)$. We then obtain a contradiction to the previously derived inequality, thus proving that the two sets in question must coincide.

Suppose that for some $\alpha \in \mathfrak{M}_{\mathrm{I}}(s_i, \beta_i)$ the states $\delta(s_i, \alpha)$ and $\delta(s_j, \alpha)$ are incompatible, i. e., there exists a word α_k such that

$$\lambda(\delta(s_i, \alpha), \alpha_k) = \beta_k b_l, \quad \lambda(\delta(s_j, \alpha), \alpha_k) = \beta_k b_m, \quad b_l \neq b_m.$$

Take an arbitrary word α_l of length N such that $\lambda(\delta(s_j, \alpha), \alpha_k\alpha_l)$ is defined. Let $\lambda(\delta(s_j, \alpha), \alpha_k\alpha_l) = \beta_k b_m \beta_l$. Since the inverse automaton is complete, the value of $\mu((s_i, \beta_i), \beta_k b_m \beta_l)$ is also defined. Hence there exist words α_n and α'_n of length N and a word α'' such that

$$\lambda(s_i, \alpha_n\alpha''\alpha'_n) = \beta_i\beta_k b_m \beta_l$$

or

$$\lambda(\delta(s_i, \alpha_n), \alpha''\alpha'_n) = \beta_k b_m \beta_l.$$

If $\alpha_n \neq \alpha$, it follows from the above formulas that the states $\delta(s_i, \alpha_n)$ and $\delta(s_j, \alpha)$ are not disjoint of order M. Since this contradicts Theorem 10_{I}, it remains only to consider the case $\alpha_n = \alpha$, i. e.,

$$\lambda(\delta(s_i, \alpha), \alpha''\alpha'_n) = \beta_k b_m \beta_l.$$

If $\alpha'' \neq \alpha_k$, we obtain a contradiction to Theorem 10_{I}, since then the states $\delta(s_i, \alpha)$ and $\delta(s_j, \alpha)$ are not consistent with delay N. We may thus assume that $\alpha'' = \alpha_k$, but then $\lambda(\delta(s_i, \alpha), \alpha_k) = \beta_k b_m$, and this contradicts a previous equality, proving the theorem.

Theorem 11_{II}. *Given a complete type II standard inverse automaton, let* (s_i, β_i) *and* (s_j, β_j) *be equivalent states. Then* $\mathfrak{M}_{\mathrm{II}}(s_i, \beta_i) = \mathfrak{M}_{\mathrm{II}}(s_j, \beta_j)$ *and, for any word* $\alpha \in \mathfrak{M}_{\mathrm{II}}(s_i, \beta_i)$ *and arbitrary words* α_k, β_k *and state* s_m *such that*

$$\delta(\delta(s_m, \alpha_k), \alpha) = s_i, \quad \lambda(s_m, \alpha_k) = \beta_k, \quad (\lambda(\delta(s_m, \alpha_k), \alpha))^{-1} = \beta_i,$$

there exists a state s_n *such that* $\delta(\delta(s_n, \alpha_k), \alpha) = s_j$, $(\lambda(\delta(s_n, \alpha_k), \alpha))^{-1} = \beta_j$ *and* $\lambda(s_n, \alpha_k) = \beta_k$, *and conversely.*

Proof. Suppose there exist a word α and a state s_k such that $\delta(s_k, \alpha) = s_i$, $(\lambda(s_k, \alpha))^{-1} = \beta_i$, but for any state s_l either $\delta(s_l, \alpha) \neq s_j$ or $(\lambda(s_l, \alpha))^{-1} \neq \beta_j$. Let α_j be any word for which there is a state s_l such that $\delta(s_l, \alpha_j) = s_j$, $(\lambda(s_l, \alpha_j))^{-1} = \beta_j$. By Theorem 10_{II}, the states s_l and s_k are inversely disjoint of order M, $M \leqslant N$, since $\alpha_j \neq \alpha$. This means that for any states s_ν, s_μ and words α_k, α_l of length N such that $\delta(s_\nu, \alpha_k) = s_l$, $\delta(s_\mu, \alpha_l) = s_k$ we have $\lambda(s_\nu, \alpha_k) \neq \lambda(s_\mu, \alpha_l)$. Since $\mu((s_j, \beta_j), \beta)$ is defined for any word β, there must exist a word α'_j of length N, a word α' and a state s_ρ such that $\delta(s_\rho, \alpha'\alpha'_j) = s_j$, $\lambda(s_\rho, \alpha'\alpha'_j) = (\beta_j\beta)^{-1}$. In particular, let β^{-1} be the word $\lambda(s_\mu, \alpha_l)$. But then it follows that there exist a word α' of length N and a state s_ρ such that

$$\delta(s_\rho, \alpha') = s_l, \ \delta(s_l, \alpha'_j) = s_j, \quad (\lambda(s_l, \alpha'_j))^{-1} = \beta_j,$$
$$\lambda(s_\rho, \alpha') = \lambda(s_\mu, \alpha_l),$$

contrary to what we have already proved. Consequently, the sets $\mathfrak{M}_{\mathrm{II}}(s_i, \beta_i)$ and $\mathfrak{M}_{\mathrm{II}}(s_j, \beta_j)$ must be identical.

Now suppose there exist words $\alpha \in \mathfrak{M}_{\mathrm{II}}(s_i, \beta_i)$, α_k and β_k such that for some state s_m it is true that $\delta(s_m, \alpha_k\alpha) = s_i$ and $(\lambda(s_m, \alpha_k\alpha))^{-1} = \beta_i\beta_k^{-1}$, but for any state s_n we have either $\delta(s_n, \alpha_k\alpha) \neq s_j$ or $(\lambda(s_n, \alpha_k\alpha))^{-1} \neq \beta_j\beta_k^{-1}$. Let α_l be a word of length N and s_μ a state such that $\delta(s_\mu, \alpha_l) = s_m$. Set $\lambda(s_\mu, \alpha_l) = \beta_l$. Since the standard inverse is complete, the value of $\mu((s_j, \beta_j), (\beta_l\beta_k)^{-1})$ is defined. But then there exist words α_n, α'_n of length N, a word α'' and a state s_π such that

$$\delta(s_\pi, \alpha'_n\alpha''\alpha_n) = s_j,$$
$$\lambda(s_\pi, \alpha'_n\alpha''\alpha_n) = \beta_l\beta_k\beta_j^{-1}.$$

If $\alpha_n \neq \alpha$, the states $\delta(s_\pi, \alpha'_n\alpha'')$ and $\delta(s_\mu, \alpha_l\alpha_k)$ are not inversely disjoint of order M with $M \leqslant N$. Since by Theorem 10_{II} this is impossible, it remains to consider the case that $\alpha_n = \alpha$, or

$$\delta(\delta(s_\pi, \alpha'_n\alpha''), \alpha) = s_j, \quad (\lambda(\delta(s_\pi, \alpha'_n\alpha''), \alpha))^{-1} = \beta_j.$$

Let $\alpha'' \neq \alpha_k$. Then the states $\delta(s_\pi, \alpha'_n\alpha'')$ and $\delta(s_\mu, \alpha_l\alpha_k)$ cannot be consistent with delay N, and this case is also impossible.

Thus $\alpha''=\alpha_k$. But then we have

$$\lambda(\delta(s_\pi, \alpha'_n), \alpha_k)=\beta_k, \; \delta(\delta(\delta(s_\pi, \alpha'_n), \alpha_k), \alpha)=s_j,$$

contrary to assumption.

Theorem 12_{I}. *Let A be a complete IL-I-N automaton. If* $\mathfrak{M}_{\text{I}}(s_i, \beta_i)=\mathfrak{M}_{\text{I}}(s_j, \beta_j)$ *and for every* $\alpha\in\mathfrak{M}_{\text{I}}(s_i, \beta_i)$ *the states* $\delta(s_i, \alpha)$ *and* $\delta(s_j, \alpha)$ *are equivalent, then the states* (s_i, β_i) *and* (s_j, β_j) *of the standard inverse automaton constructed with delay N are compatible.*

Proof. It will suffice to check that the assumptions of Theorem 10_{I} hold. Consider two words $\alpha a_k \alpha_i \in\mathfrak{M}_{\text{I}}(s_i, \beta_i)$ and $\alpha a_l \alpha_j \in\mathfrak{M}_{\text{I}}(s_j, \beta_j)$, $a_k\neq a_l$. Set $|\alpha|=M-1$. Suppose that the states $\delta(s_i, \alpha a_k \alpha_i)$ and $\delta(s_j, \alpha a_l \alpha_j)$ are not disjoint of order M, so that there exist words α'_i and α'_j of length M such that

$$\lambda(\delta(s_i, \alpha a_k \alpha_i), \alpha'_i)=\lambda(\delta(s_j, \alpha a_l \alpha_j), \alpha'_j)=\beta\,.$$

It follows from the assumptions of our theorem that $\alpha a_l \alpha_j\in\mathfrak{M}_{\text{I}}(s_i, \beta_i)$, and the states $\delta(s_i, \alpha a_l \alpha_j)$ and $\delta(s_j, \alpha a_l \alpha_j)$ are equivalent, i. e.,

$$\lambda(\delta(s_i, \alpha a_l \alpha_j), \alpha'_j)=\beta$$

or

$$\lambda(s_i, \alpha a_k \alpha_i \alpha'_i)=\lambda(s_i, \alpha a_l \alpha_j \alpha'_j)=\beta_i\beta\,.$$

Hence

$$\lambda(\delta(s_i, \alpha), a_k \alpha_i \alpha'_i)=\lambda(\delta(s_i, \alpha), a_l \alpha_j \alpha'_j)\,.$$

Since $|\alpha_i\alpha'_i|=N$, the automaton A cannot be IL-I-N. This contradiction shows that condition 1 of Theorem 10_{I} holds.

Let $\alpha\in\mathfrak{M}_{\text{I}}(s_i, \beta_i)$. Suppose that the states $\delta(s_i, \alpha)$ and $\delta(s_j, \alpha)$ are not consistent of order N, so that there exist words $\alpha_1 a_k \alpha_i$ and $\alpha_1 a_l \alpha_j$, $a_k\neq a_l$, $|\alpha_i|=|\alpha_j|=N$, such that $\lambda(\delta(s_i, \alpha), \alpha_1 a_k \alpha_i)=\lambda(\delta(s_j, \alpha), \alpha_1 a_l \alpha_j)$. Since the states $\delta(s_i, \alpha)$ and $\delta(s_j, \alpha)$ are equivalent, $\lambda(\delta(s_j, \alpha), \alpha_1 a_l \alpha_j)=\lambda(\delta(s_i, \alpha), \alpha_1 a_l \alpha_j)$. We now see that

$$\lambda(\delta(s_i, \alpha\alpha_1), a_l \alpha_j)=\lambda(\delta(s_i, \alpha\alpha_1), a_k \alpha_i)\,,$$

so that A cannot be an IL-I-N automaton. Consequently, condition 2 of Theorem 10_{I} is also satisfied and so its conclusion is also valid: (s_i, β_i) and (s_j, β_j) are compatible states.

To prove the analog of Theorem 12_{I} for type II inverses, we need two new concepts.

Definition 11. An automaton A is said to be inversely complete if for any word α and any state s_j there exists a state s_i such that $\delta(s_i, \alpha)=s_j$.

Definition 12. Two states s_i and s_j of an automaton A are said to be inversely equivalent if they satisfy the following condition. For every word α for which there is a state $s_\varkappa$ with $\delta(s_\varkappa, \alpha) = s_i$ (or $\delta(s_\varkappa, \alpha) = s_j$), there exists a state s_λ such that $\delta(s_\lambda, \alpha) = s_j$ (or $\delta(s_\lambda, \alpha) = s_i$) and $\lambda(s_\lambda, \alpha) = \lambda(s_\varkappa, \alpha)$

Theorem 12_{II}. Let $A(II, N)$ be an inversely complete automaton. States (s_i, β_i) and (s_j, β_j) of the type II standard inverse constructed with delay N are compatible if $\mathfrak{M}_{\text{II}}(s_i, \beta_i) = \mathfrak{M}_{\text{II}}(s_j, \beta_j)$ and if, for any word α and state s_k such that $\delta(s_k, \alpha) = s_i$ and $(\lambda(s_k, \alpha))^{-1} = \beta_i$, there exists a state such that $\delta(s_l, \alpha) = s_j$, $(\lambda(s_l, \alpha))^{-1} = \beta_j$, and the states s_k and s_l are inversely equivalent, and conversely.

Proof. We need only check that the assumptions of Theorem 10_{II} hold.

Consider two words $\alpha_i a_k \alpha$ and $\alpha_j a_l \alpha$, $a_k \neq a_l$ for which there exist states s_k and s_l such that

$$\delta(s_k, \alpha_i a_k \alpha) = s_i,\ \delta(s_l, \alpha_j a_l \alpha) = s_j,$$
$$(\lambda(s_k, \alpha_i a_k \alpha))^{-1} = \beta_i, \quad (\lambda(s_l, \alpha_j a_l \alpha))^{-1} = \beta_j.$$

Set $M = |\alpha| + 1$.

Suppose that the states s_k and s_l are not inversely disjoint of order M, so that there exist words α'_i, α'_j of length M and states s_ν, s_μ such that

$$\delta(s_\nu, \alpha'_i) = s_k,\ \delta(s_\mu, \alpha'_j) = s_l,\ \lambda(s_\nu, \alpha'_i) = \lambda(s_\mu, \alpha'_j).$$

It follows from the assumptions of our theorem that there is a state s_ρ for which $\delta(s_\rho, \alpha_j a_l \alpha) = s_i$ and $(\lambda(s_\rho, \alpha_j a_l \alpha))^{-1} = \beta_i$, and moreover s_ρ is inversely equivalent to s_l, i. e., there exists a state s_π such that $\delta(s_\pi, \alpha'_j) = s_\rho$, $\lambda(s_\pi, \alpha'_j) = \lambda(s_\mu, \alpha'_j)$. From these equalities we obtain

$$\delta(s_\pi, \alpha'_j \alpha_j a_l \alpha) = s_i,\ \delta(s_\nu, \alpha'_i \alpha_i a_k \alpha) = s_i,\ \lambda(s_\pi, \alpha'_j \alpha_j a_l \alpha) = \lambda(s_\nu, \alpha'_i \alpha_i a_k \alpha).$$

Hence one readily concludes that the automaton A cannot be IL-II-N, and so condition 1 of Theorem 10_{II} is satisfied.

Now let α be a word for which there exists a state s_k such that $\delta(s_k, \alpha) = s_i$ and $(\lambda(s_k, \alpha))^{-1} = \beta_i$. Then there is a state s_l such that $\delta(s_l, \alpha) = s_j$ and $(\lambda(s_l, \alpha))^{-1} = \beta_j$. Suppose that the states s_k and s_l are not inversely consistent with delay N, so that there exist words $\alpha_i a_k \alpha_1$ and $\alpha_j a_l \alpha_1$, $a_k \neq a_l$, $|\alpha_i| = |\alpha_j| = N$, and states s_ν, s_μ, such that

$$\delta(s_\nu, \alpha_i a_k \alpha_1) = s_k,\ \delta(s_\mu, \alpha_j a_l \alpha_1) = s_l,\ \lambda(s_\nu, \alpha_i a_k \alpha_1) = \lambda(s_\mu, \alpha_j a_l \alpha_1).$$

Since s_k and s_l are inversely equivalent, there is a state s_ρ such that $\delta(s_\rho, \alpha_j a_l \alpha_1) = s_k$ and $\lambda(s_\rho, \alpha_j a_l \alpha_1) = \lambda(s_\mu, \alpha_j a_l \alpha_1)$. From these equalities we easily deduce that

$$\delta(s_\rho, \alpha_j a_l \alpha_1 \alpha) = s_i,\ \delta(s_\nu, \alpha_i a_k \alpha_1 \alpha) = s_i,\ \lambda(s_\rho, \alpha_j a_l \alpha_1 \alpha) = \lambda(s_\nu, \alpha_i a_k \alpha_1 \alpha).$$

Let $\delta(s_\rho, \alpha_j a_l) = \delta(s_\nu, \alpha_i a_k)$. Then A cannot be IL-II-N, since $\lambda(s_\rho, \alpha_j a_l) = \lambda(s_\nu, \alpha_i a_k)$.

Let $\alpha' a_{i_1}$ and $\alpha'' a_{i_2}$ be the longest equal-length prefixes of the words $\alpha_j a_l \alpha_1 \alpha$ and $\alpha_i a_k \alpha_1 \alpha$ such that $\delta(s_\rho, \alpha' a_{i_1}) = \delta(s_\nu, \alpha'' a_{i_2})$ but $\delta(s_\rho, \alpha') \neq \delta(s_\nu, \alpha'')$ $(|\alpha'| > |\alpha_j|)$. Since $\lambda(s_\rho, \alpha' a_{i_1}) = \lambda(s_\nu, \alpha'' a_{i_2})$, we again conclude that A cannot be IL-II-N.

These contradictions show that condition 2 of Theorem 10_{II} must also hold, and thus so does its conclusion: the states (s_i, β_i) and (s_j, β_j) are compatible.

The following theorems are corollaries of Theorems 11 and 12.

Theorem 13_{I}. *Let* $A(I, N)$ *and assume that the type I standard inverse of A constructed with delay N is complete. States* $(s_i, \beta_i)\in\mathfrak{T}_1$ *and* $(s_j, \beta_j)\in\mathfrak{T}_1$ *are equivalent if and only if* $\mathfrak{M}_{\text{I}}(s_i, \beta_i)=\mathfrak{M}_{\text{I}}(s_j, \beta_j)$ *and, for any word* $\alpha\in\mathfrak{M}_{\text{I}}(s_i, \beta_i)$, *the states* $\delta(s_i, \alpha)$ *and* $\delta(s_j, \alpha)$ *are equivalent.*

Theorem 13_{II}. *Let* $A(II, N)$ *be inversely complete and suppose that the type II standard inverse of A with delay N is complete. Suppose that states* $(s_i, \beta_i)\in\mathfrak{T}_1$ *and* $(s_j, \beta_j)\in\mathfrak{T}_1$ *satisfy the conditions: for any words* $\alpha_1\in\mathfrak{M}_{\text{II}}(s_i, \beta_i)$ *and* $\alpha_2\in\mathfrak{M}_{\text{II}}(s_j, \beta_j)$, *there exists only one pair of states* s_ν, s_μ *such that*

$$\delta(s_\nu, \alpha_1)=s_i,\quad (\lambda(s_\nu, \alpha_1))^{-1}=\beta_i,\quad \delta(s_\mu, \alpha_2)=s_j,\quad (\lambda(s_\mu, \alpha_2))^{-1}=\beta_j.$$

Then the states (s_i, β_i) *and* (s_j, β_j) *are equivalent if and only if* $\mathfrak{M}_{\text{II}}(s_i, \beta_i)=\mathfrak{M}_{\text{II}}(s_j, \beta_j)$ *and for every word* $\alpha\in\mathfrak{M}_{\text{II}}(s_i, \beta_i)$ *the states* s_ν *and* s_μ *such that*

$$\delta(s_\nu, \alpha)=s_i,\quad (\lambda(s_i, \alpha))^{-1}=\beta_i,\quad \delta(s_\mu, \alpha)=s_j,\quad (\lambda(s_j, \alpha))^{-1}=\beta_j$$

are inversely equivalent.

The proof requires only the following observation. The inverse equivalence of two states s_k, s_l and the existence of words α_k, β_k and a state $s_\varkappa$ such that $\delta(s_\varkappa, \alpha_k)=s_k$ and $\lambda(s_\varkappa, \alpha_k)=\beta_k$ implies the existence of a state s_λ such that $\delta(s_\lambda, \alpha_k)=s_l$ and $\lambda(s_\lambda, \alpha_k)=\beta_k$.

Example 9. Consider the automaton $A(\text{SI}, 2)$ defined by Table 19.

TABLE 19.

	0	1
s_1	s_2, 0	s_3, 1
s_2	s_1, 0	s_4, 0
s_3	s_1, 1	s_4, 1
s_4	s_2, 1	s_3, 0

The principal part of the standard inverse B constructed for A with delay 2 has the states:

$$(s_1, 00),\ (s_1, 11),\ (s_2, 00),\ (s_2, 01),\ (s_3, 10),\ (s_3, 11),\ (s_4, 01),\ (s_4, 10).$$

We have

$$\begin{aligned}
&\lambda(s_1, 00)=\lambda(s_1, 01)=00, && \lambda(s_1, 10)=\lambda(s_1, 11)=11,\\
&\lambda(s_2, 00)=\lambda(s_2, 11)=00, && \lambda(s_2, 01)=\lambda(s_2, 10)=01,\\
&\lambda(s_3, 00)=\lambda(s_3, 11)=10, && \lambda(s_3, 01)=\lambda(s_3, 10)=11,\\
&\lambda(s_4, 00)=\lambda(s_4, 01)=10, && \lambda(s_4, 10)=\lambda(s_4, 11)=01.
\end{aligned}$$

Thus the first condition of Theorem 13_{I} (equality of the sets $\mathfrak{M}_{\mathrm{I}}(s_i, \beta_i)$ and $\mathfrak{M}_{\mathrm{I}}(s_j, \beta_j)$) holds for the following pairs of states:

$$\{(s_1, 00), (s_4, 10)\}, \{(s_1, 11), (s_4, 01)\}, \{(s_2, 00), (s_3, 10)\}, \{(s_2, 01), (s_3, 11)\}.$$

Next, we have

$$\begin{aligned} &\delta(s_1, 00) = \delta(s_4, 00) = s_1, \quad &&\delta(s_1, 01) = \delta(s_4, 01) = s_4, \\ &\delta(s_1, 10) = \delta(s_4, 10) = s_1, \quad &&\delta(s_1, 11) = \delta(s_4, 11) = s_4, \\ &\delta(s_2, 00) = \delta(s_3, 00) = s_2, \quad &&\delta(s_2, 11) = \delta(s_3, 11) = s_3, \\ &\delta(s_2, 01) = \delta(s_3, 01) = s_3, \quad &&\delta(s_2, 10) = \delta(s_3, 10) = s_2. \end{aligned}$$

Thus the pairs listed above also satisfy the second condition of Theorem 12_{II} (equivalence of the states $\delta(s_i, \alpha)$ and $\delta(s_j, \alpha)$.

It follows that they are pairs of equivalent states.

Certain deductions may nevertheless be made directly from Table 19.

We have

$$\delta(s_1, 0) = \delta(s_4, 0), \quad \delta(s_1, 1) = \delta(s_4, 1), \quad \lambda(s_1, 0) \neq \lambda(s_1, 1)$$

and

$$\lambda(s_4, 0) \neq \lambda(s_4, 1).$$

It is thus clear that for every state (s_1, β) there exists a state (s_4, β') such that the pair (s_1, β) and (s_4, β') satisfy the assumptions of Theorem 13_{I}. Similarly, for each state (s_2, β) there must be an equivalent state (s_3, β'), and conversely. Thus, in constructing the inverse automaton, the states (s_1, β) and (s_2, β) may be disregarded. Instead of the standard inverse one then obtains a simplification of the standard inverse.

Example 10. Consider the automaton $A(\mathrm{SII}, 2)$ defined by Table 16. It is clear from Table 17 that the following pairs of states of A are inversely disjoint of order 1:

$$\begin{aligned} &(s_1, s_2), (s_1, s_3), (s_1, s_6), (s_1, s_8), (s_2, s_4), (s_2, s_5), \\ &(s_3, s_4), (s_3, s_5), (s_4, s_6), (s_4, s_8), (s_5, s_6), (s_5, s_8). \end{aligned}$$

The pair (s_2, s_7) is inversely disjoint of order 2.

Finally we list the pairs of inversely consistent states with delay 2 (besides the pairs of inversely disjoint states of orders 1 and 2): (s_1, s_5), (s_2, s_6), (s_3, s_7), (s_3, s_8), (s_7, s_8).

All this may be established by examining Table 17.

Examining the sets $\mathfrak{M}_{\mathrm{II}}(s_i, \beta_i)$ and the pairs of inversely disjoint and inversely consistent states, one can show that the following pairs of states of the principal part of the standard inverse with delay 2 are compatible:

$$\{(s_1, 10), (s_2, 01)\}, \{(s_1, 10), (s_3, 01)\}, \{(s_1, 10), (s_5, 10)\}, \{(s_1, 10),$$
$$(s_6, 01)\}, \{(s_1, 10), (s_8, 01)\}, \{(s_2, 01), (s_3, 00)\}, \{(s_2, 01), (s_6, 01)\},$$

$\{(s_2, 01), (s_7, 10)\}$, $\{(s_3, 00), (s_3, 01)\}$, $\{(s_3, 00), (s_6, 01)\}$, $\{(s_3, 00), (s_7, 00)\}$, $\{(s_3, 00), (s_8, 01)\}$, $\{(s_3, 01), (s_7, 10)\}$, $\{(s_3, 01), (s_8, 01)\}$, $\{(s_6, 01), (s_7, 10)\}$, $\{(s_7, 10), (s_8, 01)\}$.

The results of this section were published previously in /6, 7/ (omitting the proofs for type II automata).

§8. RELATIONSHIP OF AN AUTOMATON TO ITS INVERSE

The properties of the original (direct) IL-I-N or IL-II-N automaton imply certain properties of its inverse.

Theorem 14. If the automaton A is strongly connected, the principal part of its standard inverse is also strongly connected.

Proof. We consider a type I inverse. Let $(s_i, \beta_i) \in \mathfrak{T}_1$ and $(s_j, \beta_j) \in \mathfrak{T}_1$ be states of the inverse and α_1 a word such that $\lambda(s_i, \alpha_1) = \beta_i$. Since A is strongly connected, there is a word α_2 such that $\delta(\delta(s_i, \alpha_1), \alpha_2) = s_j$. Set $\lambda(\delta(s_i, \alpha_1), \alpha_2) = \beta$. Then

$$\mu((s_i, \beta_i), \beta\beta_j) = \alpha_1\alpha_2$$

and

$$\varepsilon((s_i, \beta_i), \beta\beta_j) = (\delta(s_i, \alpha_1\alpha_2), \beta_j) = (s_j, \beta_j).$$

For a type II inverse, we consider words α_1, α_2 and a state s_{i_1} such that

$$\delta(s_{i_1}, \alpha_1) = s_i, \quad (\lambda(s_{i_1}, \alpha_1))^{-1} = \beta_i, \quad \delta(s_j, \alpha_2) = s_{i_1}.$$

Then

$$\mu((s_i, \beta_i), (\lambda(s_j, \alpha_2))^{-1}\beta_j) = (\alpha_2\alpha_1)^{-1}$$

and

$$\varepsilon((s_i, \beta_i), (\lambda(s_j, \alpha_2))^{-1}\beta_j) = (s_k, \beta_j),$$

where s_k is a state for which $\delta(s_k, \alpha_2\alpha_1) = s_i$, $\lambda(s_k, \alpha_2\alpha_1) = \lambda(s_j, \alpha_2)\beta_i^{-1}$, and there exist a state s_{k_1} and a word α such that $\delta(s_{k_1}, \alpha) = s_k$ and $(\lambda(s_{k_1}, \alpha))^{-1} = \beta_j$. For an IL-II-$N$ automaton, the state s_k is uniquely determined, so that necessarily $s_k = s_j$.

Theorem 15. For any state (s_i, β_i) of a standard inverse, there exists a letter b_l such that $\mu((s_i, \beta_i), b_l)$ is defined.

Proof. We first consider a type I inverse with delay N. For any state s_j there is a letter a_r such that $\lambda(s_j, a_r)$ is defined, and so for any state

s_i there is a word α of length $N+1$ such that $\lambda(s_i, \alpha)$ is defined. Let $\lambda(s_i, \alpha) = \beta_i b_l$; then $\mu((s_i, \beta_i), b_l)$ is defined.

The proof for type II inverses is analogous. One must only remember here that type II inverses may be constructed only for automata whose formation tables have no row containing no state—output letter pairs.

Theorem 16. Let B be a type I standard inverse with delay N for an automaton A. The principal part B_1 of B is an IL-I-N automaton and A is an inverse of B_1 with delay N.

Proof. If $(s_i, \beta) \in \mathfrak{T}_1$, it follows from the construction of the standard inverse that $\mu((s_i, \beta), \beta_1\beta_2) = \alpha$, where $\lambda(s_i, \alpha) = \beta\beta_1$ $(|\beta_2| = N)$. Hence $\lambda(s_i, \mu((s_i, \beta), \beta_1\beta_2)) = \beta\beta_1$. This shows that for every state of the principal part of B we may select a state of the original automaton A satisfying the conditions of Definition 5. It follows from Theorem 6 that the principal part of B is IL-I-N.

In the next chapter we shall study the question of determining the number N_1 for which B_1 is ILS-I-N_1; we shall see that it is not always true that $N_1 = N$.

Up to now, our results concerning respectively type I and type II automata have been essentially the same: each result for type I has an analog for type II and vice versa. The next theorem shows that the analogy may collapse: for type I inverses we may have $N_1 > 0$.

Theorem 17. Let B be a type II standard inverse automaton. Then the principal part B_1 of B is an IL-II-0 automaton.

Proof. Suppose that for some state $(s_k, \beta_k) \in \mathfrak{T}_1$ there exist states $(s_i, \beta_i) \in \mathfrak{T}_1$, $(s_j, \beta_j) \in \mathfrak{T}_1$ and letters b_l, b_r such that

$$\varepsilon((s_i, \beta_i), b_l) = \varepsilon((s_j, \beta_j), b_r) = (s_k, \beta_k)$$

and

$$\mu((s_i, \beta_i), b_l) = \mu((s_j, \beta_j), b_r) = a_m.$$

By the construction of type II inverses, this implies that $\delta(s_k, a_m) = s_i$ and $\delta(s_k, a_m) = s_j$. Let β be an arbitrary word of length $N-1$ for which $\varepsilon((s_k, \beta_k), \beta)$ is defined.

Set

$$\varepsilon((s_k, \beta_k), \beta) = (s_p, \beta'), \ \mu((s_k, \beta_k), \beta) = \alpha.$$

Then

$$\delta(s_p, \alpha^{-1}a_m) = s_i, \quad (\lambda(s_p, \alpha^{-1}a_m))^{-1} = \beta_i,$$
$$\delta(s_p, \alpha^{-1}a_m) = s_j, \quad (\lambda(s_p, \alpha^{-1}a_m))^{-1} = \beta_j,$$

i. e., $(s_i, \beta_i) = (s_j, \beta_j)$. Consequently, a knowledge of the output letter a_m and the state (s_k, β_k) entered by the automaton B_1 after producing this letter is sufficient to uniquely determine the previous state and input letter, so that B_1 is IL-II-0.

Chapter II

STRUCTURE OF INFORMATION-LOSSLESS AUTOMATA

§1. GRAPHS AS VERTICES OF OTHER GRAPHS. DIAGRAMS OF INFORMATION-LOSSLESS AUTOMATA

In Chapter I we defined the sets $\mathfrak{M}_{\mathrm{I}}(s_i, \beta_i)$ and $\mathfrak{M}_{\mathrm{II}}(s_i, \beta_i)$, which play a central role in the theory of IL-I-N and IL-II-N automata. We therefore propose a method for defining sets of words as labeled graphs. It thus becomes possible to formulate properties of sets of words in terms of graphs, which not only imparts to the theory a greater degrees of lucidity but also enables one to formulate properties of the sets $\mathfrak{M}(s_i, \beta_i)$ which would otherwise be difficult to describe.

We begin with a few definitions connected with this formulation of the problem.

Definition 13. A complete tree of type (K, N) is a rooted tree with $(K^{N+1}-1)/(K-1)$ vertices, such that there are K arcs emanating from each vertex and the maximum length of a path in the tree is N.

Definition 14. A complete input tree of type (K, N) is a labeled complete tree of type (K, N), with letters of the alphabet $\mathfrak{A}$ attached to the arcs in such a way that any two arcs emanating from the same vertex are assigned different letters.

Definition 15. A complete automaton tree of type (K, N) is a complete input tree of type (K, N) whose labels are pairs of letters, a letter from the alphabet $\mathfrak{A}$ and one from the alphabet $\mathfrak{B}$.

We shall be concerned with certain subgraphs of complete trees, satisfying the following conditions:

(1) each subgraph contains the root of the tree;

(2) every leaf of the subgraph is also a leaf of the tree.

Any subgraph satisfying these conditions will be called a subtree, specifically: input subtree or automaton subtree, depending on the type of complete tree of which it is part. Subtrees will also preserve the original labels of their arcs.

It is readily seen that a complete input tree defines the set of all words of length N over the alphabet $\mathfrak{A}$.

An input subtree defines a certain set of words of length N over $\mathfrak{A}$. In this sense, we shall refer in the sequel to intersections of input subtrees (meaning the set of words defined by all the subtrees in question), unions of subtrees (the union of the sets of words defined by the subtrees), partitions of input subtrees (the partial subtrees define sets of words which form a partition of the set of words defined by the original subtree), and so on.

A vertex of a subtree will be called a vertex of level n if it is the end of some path of length n. The root is a vertex of level 0.

There is a natural correspondence between the graphs just defined and the states of automata (not necessarily IL-I-N). Let s_i be any state of an automaton A. Define a graph $\Gamma'(s_i, N)$ as a subtree of a complete input tree of type (K, N) in which the paths from the root define those, and only those words α for which $\lambda(s_i, \alpha)$ is defined. For the automata considered in this book, the graphs $\Gamma'(s_i, N)$ have the property that their only leaves belong to level N, since for any state s_j there is a letter a_k such that $\lambda(s_j, a_k)$ is defined. Starting from the input subtree $\Gamma'(s_i, N)$, we now form an automaton subtree $\Gamma(s_i, N)$ by assigning letters of $\mathfrak{B}$ to the arcs of $\Gamma'(s_i, N)$ in such a way that any path from the root defines a pair of words $(\alpha, \lambda(s_i, \alpha))$.

In connection with IL-I-N automata, it is convenient to partition each graph $\Gamma(s_i, N)$ into subgraphs $\Gamma(s_i, \beta_{i_1}), \ldots, \Gamma(s_i, \beta_{i_n})$ (where $\beta_{i_j} \neq \beta_{i_l}$ if $j \neq l$) with the maximum number of vertices in such a way that in each graph $\Gamma(s_i, \beta_{i_j})$ every path from the root defines the word β_{i_j} $(j = 1, \ldots, n)$. *

It is clear that the graph $\Gamma(s_i, \beta_{i_j})$ generates those, and only those words of length N over $\mathfrak{A}$ which are elements of the set $\mathfrak{M}_{\mathrm{I}}(s_i, \beta_{i_j})$. Thus specification of the set $\mathfrak{M}_{\mathrm{I}}(s_i, \beta_{i_j})$ is equivalent to specification of the subtree $\Gamma(s_i, \beta_{i_j})$.

Let B be a type I standard inverse with delay N for some automaton $A(\mathrm{I}, N)$. We construct a diagram of B in which the vertices are automaton subgraphs — each state (s_i, β_i) is represented by the subtree $\Gamma(s_i, \beta_i)$; denote this diagram by $\Gamma(B)$. For simplicity's sake we shall denote the vertices of the graph $\Gamma(B)$ by the same letters t_k as the states of the automaton B. Let $\Gamma(Bx)$ denote the graph obtained from $\Gamma(B)$ by deleting the letters of $\mathfrak{B}$ in the graph $\Gamma(B)$, and $\Gamma(By)$ the graph obtained by deleting the letters of both alphabets $\mathfrak{A}$ and $\mathfrak{B}$. (The letters are deleted in both cases both from the arcs of $\Gamma(B)$ and from the arcs of the subtrees $\Gamma(s_i, \beta_j)$.)

The vertex of the graph $\Gamma(Bx)$ obtained from the vertex t_k of $\Gamma(B)$ in this process will be denoted by x_k, and the corresponding vertex of $\Gamma(By)$ by y_k.

To avoid misunderstandings, the vertices of the graphs $\Gamma(B)$, $\Gamma(Bx)$ and $\Gamma(By)$ will be called subtrees, reserving the term "vertices" to designate the vertices of the vertices of the graphs $\Gamma(B)$, $\Gamma(Bx)$ and $\Gamma(By)$. We shall make no distinction between the automaton B and the corresponding graph $\Gamma(B)$.

We denote the root of a subtree t_i by τ_i, and each of its other vertices by $\tau_{ij\alpha}$, where i designates the subtree, j the level and α the word defined by the path from τ_i to the vertex. The symbols χ_i, ξ_i and $\chi_{ij\alpha}$ will denote the vertices of the subtrees x_i and y_i corresponding to the vertices τ_i and $\tau_{ij\alpha}$ when the graphs $\Gamma(Bx)$ and $\Gamma(By)$ are formed from $\Gamma(B)$. A vertex of the subtree y_i will be denoted by ξ_{ijk}, where the third subscript k indexes the vertices on the same level. In some cases, in the interests of a unified notation, we shall also designate roots of subtrees by three indices.

The weight of a vertex $\tau_{ij\alpha}$ in a subtree t_i is defined as the number of leaves of the subtree which are ends of paths from $\tau_{ij\alpha}$. The weight of $\tau_{ij\alpha}$ will be denoted by $|\tau_{ij\alpha}|$. The weight of a subtree t_i, denoted by $|t_i|$, is defined as the weight of its root. Similar terminology and notation will be

* A path in the graph $\Gamma(s_i, \beta_i)$ defines a sequence of pairs $(a_{i_1}, b_{k_1}), \ldots, (a_{i_N}, b_{k_N})$. The above formulation refers to the word $b_{i_1} \ldots b_{i_N}$. Simplified terminology of this kind will be employed throughout when we are interested in only one letter of each pair.

employed for the subtrees x_i, and their vertices. Figure 10 illustrates the graph $\Gamma(B)$ for the principal part of the standard inverse automaton in Example 9. To simplify the figure, the letters attached to the subtree arcs are omitted. Instead, we adopt the convention that any arc / should be assigned the letter $a_1=0$, and any arc\the letter $a_2=1$. All arcs of subtrees point downward. The letters of the alphabet $\mathfrak{B}$ to be attached to the arcs of the subtrees are evident from the designations of the states.

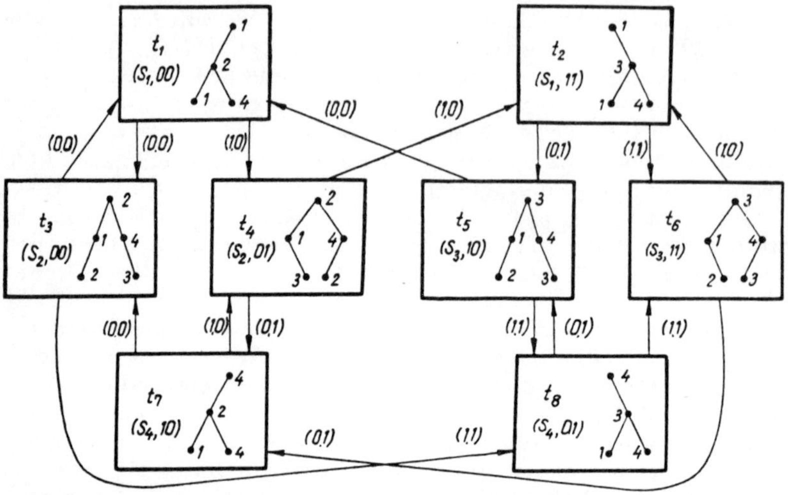

FIGURE 10.

We correlate the vertices of a subtree $t_k=(s_i, \beta)\in\mathfrak{T}_1$ and the states of the automaton A as follows: the root of (s_i, β) corresponds to the state s_i, the vertex $\tau_{kl\alpha}$ to the state $\delta(s_i, \alpha)$. (The numbers at the subtree vertices in Figure 10 are the indices of the appropriate states.)

We shall say that vertices $\tau_{ij\alpha_1}$ and $\tau_{kl\alpha_2}$ are e q u i v a l e n t in $\Gamma(B)$ if they correspond to the same state of the automaton A. Vertices $\chi_{ij\alpha_1}$ and $\chi_{kl\alpha_2}$ (ξ_{ijk} and ξ_{klp}) are said to be equivalent if the corresponding vertices $\tau_{ij\alpha_1}$ and $\tau_{kl\alpha_2}$ are equivalent.

To facilitate the reader's understanding of what follows, it is important to clarify two approaches to the differentiation of subtrees. According to the first approach, two subtrees are viewed as distinct if they represent different states of the automaton (in the case of the graph $\Gamma(B)$) or if they are obtained from such subtrees when the graphs $\Gamma(Bx)$ and $\Gamma(By)$ are formed from $\Gamma(B)$. In that case we shall say that the subtrees are d i s t i n c t. According to the second approach we must consider each type of subtree separately. Two subtrees are viewed as different if they are nonisomorphic. Two input or automaton subtrees are said to be different if they define different sets of words over $\mathfrak{A}$. We shall say in this case too that the corresponding subtrees are nonisomorphic.

Two input or automaton subtrees are said to be isomorphic if they define the same sets of words over the alphabet $\mathfrak{A}$.

The graph of Figure 10 may be viewed equally well as $\Gamma(Bx)$ or $\Gamma(By)$, provided only that we disregard the letters of the appropriate alphabets. This approach makes the subtrees t_1 and t_7, x_1 and x_7, y_1 and y_7 distinct. However, the subtrees x_1 and are isomorphic, as are y_1 and y_7.

Definition 16. The type of a state s_i in an automaton $A(\mathrm{I}, N)$ is the set of all distinct subtrees $y_{j_1},\ldots,y_{j_n}$ of the graph $\Gamma(By)$, together with the equivalence relation between their vertices, such that $\Gamma(B)$ contains vertices t_{j_k} of the form (s_i, β_k) $(k=1,\ldots,n)$.

It is sometimes possible to construct a system of invariant classes of states of the standard inverse B such that, for all states $(s_{i_1}, \beta_1),\ldots,(s_{i_n}, \beta_n)$ in the same invariant class, $\mathfrak{M}_{\mathrm{I}}(s_{i_k}, \beta_k)=\mathfrak{M}_{\mathrm{I}}(s_{i_l}, \beta_l)$ $(k, l=1,\ldots,n)$. We denote the automaton produced by the corresponding simplification of B by B'. Simplification of B with respect to a system of invariant classes with this property will be called standard simplification.

Now let $\Gamma(B')$ be the diagram of B' in which the vertices are represented by input subtrees.

Externally, the graph $\Gamma(B')$ differs from $\Gamma(B)$ in that the subtree arcs in $\Gamma(B')$ are not assigned letters from the alphabet $\mathfrak{B}$. Deleting the letters of $\mathfrak{B}$ from $\Gamma(B')$, we get the graph $\Gamma(B'x)$; doing the same for the letters of $\mathfrak{A}$ and $\mathfrak{B}$, we get the graph $\Gamma(B'y)$. The subtrees of the graphs $\Gamma(B')$, $\Gamma(B'x)$ and $\Gamma(B'y)$ are denoted respectively by t'_k, x'_k and y'_k, and the vertices of these subtrees by suitably indexed symbols τ', χ' and ξ', following the same pattern as when indexing the symbols τ, χ and ξ for the subtree vertices of $\Gamma(B)$, $\Gamma(Bx)$ and $\Gamma(By)$.

Suppose that a subtree t'_k in the graph $\Gamma(B')$ is a state of the automaton B' — a class of states $\{(s_{i_1}, \beta_1),\ldots,(s_{i_n}, \beta_n)\}$. Let us identify the root τ'_k with any of the states $s_{i_1},\ldots,s_{i_n}$ and each vertex $\tau'_{ki\alpha}$ with any of the states $\delta(s_{i_j}, \alpha)$ $(j=1,\ldots,n)$. We shall say that vertices $\tau_{ij\alpha_1}$ and $\tau_{kl\alpha_2}$ are identifiable if they may be identified with the same state of the automaton A. Preserving an analogy with our previous notation, we let $\mathfrak{M}(z)$ denote the set of all words of length N over $\mathfrak{A}$ defined by the subtree z.

Consider Figure 11, which shows the graph $\Gamma(B')$ for the automaton obtained from the automaton of Example 9 by simplification with respect to the equivalent states specified in that example.

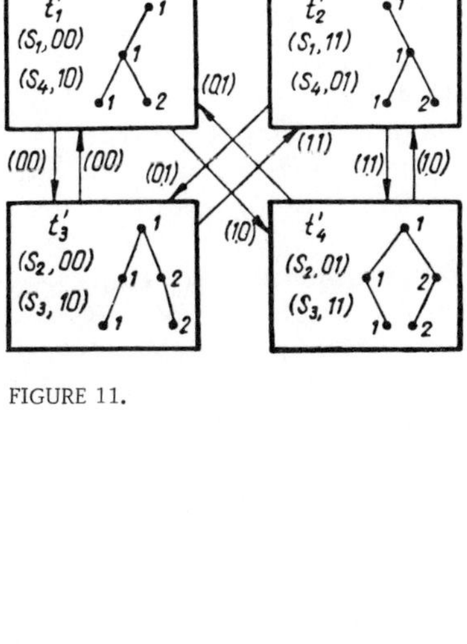

FIGURE 11.

The vertices τ'_{211}, τ'_{322}, τ'_{421}, τ'_3 and τ'_4 are identifiable, since they may all be identified with the state s_3 of A. Similarly, the vertices τ'_{122}, τ'_{222}, τ'_{312}, τ'_{412}, τ'_1 and τ'_2 are identifiable, since they may be identified with the state s_4. (To simplify matters, the third subscript indexes the vertices in each level.)

The relationship between subtrees $t_i, t_{i_1}, t_{i_2}, \ldots, t_{i_n}$ with the property that there are arcs going from t_i to all the subtrees t_{i_j} $(j=1, \ldots, n)$ is established by the following lemmas.

Lemma 3. If $a_m\alpha \in \mathfrak{M}(t_i)$ $(a_m\alpha \in \mathfrak{M}(t'_i))$, the graph $\Gamma(B)$ $(\Gamma(B'))$ contains a subtree t_{i_j} (t'_{i_j}) which is the end of an arc emanating from t_i (t'_i) labeled a_m, such that for some a_l we have $\alpha a_l \in \mathfrak{M}(t_{i_j})$ $(\alpha a_l \in \mathfrak{M}(t'_{i_j}))$.

Proof. Let $t_i = (s_j, b_k\beta)$ and $\lambda(s_j, a_m\alpha) = b_k\beta$. Then there is a letter a_l such that $\lambda(\delta(s_j, a_m\alpha), a_l)$ is defined and equal to some letter b_r. But then $\varepsilon((s_i, b_k\beta), b_r) = (\delta(s_i, a_m), \beta b_r)$. It is clear that $\alpha a_l \in \mathfrak{M}(\delta(s_i, a_m), \beta b_r))$.

The graph $\Gamma(B')$ of the automaton obtained by standard simplification of B contains no subtrees other than those of $\Gamma(B)$, and the arcs in the two graphs always join isomorphic subtrees. This implies the conclusion of the theorem for $\Gamma(B')$.

Lemma 4. If the automaton A is complete, then for any subtree $t_i(t'_i)$, any word $a_m\alpha \in \mathfrak{M}(t_i)$ $(a_m\alpha \in \mathfrak{M}(t'_i))$, and any letter a_l, there exists a subtree $t_j(t'_j)$ such that there is an arc from t_i to t_j (from t'_i to t'_j) labeled a_m, with $\alpha a_l \in \mathfrak{M}(t_j)$ $(\alpha a_l \in \mathfrak{M}(t'_j))$.

The proof is similar to that of Lemma 3.

§2. PROPERTIES OF AN IL-I-N AUTOMATON DEDUCIBLE FROM THE PROPERTIES OF THE SUBTREES OF ITS GRAPH

A subgraph Γ of a graph X is said to be attached to a vertex a of X if its vertices are a and all vertices of X which are ends of paths from a; we shall sometimes call Γ the attached subgraph at a.

Definition 17. A subtree is a panicle* of type (K, N, M) if it contains only one vertex on each of levels $0, 1, \ldots, N-M$ and more than one vertex on level $N-M+1$. A subtree is a complete panicle of type (K, N, M) if it is a panicle of type (K, N, M) and the subgraph attached to the vertex on level $N-M$ is a complete tree of type (K, M). (The property of being a panicle or a complete panicle, as described in Definition 17, is meaningful for both automaton and input subtrees.)

It was proved in Theorem 16 that a type I standard inverse with delay N is an IL-I-N automaton. It is quite possible, however, for this inverse to be ILS-I-N_1 for some $N_1 < N$.

The notions we have defined make it possible to characterize the number N_1 in terms of properties of the subtrees of $\Gamma(B)$ or $\Gamma(B')$.

Theorem 18. The principal part B_1 of a type I standard inverse B with delay N is IL-I-M, $M < N$, if and only if the following condition is not satisfied. The graph $\Gamma(B)$ contains three subtrees t_i, t_{i_1} and t_{i_2} such that arcs

* [The Russian word also means "broom," but it seems clear in view of the "arboreal" imagery throughout that the author is thinking of this more specific botanical term. — Trans.]

lead from t_i to both t_{i_1} and t_{i_2} and there are two equivalent vertices $\tau_{i_1 M\alpha_1}$ and $\tau_{i_2 M\alpha_2}$.

Proof. Suppose that B_1 is not IL-I-M. Then there exist a state $t_i = (s_j, b_n\beta)$ and words $b_k\beta_1$ and $b_l\beta_2$ $(b_k \neq b_l)$ of length $M+1$ such that

$$\mu((s_j, b_n\beta), b_k\beta_1) = \mu((s_j, b_n\beta), b_l\beta_2) = a_m\alpha.$$

Let

$$\varepsilon(t_i, b_k) = t_{i_1} = (s_r, \beta b_k)$$

and

$$\varepsilon(t_i, b_l) = t_{i_2} = (s_r, \beta b_l),$$

where $s_r = \delta(s_j, a_m)$. Each of the subtrees t_{i_1} and t_{i_2} has an M-th level vertex corresponding to the state $\delta(s_r, \alpha)$, so that the vertices $\tau_{i_1 M\alpha}$ and $\tau_{i_2 M\alpha}$ are equivalent.

Now suppose that there are arcs from the subtree t_i to subtrees t_{i_1} and t_{i_2}, whose M-th levels $(M<N)$ contain two equivalent vertices, i.e., vertices $\tau_{i_1 M\alpha_1}$ and $\tau_{i_2 M\alpha_2}$ corresponding to the same states s_p of the automaton A. Let the vertex τ_{i_1} correspond to a state s_{j_1}, and τ_{i_2} to a state s_{j_2}. Then $\delta(s_{j_1}, \alpha_1) = s_p$, $\delta(s_{j_2}, \alpha_2) = s_p$. Let

$$\varepsilon((s_j, b_n\beta), b_k) = (s_{j_1}, \beta b_k) \quad ((s_j, b_n\beta) = t_i),$$
$$\varepsilon((s_j, b_n\beta), b_l) = (s_{j_2}, \beta b_l),$$
$$\mu((s_j, b_n\beta), b_k) = a_m, \quad \mu((s_j, b_n\beta), b_l) = a_r.$$

Suppose that $a_m \neq a_r$. Since $|a_m\alpha_1| = |a_r\alpha_2| = M+1 \leqslant N$, it follows that $\lambda(s_j, a_m\alpha_1) = \lambda(s_j, a_r\alpha_2)$. In view of the foregoing arguments, $\delta(s_j, a_m\alpha_1) = \delta(s_j, a_r\alpha_2) = s_p$, and the automaton A cannot be IL-I-N, contrary to assumption. Thus necessarily $a_m = a_r$. One shows similarly that $\alpha_1 = \alpha_2$.

Let

$$\lambda(\delta(s_j, a_r), \alpha_1\alpha') = \beta b_k,$$

and

$$\lambda(\delta(s_j, a_r), \alpha_1\alpha'') = \beta b_l.$$

Let α_3 and α_4 be arbitrary words of length N such that $\lambda(\delta(s_j, a_r\alpha_1\alpha'), \alpha_3)$ and $\lambda(\delta(s_j, a_r\alpha_1\alpha''), \alpha_4)$ are defined. Then $\lambda(s_j, a_r\alpha_1\alpha'\alpha_3) = b_n\beta b_k\beta_3$ and $\lambda(s_j, a_r\alpha_1\alpha''\alpha_4) = b_n\beta b_l\beta_4$, where $\lambda(\delta(s_j, a_r\alpha_1\alpha'), \alpha_\gamma) = \beta_\gamma$ $(\gamma = 3, 4)$. In the inverse automaton, we have

$$\mu((s_j, b_n\beta), b_k\beta_3) = a_r\alpha_1\alpha', \quad \mu((s_j, b_n\beta), b_l\beta_4) = a_r\alpha_1\alpha''.$$

Since $|a_r\alpha_1| = M+1$, the automaton B cannot be IL-I-N.

Theorem 19. *Let B' be obtained by standard simplification of the principal part B_1 of a type I standard inverse B constructed with delay N for an automaton A. Then B' is IL-I-M, $M<N$, if and only if the following condition is not satisfied. The graph $\Gamma(B')$ contains three subtrees t'_i, t'_{i_1} and t'_{i_2}, with identifiable vertices $\tau'_{i,M+1,a_m\alpha}$, $\tau'_{i_1,M,\alpha}$ and $\tau'_{i_2,M,\alpha}$, such that there are arcs labeled a_m from t'_i to t'_{i_1} and t'_{i_2}.*

Proof. Suppose that B' is not IL-I-M, so that there exist a state t'_i and words $b_k\beta_1$ and $b_l\beta_2$ ($b_k \neq b_l$) of length $M+1$ with

$$\mu'(t'_i, b_k\beta) = \mu'(t'_i, b_l\beta) = a_m\alpha.$$

Let $\varepsilon'(t'_i, b_k) = t'_{i_1}$, $\varepsilon'(t'_i, b_l) = t'_{i_2}$. Then $\Gamma(B')$ contains arcs from the subtree t'_i to subtrees t'_{i_1} and t'_{i_2}, and these arcs are labeled a_m. Let $(s_j, b_n\beta) \in t'_i$ be any state. In the automaton B, we have

$$\mu((s_j, b_n\beta), b_k\beta_1) = \mu((s_j, b_n\beta), b_l\beta_2) = a_m\alpha.$$

Therefore,

$$\varepsilon((s_j, b_n\beta), b_k) = (\delta(s_j, a_m), \beta b_k) \in t'_{i_1}$$

and

$$\varepsilon((s_j, b_n\beta), b_l) = (\delta(s_j, a_m), \beta b_l) \in t'_{i_2}.$$

Consequently, the vertices $\tau'_{i_1 M\alpha}$ and $\tau'_{i_2 M\alpha}$ are identifiable with the state $\delta(\delta(s_j, a_m), \alpha)$, and the vertex $\tau'_{i, M+1, a_m\alpha}$ is identifiable with $\delta(s_i, a_m\alpha) = \delta(\delta(s_i, a_m), \alpha)$. Thus the vertices $\tau'_{i, M+1, a_m\alpha}$, $\tau'_{i_1 M\alpha}$ and $\tau'_{i_2 M\alpha}$ are identifiable.

Now suppose that there are arcs from a subtree t'_i to subtrees t'_{i_1} and t'_{i_2}, labeled (b_k, a_m) and (b_l, a_m), respectively, so that

$$\varepsilon'(t'_i, b_k) = t'_{i_1}, \quad \varepsilon'(t'_i, b_l) = t_{i_2}, \quad \mu'(t'_i, b_k) = \mu'(t'_i, b_l) = a_m.$$

Let $(s_i, b_r\beta) \in t'_i$. Then $\varepsilon((s_i, b_r\beta), b_k) = (\delta(s_i, a_m), \beta b_k) \in t'_{i_1}$. Suppose that the vertices $\tau'_{i, M+1, a_m\alpha}$, $\tau'_{i_1 M\alpha}$ and $\tau'_{i_2 M\alpha}$ are identifiable. Then there exist words α_1 and α_2 such that $\alpha\alpha_1 \in \mathfrak{M}(t'_{i_1})$ and $\alpha\alpha_2 \in \mathfrak{M}(t'_{i_2})$, and also words α_3 and α_4 of length N such that $\lambda(\delta(s_i, a_m\alpha\alpha_1), \alpha_3)$ and $\lambda(\delta(s_i, a_m\alpha\alpha_2), \alpha_4)$ are defined. Then

$$\mu((s_i, b_r\beta), b_k\lambda(\delta(s_i, a_m\alpha\alpha_1), \alpha_3)) = a_m\alpha\alpha_1,$$
$$\mu((s_i, b_r\beta), b_l\lambda(\delta(s_i, a_m\alpha\alpha_2), \alpha_4)) = a_m\alpha\alpha_2$$

and

$$\mu'(t'_i, b_k\lambda(\delta(s_i, a_m\alpha\alpha_1), \alpha_3)) = a_m\alpha\alpha_1,$$
$$\mu'(t'_i, b_l\lambda(\delta(s_i, a_m\alpha\alpha_2), \alpha_4)) = a_m\alpha\alpha_2.$$

Hence it follows that B' cannot be IL-I-M, since $|a_m\alpha| = M+1$.

In the special case that the automaton A is complete, we obtain the following theorem.

Theorem 20. Let the automaton $A(I, N)$ be complete. Then the principal part B_1 of a type I standard inverse constructed with delay N for A, or the automaton B' obtained by standard simplification of B_1, is IL-I-M if and only if the subgraphs attached to all M-th level vertices in every subtree of $\Gamma(B)$ or $\Gamma'(B')$ are complete trees of type $(K, N-M)$.

Proof. Suppose that B_1 is not IL-I-M. By Theorem 18, there exist subtrees t_i, t_{i_1} and t_{i_2}, with arcs from t_i to t_{i_1} and t_{i_2}, such that certain vertices

$\tau_{i_1 M\alpha_1}$ and $\tau_{i_2 M\alpha_2}$ are equivalent. Let $t_{i_1}=(s_{j_1}, \beta b_k)$ and $t_{i_2}=(s_{j_2}, \beta b_l)$. It follows from the proof of Theorem 18 that $\alpha_1=\alpha_2$, $s_{j_1}=s_{j_2}$, $\varepsilon(t_i, b_k)=t_{i_1}$, $\varepsilon(t_i, b_l)=t_{i_2}$ and $\mu(t_i, b_k)=\mu(t_i, b_l)=a_m$. But then there must be two different words α_3 and α_4 such that $\lambda(s_{j_1}, \alpha_1\alpha_3)=\beta b_k$, $\lambda(s_{j_1}, \alpha_1\alpha_4)=\beta b_l$. Hence the subgraph attached to $\tau_{i_1 M\alpha_1}$ cannot be a complete tree, since the word $\alpha_1\alpha_4$ is not in $\mathfrak{M}_{\mathrm{I}}(s_{j_1}, \beta b_k)$ while the word $\alpha_1\alpha_3$ is in this set ($|\alpha_1|=M$).

Suppose that B' is not IL-I-M. By Theorem 19, there exist states t'_i, t'_{i_1} and t'_{i_2} and letters b_k, b_l ($b_k\neq b_l$) and a_m such that $\varepsilon'(t'_i, b_k)=t'_{i_1}$, $\varepsilon'(t'_i, b_l)=t'_{i_2}$ and $\mu'(t'_i, b_k)=\mu'(t'_i, b_l)=a_m$, and the vertices $\tau'_{i,M+1,a_m\alpha}$, $\tau'_{i_1 M\alpha}$ and $\tau'_{i_2 M\alpha}$ are identifiable for some word α of length M. Let $(s_j, b_r\beta)\in t'_i$. Then the states $\tau'_{i,M+1,a_m\alpha}$, $\tau'_{i_1 M\alpha}$ and $\tau'_{i_2 M\alpha}$ are identifiable with the state $\delta(s_j, a_m\alpha)$ and

$$\varepsilon((s_j, b_r\beta), b_k)=(\delta(s_j, a_m), \beta b_k),\ \varepsilon((s_j, b_r\beta), b_l)=(\delta(s_j, a_m), \beta b_l).$$

There exist words α_3 and α_4 such that $\lambda(\delta(s_j, a_m), \alpha\alpha_3)=\beta b_k$ and $\lambda(\delta(s_j, a_m), \alpha\alpha_4)=\beta b_l$. Thus the set $\mathfrak{M}_{\mathrm{I}}(\delta(s_j, a_m), \beta b_k)$ contains the word $\alpha\alpha_3$ but not $\alpha\alpha_4$, so that the subgraph attached to the vertex $\tau'_{i_1 M\alpha}$ cannot be a complete tree.

Suppose that the graph $\Gamma(B)$ contains a subtree t_{i_1} such that the tree attached to one of its vertices $\tau_{i_1 M\alpha}$ is not complete; that is to say, there is a word α_3 of length $N-M$ such that $\alpha\alpha_3\overline{\in}\mathfrak{M}(t_{i_1})$. We may assume that no other subtree contains an M_1-th level vertex ($M_1>M$) whose attached subgraph is not a complete tree. Suppose that the subtree t_{i_1} is the end of an arc labeled a_m from a subtree t_i, the vertex $\tau_{i_1 M\alpha}$ is equivalent to $\tau_{i,M+1,a_m\alpha}$ and the attached subgraph at the vertex $\tau_{i,M+1,a_m\alpha}$ is a complete panicle, i. e., $a_m\alpha\alpha_1\in\mathfrak{M}(t_i)$ for any word α_1 of length $N-|a_m\alpha|$. Then, by Lemma 4, there is a subtree t_{i_2} such that $\alpha\alpha_3\in\mathfrak{M}(t_{i_2})$, and there is an arc from t_i to t_{i_2} labeled a_m. But then the vertex $\tau_{i_2 M\alpha}$ is equivalent to $\tau_{i,M+1,a_m\alpha}$. The desired conclusion now follows from Theorem 18.

The reasoning for the automaton B' is analogous, except that one must refer to Theorem 19 instead of Theorem 18.

If B is a type I standard inverse for an automaton A, the properties of subtrees of the graphs $\Gamma(B)$ and $\Gamma(B')$ also yield information concerning the properties of A.

Theorem 21. Let $A(I, N)$ be strongly connected, B_1 the principal part of a type I standard inverse B constructed for A with delay N, and B' the automaton obtained by standard simplification of B_1. Then A is an ILS-I-L automaton if and only if:

(1) *any subtree $t_\nu(t'_\nu)$ of type (K, N) in the graph $\Gamma(B_1)(\Gamma(B'))$ is a panicle of type (K, N, L_ν) with $L_\nu\leqslant L$;*

(2) *at least one subtree $t_\mu(t'_\mu)$ of type (K, N) is a panicle of type (K, N, L).*

Proof. If A(SI, L), there exists a state s_i such that, for certain words $a_k\alpha_1$ and $a_l\alpha_2$ ($a_k\neq a_l$) of length L, $\lambda(s_i, a_k\alpha_1)=\lambda(s_i, a_l\alpha_2)=\beta$. Since A is strongly connected, there exist a state s_j and a word α of length $N-L$ such that $\delta(s_j, \alpha)=s_i$. Set $\lambda(s_j, \alpha)=\beta_1$. Then the automaton B_1 has a state $(s_j, \beta_1\beta)$ such that $\alpha a_k\alpha_1\in\mathfrak{M}_{\mathrm{I}}(s_j, \beta_1\beta)$ and $\alpha a_l\alpha_2\in\mathfrak{M}_{\mathrm{I}}(s_j, \beta_1\beta)$. Thus the subtree $t_\varkappa=(s_j, \beta_1\beta)$ is a panicle of type (K, N, L_1) ($L_1\geqslant L$). For every subtree of $\Gamma(B_1)$ there is an isomorphic subtree of $\Gamma(B')$, and so $\Gamma(B')$ also contains a panicle of type (K, N, L_1), $L_1\geqslant L$, if A(SI, L).

Suppose now that $\Gamma(B_1)$ contains a subtree $t_v = (s_i, \beta_i)$ which is a panicle of type (K, N, L_1) with $L_1 > L$, i. e., there exist words α, $a_k\alpha_1$ and $a_l\alpha_2$, $a_k \neq a_l$, $|a_k\alpha_1| = |a_l\alpha_2| = L_1$, such that $\alpha a_k \alpha_1 \in \mathfrak{M}_I(s_i, \beta_i)$, $\alpha a_l \alpha_2 \in \mathfrak{M}_I(s_i, \beta_i)$. Then

$$\lambda(\delta(s_i, \alpha), a_k\alpha_1) = \lambda(\delta(s_i, \alpha), a_l\alpha_2),$$

so that A is not IL-I-L. For every subtree of $\Gamma(B')$ there is an isomorphic subtree in $\Gamma(B_1)$; thus A is not IL-I-L if $\Gamma(B')$ contains a panicle of type (K, N, L_1) with $L_1 > L$. Hence it follows that any automaton A (SI, L) satisfies conditions 1 and 2 of the theorem. Condition 2 implies that A is ILS-I-L_1 with $L_1 \geqslant L$. But if it were true that $L_1 > L$, it would follow that $\Gamma(B_1)$ (or $\Gamma(B')$) contains a panicle of type (K, N, L_1) with $L_1 > L$, contrary to condition 1.

This completes the proof.

The statements embodied in the next theorem are corollaries of the above theorems.

Theorem 22. Let $A(I, N)$ be a strongly connected automaton, B a type I standard inverse of A with delay N, B_1 its principal part, and B' the automaton obtained by standard simplification of B_1. Then A is ILS-I-L and B_1, B' are ILS-I-M if and only if the following conditions hold:

(1) Every subtree in $\Gamma(B_1)$ or $\Gamma(B')$ of type (K, N) is a panicle of type (K, N, L_1), $L_1 \leqslant L$, and $\Gamma(B_1)$ or $\Gamma(B')$ contains a panicle of type (K, N, L).

(2) For the automaton B_1: there is no triple of subtrees t_i, t_{i_1}, t_{i_2} of type (K, N), with arcs from t_i to t_{i_1} and t_{i_2}, such that the vertices $\tau_{i_1 M\alpha}$ and $\tau_{i_2 M\alpha}$ are equivalent for some word α.

For the automaton B': there is no triple of subtrees t'_i, t'_{i_1}, t'_{i_2} of type (K, N), with arcs from t'_i to t'_{i_1} and t'_{i_2} labeled by the same letter of $\mathfrak{A}$, say a_m, such that the vertices $\tau'_{i, M+1, a_m\alpha}$, $\tau'_{i_1 M\alpha}$ and $\tau'_{i_2 M\alpha}$ are identifiable for some word α.

(3) For the automaton B_1: there exist subtrees t_j, t_{j_1}, t_{j_2}, with arcs from t_j to t_{j_1} and t_{j_2}, such that the vertices $\tau_{j_1, M-1, \alpha_1}$, and $\tau_{j_2, M-1, \alpha_1}$ are equivalent for some α_1.

For the automaton B': there exist subtrees t'_j, t'_{j_1}, t'_{j_2} with arcs from t'_j to t'_{j_1} and t'_{j_2} labeled by the same letter a_m of $\mathfrak{A}$, such that the vertices $\tau'_{j, M, a_m\alpha_1}$, $\tau'_{j_1, M-1, \alpha_1}$ and $\tau'_{j_2, M-1, \alpha_1}$ are identifiable for some word α_1.

If the automaton A is complete, conditions 2 and 3 may be replaced by the following:

(2^1) there are complete trees of type $(K, N-M)$ attached to any vertex of level M in $\Gamma(B)$ and $\Gamma(B')$;

(3^1) $\Gamma(B)$ and $\Gamma(B')$ contain a subtree of type (K, N) to one of whose vertices of level $M-1$ no complete tree of type $(K, N-M+1)$ is attached.

§3. ADMISSIBLE GRAPHS WHOSE VERTICES ARE SUBTREES. PROPERTIES OF AUTOMATA DEFINED BY ADMISSIBLE GRAPHS

In the last two sections we showed how to construct the graphs $\Gamma(B)$, $\Gamma(Bx)$, $\Gamma(By)$, $\Gamma(B')$, $\Gamma(B'x)$ and $\Gamma(B'y)$ for a standard inverse automaton.

We are now interested in the converse situation: given graphs whose arcs are labeled by letters of the alphabets $\mathfrak{A}$ and $\mathfrak{B}$ and whose vertices are subtrees, input subtrees or automaton subtrees, what conditions must hold for them to be the graphs $\Gamma(B)$, $\Gamma(Bx)$, $\Gamma(By)$, $\Gamma(B')$, $\Gamma(B'x)$ or $\Gamma(B'y)$ for some type I standard inverse B constructed with delay N for some automaton $A(\mathrm{I}, N)$? Theorem 22 also raises an additional question: can the graph be so constructed that it be $\Gamma(B)$ for some automaton $B(\mathrm{SI}, M_1)$, where B is constructed for some automaton $A(\mathrm{SI}, M_2)$, M_1 and M_2 being prescribed numbers? Yet another question to be considered later is whether one can construct ILS-I-N automata with states of a prescribed type.

In order to solve these and certain other problems, we introduce the concept of an admissible input or automaton graph. We assume the alphabets $\mathfrak{A}$ and $\mathfrak{B}$ given, $|\mathfrak{A}|=K$.

Let $\Gamma(t)$, $\Gamma(x)$ and $\Gamma(y)$ denote respectively graphs whose vertices are automaton subtrees, input subtrees and subtrees of type (K, N). The subtrees of these graphs will be denoted, as before, by t_i, x_i and y_i, and the vertices of the subtrees by τ_i, $\tau_{ij\alpha}$, χ_i, $\chi_{ij\alpha}$, ξ_i and ξ_{ijk}. The arcs of the graph $\Gamma(x)$ are labeled by letters of $\mathfrak{A}$, those of $\Gamma(t)$ by pairs of letters from $\mathfrak{A}$ and $\mathfrak{B}$.

Suppose there is an arc in $\Gamma(y)$ from a subtree y_i to a subtree y_j. Let $\mathfrak{F}(y_i, y_j)$ be a set of pairs $(\xi_{i,n+1,r};\ \xi_{j,n,\rho})$, where each vertex $\xi_{jn\rho}$ $(n=0, 1, \ldots, N-1)$ appears in exactly one pair, and each vertex $\xi_{i,n+1,r}$ $(n=0, 1, \ldots, N-1)$ in at most one pair. Let us say that the vertices $\xi_{i,n+1,r}$ and $\xi_{j,n,\rho}$ are *identifiable* if $(\xi_{i,n+1,r};\ \xi_{j,n,\rho})\in\mathfrak{F}(y_i, y_j)$.

We shall say that a set $\mathfrak{F}(y_i, y_j)$ is *admissible* provided the following condition holds: if $(\xi_{i,n+1,k};\ \xi_{j,n,l})\in\mathfrak{F}(y_i, y_j)$, $(\xi_{i,r+1,m};\ \xi_{j,r,p})\in\mathfrak{F}(y_i, y_j)$, $0\leqslant r<n\leqslant N-1$, then either there are paths in both subtrees y_i and y_j from $\xi_{i,r+1,m}$ to $\xi_{i,n+1,k}$ and from $\xi_{j,r,p}$ to $\xi_{j,n,l}$, respectively, or neither of these paths exists.

Let y_i be a subtree in the graph $\Gamma(y)$, from which there are arcs to subtrees $y_{i_1}, \ldots, y_{i_n}$ and only to these subtrees. We define an *admissible set* $\mathfrak{G}(y_i)$ to be a set of admissible sets $\mathfrak{F}(y_i, y_{i_j})$ $(j=1, \ldots, n)$* satisfying the following conditions:

(1) for any vertex $\xi_{i,m+1,k}$ $(m=0, 1, \ldots, N-1)$ there is a set $\mathfrak{F}(y_i, y_{i_j})\in\mathfrak{G}(y_i)$ such that $(\xi_{i,m+1,k};\xi_{i_j,m,\rho})\in\mathfrak{F}(y_i, y_{i_j})$ for some vertex $\xi_{i_jm\rho}$;

(2) for any vertex ξ_{iNn}, the sum of weights of all the vertices $\xi_{i_j,N-1,k}$ identifiable with ξ_{iNn} is at most K.

Definition 18. A graph $\Gamma(y)$ is said to be *admissible* if each of its subtrees y_i has an admissible set $\mathfrak{G}(y_i)$ and at most $|\mathfrak{B}|$ arcs emanate from each subtree.

Now consider a graph $\Gamma(x)$ (or $\Gamma(t)$). For any pair of subtrees (x_i, x_j) (or (t_i, t_j)) such that there is an arc from x_i (t_i) to x_j (t_j), let $\mathfrak{F}(x_i, x_j)$ (or $\mathfrak{F}(t_i, t_j)$) be a set of pairs $(\chi_{i,m+1,a_r\alpha};\ \chi_{jm\alpha})$ (or $(\tau_{i,m+1,a_r\alpha};\ \tau_{jm\alpha})$) $(m=0, 1, \ldots, N-1)$, where a_r is fixed.

Let us say that a set $\mathfrak{F}(x_i, x_j)$ (or $\mathfrak{F}(t_i, t_j)$) is *admissible* if every vertex $\chi_{jm\alpha}$ (or $\tau_{jm\alpha}$) $(m=0, 1, \ldots, N-1)$ is contained in a pair of the set $\mathfrak{F}(x_i, x_j)$ (or $\mathfrak{F}(t_i, t_j)$).

* The subtrees $y_{i_1}, \ldots, y_{i_n}$ need not be distinct. Sets $\mathfrak{F}(y_i, y_{i_j})$ and $\mathfrak{F}(y_i, y_{i_k})$ for identical y_{i_j} and y_{i_k} may be different.

Vertices $\chi_{i,m+1,a_r\alpha}$ and $\chi_{jm\alpha}$ (or $\tau_{i,m+1,a_r\alpha}$ and $\tau_{jm\alpha}$) are said to be identifiable if $(\chi_{i,m+1,a_r\alpha};\ \chi_{jm\alpha}) \in \mathfrak{F}(x_i, x_j)$ (or $(\tau_{i,m+1,a_r,\alpha};\ \tau_{jm\alpha}) \in \mathfrak{F}(t_i, t_j)$).

Any specification of sets $\mathfrak{F}(y_i, y_j)$ (or ($\mathfrak{F}(x_i, x_j)$, or $\mathfrak{F}(t_i, t_j)$) for all pairs of subtrees (y_i, y_j) ((x_i, x_j) or (t_i, t_j)) such that the graph $\Gamma(y)$ ($\Gamma(x)$ or $\Gamma(t)$) contains an arc from y_i to y_j (from x_i to x_j, or from t_i to t_j) will be called an identification of subtree vertices in $\Gamma(y)$ ($\Gamma(x)$ or $\Gamma(t)$).

Suppose that there are arcs in a graph $\Gamma(x)$ (or $\Gamma(t)$) from a subtree x_i (or t_i) to subtrees $x_{i_1}, x_{i_2}, \ldots, x_{i_n}$ (or $t_{i_1}, t_{i_2}, \ldots, t_{i_n}$) and only to these subtrees. We define an admissible set $\mathfrak{G}(x_i)$ (or $\mathfrak{G}(t_i)$) to be a set of admissible sets $\mathfrak{F}(x_i, x_{i_j})$ (or $\mathfrak{F}(t_i, t_{i_j})$) $(j=1, \ldots, n)$ satisfying the conditions: 1) for any vertex $\chi_{i,m+1,\alpha}$ (or $\tau_{i,m+1,\alpha}$) $(m=0, 1, \ldots, N-1)$, there is a set $\mathfrak{F}(x_i, x_{i_j}) \in \mathfrak{G}(x_i)$ (or $\mathfrak{F}(t_i, t_{i_j}) \in \mathfrak{G}(t_i)$) $(j=1, 2, \ldots, n)$ such that $(\chi_{i,m+1,\alpha};\ \chi_{i_j,m,\alpha_1}) \in \mathfrak{F}(x_i, x_{i_j})$ (or $(\tau_{i,m+1,\alpha};\ \tau_{i_j,m,\alpha_1}) \in \mathfrak{F}(t_i, t_{i_j})$) for some vertex χ_{i_j,m,α_1} (or τ_{i_j,m,α_1}); 2) for any vertex $\chi_{i,N,a_m\alpha}$ (or $\tau_{i,N,a_m\alpha}$) there are no vertices $\chi_{i_k,N-1,\alpha}$ and $\chi_{i_l,N-1,\alpha}$ (or $\tau_{i_k,N-1,\alpha}$ and $\tau_{i_l,N-1,\alpha}$) $(1 \leqslant k,\ l \leqslant n)$, identifiable with the vertex $\chi_{i,N,a_m\alpha}$ (or $\tau_{i,N,a_m\alpha}$), from which there are arcs labeled by the same letter of $\mathfrak{A}$.

Definition 19. A graph $\Gamma(x)$ is said to be admissible if the following conditions are satisfied:

(1) every subtree x_i of the tree has an admissible set $\mathfrak{G}(x_i)$;

(2) at most $|\mathfrak{B}|$ arcs emanate from each subtree;

(3) any arc from a subtree x_i to a subtree x_j with identifiable vertices χ_{ila_m} and χ_j is labeled a_m.

A graph $\Gamma(x)$ is said to be semi-admissible if it satisfies all the conditions for admissibility except that the sets $\mathfrak{G}(x_i)$ are not required to satisfy condition 1 in the definition of admissible sets.

Definition 20. A graph $\Gamma(t)$ is said to be admissible if the following conditions are satisfied:

(1) every subtree t_i of the graph has an admissible set $\mathfrak{G}(t_i)$;

(2) any arc from a subtree t_i to a subtree t_j with identifiable vertices τ_{ila_m} and τ_j is labeled a_m;

(3) no two arcs emanating from the same subtree may be labeled by the same letter of $\mathfrak{B}$;

(4) all paths of length N in the same subtree define the same word over $\mathfrak{B}$;

(5) if some arc from t_i to t_j is labeled b_l, the words over $\mathfrak{B}$ defined by these subtrees have the form $b_k\beta$ and βb_l, respectively (it may happen that $b_k = b_l$).

Theorem 23. Any admissible graph $\Gamma(t)$ is the graph $\Gamma(B)$ for some IL-I-N automaton B. The automaton B is ILS-I-M if and only if the following conditions hold:

(1) For any subtrees t_i, t_{i_1} and t_{i_2} with arcs from t_i to t_{i_1} and t_{i_2}, both labeled a_m, there cannot be two vertices of the form $\tau_{i_1M\alpha}$ and $\tau_{i_2M\alpha}$.

(2) There exist subtrees t_j, t_{j_1} and t_{j_2} with arcs from t_j to t_{j_1} and t_{j_2}, both labeled a_m, such that for some word α there exist vertices $\tau_{j_1,M-1,\alpha}$, $\tau_{j_2,M-1,\alpha}$.

Proof. It follows from condition 3 in Definition 20 that an admissible graph $\Gamma(t)$ defines an automaton with input alphabet $\mathfrak{B}$ and output alphabet $\mathfrak{A}$. Denote this automaton by B and let $\mathfrak{M}(t_i)$ be the set of all words over $\mathfrak{A}$ of length N defined by paths in the subtree t_i. It follows from condition 2 of Definition 20 and from the admissibility of $\mathfrak{F}(t_i, t_j)$ and $\mathfrak{G}(t_i)$ that there is a word β with $\mu(t_i, \beta) = \alpha$ if and only if $\alpha \in \mathfrak{M}(t_i)$. Let t_i be any state for which there exist words $b_k\beta_1$ and $b_l\beta_2$ $(b_k \neq b_l)$ of length $N+1$ such that $\mu(t_i, b_k\beta_1)$ and $\mu(t_i, b_l\beta_2)$ are defined. Suppose that

$$\mu(t_i, b_k\beta_1) = a_\varkappa\alpha_1 a_{p_1}, \quad \mu(t_i, b_l\beta_2) = a_\lambda\alpha_2 a_{p_2}, \quad \varepsilon(t_i, b_k) = t_{i_1}, \quad \varepsilon(t_i, b_l) = t_{i_2}.$$

Let $a_\varkappa\alpha_1 = a_\lambda\alpha_2$. Then

$$a_\varkappa\alpha_1 \in \mathfrak{M}(t_i), \ \alpha_1 a_{p_1} \in \mathfrak{M}(t_{i_1}), \ \alpha_1 a_{p_2} \in \mathfrak{M}(t_{i_2})$$

and the vertices $\tau_{i1a_\varkappa}$, τ_{i_1} and τ_{i_2} are identifiable. But then $\tau_{i,N,a_\varkappa\alpha_1}$, $\tau_{i_1,N-1,\alpha_1}$ and $\tau_{i_2,N-1,\alpha_2}$ are also identifiable. By condition 2 in the definition of admissible sets $\mathfrak{G}(t_i)$, there cannot be arcs from the two last-named vertices labeled by the same letters of $\mathfrak{A}$. Therefore $a_{p_1} \neq a_{p_2}$. This shows that for any state t_i and any two words $b_k\beta_1$, $b_l\beta_2$ $(b_k \neq b_l)$ of length $N+1$,

$$\mu(t_i, b_k\beta_1) \neq \mu(t_i, b_l\beta_2),$$

provided both these values are defined. In other words, B is an IL-I-N automaton.

Now let t_i, t_{i_1} and t_{i_2} satisfy condition 2 of the theorem and suppose b_k and b_l are letters such that $\varepsilon(t_i, b_k) = t_{i_1}$, $\varepsilon(t_i, b_l) = t_{i_2}$. Then $\mu(t_{i_1}, \beta_1) \neq \mu(t_{i_2}, \beta_2)$ for any words β_1 and β_2 of length M, provided both values are defined. But then $\mu(t_i, b_k\beta_1) \neq \mu(t_i, b_l\beta_2)$ for any words $b_k\beta_1$, $b_l\beta_2$ of length $M+1$ such that $b_k \neq b_l$ and both values of μ are defined.

Now suppose that t_j, t_{j_1} and t_{j_2} satisfy condition 2 of the theorem and the letters b_k and b_l $(b_k \neq b_l)$ are such that $\varepsilon(t_j, b_k) = t_{j_1}$, $\varepsilon(t_j, b_l) = t_{j_2}$, $\mu(t_j, b_k) = \mu(t_j, b_l) = a_m$. It also follows from condition 2 that there are words β_1 and β_2 of length $M-1$ with $\mu(t_{j_1}, \beta_1) = \mu(t_{j_2}, \beta_2)$, or $\mu(t_j, b_k\beta_1) = \mu(t_j, b_l\beta_2)$, $b_k \neq b_l$. Thus B is not IL-I-$M-1$.

It thus follows that B is an ILS-I-M automaton.

Conversely, suppose that $B(\mathrm{SI}, M)$. Then there exist a state t_j and words $b_k\beta_1$ and $b_l\beta_2$ of length M $(b_k \neq b_l)$ such that $\mu(t_j, b_k\beta_1) = \mu(t_j, b_l\beta_2) = a_m\alpha$. Set $\varepsilon(t_j, b_k) = t_{j_1}$, $\varepsilon(t_j, b_l) = t_{j_2}$; in other words, there are arcs in $\Gamma(t)$ leading from t_j to the subtrees t_{j_1} and t_{j_2}, both labeled a_m. It follows from the equality $\mu(t_{j_1}, \beta_1) = \mu(t_{j_2}, \beta_2) = \alpha$ that $\alpha\alpha_1 \in \mathfrak{M}(t_{j_1})$ and $\alpha\alpha_2 \in \mathfrak{M}(t_{j_2})$ for some α_1, α_2. But then we have vertices $\tau_{j_1,M-1,\alpha}$ and $\tau_{j_2,M-1,\alpha}$, i. e., condition 2 of the theorem holds. Now, if there existed subtrees t_i, t_{i_1} and t_{i_2}, with arcs labeled a_m leading from t_i to both t_{i_1} and t_{i_2}, and also vertices $\tau_{i_1M\alpha}$ and $\tau_{i_2M\alpha}$, one could prove in the same way that B is not an IL-I-M automaton.

Thus the automaton $B(\mathrm{SI}, M)$ satisfies conditions 1 and 2. This completes the proof.

Now consider a graph $\Gamma(x)$. Let us attach letters of the alphabet $\mathfrak{B}$ to its arcs, apart from the letters of $\mathfrak{A}$ labeling them. Denote the resulting graph by $\Gamma(tx)$, retaining the previous notation for its subtrees.

Definition 21. A graph $\Gamma(tx)$ is said to be *admissible* if the underlying graph $\Gamma(x)$ is admissible and no two arcs issuing from the same subtree are labeled by identical letters of $\mathfrak{B}$.

Theorem 24. Any admissible graph $\Gamma(tx)$ is the graph $\Gamma(B)$ for some automaton $B(I, N)$. The automaton B is ILS-I-M if and only if the following conditions hold:

(1) *For any subtrees x_i, x_{i_1} and x_{i_2} such that there are arcs from x_i to x_{i_1} and x_{i_2}, both labeled a_m, there cannot be two vertices of the form $\chi_{i_1 M\alpha}$ and $\chi_{i_2 M\alpha}$.*

(2) *There exist subtrees x_j, x_{j_1} and x_{j_2} such that there are arcs from x_j to x_{j_1} and x_{j_2}, both labeled a_m, such that vertices $\chi_{j_1, M-1, \alpha}$ and $\chi_{j_2, M-1, \alpha}$ exist for some word α.*

Since the properties of an admissible graph $\Gamma(t)$ utilized in the proof of Theorem 23 are also valid for an admissible graph $\Gamma(tx)$, Theorem 24 may be proved in exactly the same way.

Theorem 25. *The automaton B defined by an admissible graph $\Gamma(t)$ or $\Gamma(tx)$ is complete if and only if there are $|\mathfrak{B}|$ arcs emanating from each subtree of the graph.*

The proof is obvious.

§4. INVERSE AUTOMATA FOR AUTOMATA DEFINED BY ADMISSIBLE GRAPHS

The preceding theorems concern the properties of an automaton B defined by an admissible graph. However, the properties of subtrees in the graphs $\Gamma(t)$ and $\Gamma(tx)$ also determine certain properties of the inverse automaton A of B. To show this, we shall have to extend our concept of identifiable vertices of $\Gamma(t)$ and $\Gamma(x)$, applying it also to vertices of non-adjacent subtrees. This will be done by an inductive definition.

Suppose that the graph $\Gamma(z)$* contains a path passing through subtrees $z_{i_1}, z_{i_2}, \ldots, z_{i_n}$ $(n \leqslant N)$ and that each pair of vertices

$$(\zeta_{i_1, j, \alpha_1}; \zeta_{i_2, j-1, \alpha_2}),$$
$$(\zeta_{i_2, j-1, \alpha_2}; \zeta_{i_3, j-2, \alpha_3}), \ldots, (\zeta_{i_{n-1}, j-n+2, \alpha_{n-1}}; \zeta_{i_n, j-n+1, \alpha_n})$$
$$(n-1 \leqslant j \leqslant N)$$

is identifiable. Then any vertex $\zeta_{i_k, j-k+1, \alpha_k}$ $(k \leqslant n)$ is identifiable with any vertex $\zeta_{i_l, j-l+1, \alpha_l}$, $l = 1, \ldots, k-1$.

Theorem 26. *Let $\Gamma(t)$ be an admissible graph in which the roots of subtrees $t_{i_1}, \ldots, t_{i_n}$ defining words $\beta_1, \ldots, \beta_n$ are identifiable with the same leaf of some subtree t_i. Then any type I standard inverse A constructed with delay N for the automaton B defined by $\Gamma(t)$ has a state s_k such that $\mathfrak{M}_1(s_k, \beta_j) = \mathfrak{M}(t_{i_j})$ $(j = 1, \ldots, n)$.*

Proof. Let the roots of $t_{i_1}, \ldots, t_{i_n}$ be identifiable with $\tau_{iN\alpha}$. In the automaton B, we have $\mu(t_i, \beta) = \alpha$ if and only if β is the word defined by some subtree t_{i_j} whose root is identifiable with $\tau_{iN\alpha}$ (this follows from conditions 2 and 5 of Definition 20). Similarly, if the root of a subtree t_r defining a word β_l is identifiable with a vertex $\tau_{i_j N \alpha_1}$, then $\mu(t_{i_j}, \beta_l) = \alpha_1$. Consequently, $\mu(t_i, \beta_j\beta_l) = \alpha\alpha_1$, the standard inverse has a state (t_i, α) and $\lambda((t_i, \alpha), \alpha_1) = \beta_j$. This is true for any $\alpha_1 \in \mathfrak{M}(t_{i_j})$ for fixed j. Therefore $\mathfrak{M}_1(s_k, \beta_j) = \mathfrak{M}(t_{i_j})$, where $s_k = (t_i, \alpha)$. But this equality is true for any $j = 1, \ldots, n$, and the proof is complete.

* Here z and ζ stand respectively for any of the letters t, x, y and τ, χ, ξ. When $\zeta = \xi$ the symbols α_l should be interpreted as numbers.

Theorem 27. Let $\Gamma(tx)$ be an admissible graph in which the roots of subtrees $x_{i_1},\ldots,x_{i_n}$ are identifiable with the same leaf of some subtree x_i. Then any type I standard inverse A constructed with delay N for the automaton B defined by the graph $\Gamma(tx)$ has a state s_k for which there are words $\beta_1,\ldots,\beta_n$ with $\mathfrak{M}_{\rm I}(s_k, \beta_j)=\mathfrak{M}(x_{i_j})$ $(j=1,\ldots,n)$.

Proof. We construct a graph $\Gamma(t)$ as follows. For each subtree x_i of $\Gamma(tx)$, find all words $\beta_1,\ldots,\beta_n$ of length N such that there are paths in $\Gamma(tx)$ defining these words and leading to the vertex x_i. Form automaton subtrees $t_{i_1},\ldots,t_{i_n}$ such that $\mathfrak{M}(t_{i_j})=\mathfrak{M}(x_i)$ and the subtree t_{i_j} defines the word β_j $(j=1,\ldots,n)$.

Denote the set of automaton subtrees so constructed for a subtree x_i by $\mathfrak{N}(x_i)$. The set of subtrees of the graph $\Gamma(t)$ is the union of the subtrees in all sets $\mathfrak{N}(x_i)$, where x_i is a subtree in $\Gamma(tx)$.

Take an arbitrary subtree t_i defining the word $\beta_j=b_k\beta$ corresponding to the subtree x_i and consider all subtrees $x_{i_1},\ldots,x_{i_n}$ which are ends of arcs in $\Gamma(tx)$ emanating from the subtree x_i. If the arc from x_i to x_{i_j} is labeled (a_{l_j}, b_{m_j}) $(j=1,\ldots,n)$, each set $\mathfrak{N}(x_{i_j})$ contains a subtree defining the word βb_{m_j}; this subtree we denote by t_{i_j}. We stipulate that arcs go from t_i to all the subtrees t_{i_j}, labeled respectively (a_{l_j}, b_{m_j}). If the subtrees x_i and x_{i_j} contain identifiable vertices $\chi_{i,M+1,a_{l_j}\alpha}$ and $\chi_{i_j,M,\alpha}$, we identify the vertices $\tau_{i,M+1,a_{l_j}\alpha}$ and $\tau_{i_j,M,\alpha}$ in the subtrees t_i and t_{i_j}. We have thus constructed a graph $\Gamma(t)$. Now the graph $\Gamma(x)$ underlying the graph $\Gamma(tx)$ of our construction satisfies conditions 1 and 3 of Definition 19, and so the analogous conditions 1 and 2 of Definition 20 are satisfied. By Definition 21, condition 3 of Definition 20 is also valid. Furthermore, it is clear from the construction that conditions 4 and 5 of Definition 20 are also satisfied, and so $\Gamma(t)$ is an admissible graph.

Now consider an arbitrary subtree $t_k\in\mathfrak{N}(x_i)$. Suppose that the root of a subtree x_{i_j} is identifiable with a leaf $\chi_{iN\alpha}$ of x_i, via a path passing through subtrees $x_i, x_{j_1},\ldots,x_{j_N}=x_{i_j}$. Then the graph $\Gamma(t)$ contains a path through vertices $t_k, t_{k_1},\ldots,t_{k_N}$ with $t_{k_l}\in\mathfrak{N}(x_{j_l})$ $(l=1,\ldots,N)$. Thus the root of the subtree t_{k_N} is identifiable with the leaf $\tau_{kN\alpha}$. Hence, by Theorem 26, the standard inverse A constructed with delay N for the automaton B defined by $\Gamma(t)$ has a state s_k for which there are words β_i $(i=1,\ldots,N)$ with $\mathfrak{M}_{\rm I}(s_k, \beta_j)=\mathfrak{M}(x_{i_j})$ $(j=1,\ldots,n)$.

The sets $\mathfrak{N}(x_i)$ constitute a complete system of invariant classes. Indeed, for any two states $t_{i_1}\in\mathfrak{N}(x_i)$ and $t_{i_2}\in\mathfrak{N}(x_i)$ and any letter b_l such that both $\varepsilon(t_{i_1}, b_l)$ and $\varepsilon(t_{i_2}, b_l)$ are defined, we have

$$\varepsilon(t_{i_1}, b_l)\in\mathfrak{N}(\varepsilon(x_i, b_l)),\quad \varepsilon(t_{i_2}, b_l)\in\mathfrak{N}(\varepsilon(x_i, b_l))$$

by virtue of the construction of $\Gamma(t)$. Similarly,

$$\mu(t_{i_1}, b_l)=\mu(t_{i_2}, b_l)=\mu(x_i, b_l).$$

Thus, simplification of the automaton $\Gamma(t)$ produces the automaton $\Gamma(tx)$. But then we have $\mu(x_i, \beta)=\mu(t_j, \beta)$ for any x_i and β, provided that $t_j\in\mathfrak{N}(x_i)$ and both values are defined. It follows that for every state (t_j, α) of the standard inverse of the automaton with diagram $\Gamma(t)$ there is a state (x_i, α) of the standard inverse of $\Gamma(tx)$, provided $t_j\in\mathfrak{N}(x_i)$, and for any word α_1

$$\lambda((t_j, \alpha), \alpha_1) = \lambda((x_t, \alpha), \alpha_1),$$

provided both values are defined. This completes the proof of our theorem.

Based on the properties of subtrees in the graph $\Gamma(t)$ or $\Gamma(tx)$, one may deduce various properties of standard inverses of the automata that they define.

Theorem 28. Suppose that all subtrees of an admissible graph $\Gamma(t)$ *(or* $\Gamma(tx)$*) are panicles of type* (K, N, L_v), $L_v \leqslant M$, *and at least one subtree is a panicle of type* (K, N, M). *Then the principal part of a type I inverse A constructed with delay N for the automaton defined by* $\Gamma(t)$ *(or* $\Gamma(tx)$*) is an ILS-I-M automaton.*

Proof. It follows from Theorems 26 and 27 that, for any subtree t_i (x_i), the standard inverses A have a state s_k and a word β_k such that $\mathfrak{M}_I(s_k, \beta_k) = \mathfrak{M}(t_i)$ ($\mathfrak{M}_I(s_k, \beta_k) = \mathfrak{M}(x_i)$). There exist no state s_l and word β_l of length N such that $\mathfrak{M}_I(s_l, \beta_l) \neq \mathfrak{M}(t_i)$ ($\mathfrak{M}_I(s_l, \beta_l) \neq \mathfrak{M}(x_i)$) for all subtrees t_i (x_i) of $\Gamma(t)$ $\Gamma(tx)$). By Theorem 16, the principal part of A, which we denote by A_1, is an IL-I-N automaton.

Let B_1 be a type I standard inverse constructed for A_1 with delay N. Now the subtrees of B_1 are exactly those defining the sets of words $\mathfrak{M}_I(s_l, \beta_l)$, where s_l is a state of A_1 and β_l a word of length N such that $\lambda(s_l, \alpha) = \beta_l$ for some α. But this means that the subtrees of the graph $\Gamma(B_1)$ satisfy the assumptions of Theorem 22, and this implies the desired conclusion.

Theorem 29. Let A_1 *be the principal part of a type I standard inverse constructed with delay N for the automaton defined by an admissible graph* $\Gamma(t)$ *(or* $\Gamma(tx)$*). Then* A_1 *is complete if and only if: for any letter* a_m, *any set of subtrees* $t_i, t_{i_1}, \ldots, t_{i_n}$ *such that* $t_{i_1}, \ldots, t_{i_n}$ *are the only subtrees to which arcs labeled* a_m *converge from the subtree* t_i, *any vertex* $\tau_{i,N,a_m\alpha}$ *(or* $\chi_{i,N,a_m\alpha}$*) and any letter* $a_l \in \mathfrak{A}$, *there exists a subtree* t_{i_j} (x_{i_j}) $(1 \leqslant j \leqslant n)$ *such that some arc labeled* a_l *emanates from the vertex* $\tau_{i_j,N-1,\alpha}$ *(or* $\chi_{i_j,N-1,\alpha}$*).*

Proof. The truth of the theorem for $\Gamma(t)$ follows from the fact that, for any subtree t_i, any word $\alpha \in \mathfrak{M}(t_i)$ and any word α_1, there is a path in $\Gamma(t)$ issuing from t_i and defining the word $\alpha\alpha_1$. If the automaton A_1 is complete, then for any subtree t_i, any word $\alpha \in \mathfrak{M}(t_i)$ and any word α_1, there is a path in the graph issuing from t_i and defining the word $\alpha\alpha_1$. This implies the conditions of the theorem.

The proof for $\Gamma(tx)$ is analogous.

§5. PASSAGE BETWEEN ADMISSIBLE GRAPHS OF DIFFERENT KINDS

The motivation for our interest in the problem indicated in the above heading is the concept of the type of a state (see Definition 16). As we shall see later, one can assign the types of states of an automaton A in advance by suitable choice of an admissible graph $\Gamma(y)$; moreover, an automaton A with a state of the prescribed type may even be stipulated to meet various other conditions.

To carry out this program, we shall have to introduce a few new concepts, among other things defining for each subtree z_i of $\Gamma(z)$ a special graph.

Definition 22. Let the graph $\Gamma(y)$ contain arcs going from a subtree y_i to subtrees $y_{i_1}, \ldots, y_{i_n}$ and only to these subtrees. We shall say that an assignment of letters of $\mathfrak{A}$ to the arcs of the subtrees $y_{i_1}, \ldots, y_{i_n}$, producing subtrees $x_{j_1}, \ldots, x_{j_n}$, is admissible if the following condition holds. Let $\xi_{i_j M k_j}$ and $\xi_{i_\rho M k_\rho}$ be vertices identifiable with the same vertex $\xi_{i,M+1,l}$. Then the paths from the roots of y_{i_j} and y_{i_ρ} to the vertices $\xi_{i_j M k_j}$ and $\xi_{i_\rho M k_\rho}$, respectively, define the same word.

Letters of the alphabet $\mathfrak{B}$ may now be assigned to the arcs of the subtrees x_i. If this is done in such a way that all paths from root to leaf define the same word β, we shall say in the interests of brevity that the word β is assigned to the subtree x_i, or that the subtree is labeled β.

Definition 23. Let the graph $\Gamma(x)$ contain arcs from a subtree x_i to subtrees $x_{i_1}, \ldots, x_{i_n}$ and only to these subtrees. We shall say that an assignment of words of length N over $\mathfrak{B}$ to these subtrees, producing subtrees $t_{j_1}, \ldots, t_{j_n}$, is admissible if the following condition holds. Let $\tau_{i_j M\alpha}$ and $\tau_{i_\rho M\alpha}$ be vertices identifiable with a vertex $\tau_{i,M+1,a_m \alpha}$. Then the paths from the roots of the subtrees t_{i_j} and t_{i_ρ} to the vertices $\tau_{i_j M\alpha}$ and $\tau_{i_\rho M\alpha}$ define identical words over $\mathfrak{B}$.

Let $\Gamma(z)$ be some admissible graph and z_k one of its subtrees. We are going to construct a new graph $T(z_k, \Gamma(z), h)$. This graph will be a rooted tree whose vertices are subtrees. The construction is inductive; together with the graph, we shall also construct certain sets $\mathfrak{Z}_k(z_i)$, where z_i is any subtree of $\Gamma(z)$.

Step 0. The root of the graph is a subtree z'_l isomorphic to z_k and defining the same word over $\mathfrak{B}$ as z_k. The subtree z'_l is an element of the set $\mathfrak{Z}_k(z_k)$.

Step $n+1$ ($n=0, 1, \ldots, h-1$). Let the new subtrees introduced at Step n be $z'_{i_1}, \ldots, z'_{i_m}$.

Substep 1. Let $z'_{i_1} \in \mathfrak{Z}_k(z_j)$, and suppose that $\Gamma(z)$ contains arcs from z_j to subtrees $z_{j_1}, \ldots, z_{j_p}$ and only to these subtrees. For each subtree z_{j_l} ($1 \leqslant l \leqslant p$), we define a new subtree $z'_{\varkappa_l}$ such that each $z'_{\varkappa_l}$ is isomorphic to z_{j_l} and defines the same word over $\mathfrak{B}$. The subtrees $z'_{\varkappa_l}$ are distinct from one another and also from all previously introduced subtrees of the new graph. Each subtree $z'_{\varkappa_l}$ is an element of $\mathfrak{Z}_k(z_{j_l})$. Arcs lead from each subtree z'_{i_1} to all subtrees $z'_{\varkappa_l}$ ($l=1, \ldots, p$). Suppose that the subtrees z_j and z_{j_l} contain identifiable vertices $\zeta_{j,M+1,a_m \alpha}$ and $\zeta_{j_l,M,\alpha}$. Then the vertices $\zeta'_{i_1,M+1,a_m \alpha}$ and $\zeta'_{\varkappa_l,M,\alpha}$ of the subtrees z'_{i_1} and $z'_{\varkappa_2}$ are identifiable. Let the arc from z_j to z_{j_l} be labeled w. Then the arc from z'_{i_1} to $z'_{\varkappa_l}$ is also labeled w. *

Substep $k+1$ ($k=1, \ldots, m-1$). Repeat substep 1 with the subtree z'_{i_1} replaced by $z'_{i_{k+1}}$.

Lemma 5. For any h, any admissible graph $\Gamma(z)$ and subtree z_k, the graph $T(z_k, \Gamma(z), h)$ is semi-admissible.

Proof. For any arc in $T(z_k, \Gamma(z), h)$ from $z'_i \in \mathfrak{Z}_k(z_j)$ to $z'_l \in \mathfrak{Z}_k(z_m)$, there is an arc from z_j to z_m in $\Gamma(z)$. In view of the identification relations for the vertices of subtrees in $T(z_k, \Gamma(z), h)$, if the subtrees z_m and z_j satisfy certain conditions, these conditions also hold for the subtrees z'_i and z'_l. The same holds in regard to all labels of arcs, thanks to the way in which the labels are assigned.

* The label w may also be empty, i.e., the arcs of the graph $\Gamma(z)$ need not be labeled.

Theorem 30. Let $\Gamma(y)$ be an admissible graph with subtrees $y_1, \ldots, y_I$. Then we can construct an admissible graph $\Gamma(x)$ satisfying the following condition. The set of subtrees of $\Gamma(x)$ may be partitioned into disjoint subsets $\mathfrak{X}_1, \ldots, \mathfrak{X}_I$, corresponding in one-to-one fashion with the subtrees $y_1, \ldots, y_I$, so that the following conditions hold:

(1) *If the letters of $\mathfrak{A}$ are discarded, each subtree $x_j \in \mathfrak{X}_n$ is isomorphic to y_n.*

(2) *If $\Gamma(y)$ contains an arc from y_j to y_i, there are subtrees $x_{j_1} \in \mathfrak{X}_j$ and $x_{i_1} \in \mathfrak{X}_i$ such that the graph $\Gamma(x)$ contains an arc from x_{j_1} to x_{i_1}.*

(3) *If there are subtrees $x_i \in \mathfrak{X}_{i_1}$ and $x_j \in \mathfrak{X}_{j_1}$ such that $\Gamma(x)$ contains an arc from x_i to x_j, then $\Gamma(y)$ contains an arc from y_{i_1} to .*

(4) *If y_i and y_j occur in a cycle in the graph $\Gamma(y)$, then any subtrees $x_{i_1} \in \mathfrak{X}_i$ and $x_{j_1} \in \mathfrak{X}_j$ occur in a cycle in $\Gamma(x)$.*

(5) *If x_i and x_j occur in a cycle in $\Gamma(x)$ and $x_i \in \mathfrak{X}_{i_1}$, $x_j \in \mathfrak{X}_{j_1}$, then y_{i_1} and y_{j_1} occur in a cycle in $\Gamma(y)$.*

(6) *Let $y_{i_1}, \ldots, y_{i_n}$ be any given set of subtrees whose roots are identifiable with a leaf of some subtree in $\Gamma(y)$; then, for any admissible assignment of letters of $\mathfrak{A}$ to the arcs of $y_{i_1}, \ldots, y_{i_n}$, producing subtrees $x_{l_1}, \ldots, x_{l_n}$, there is a set of subtrees $x_{j_1}, \ldots, x_{j_n}$ of $\Gamma(x)$ such that $x_{j_k} \in \mathfrak{X}_{i_k}$ $(k = 1, \ldots, n)$, the roots of these subtrees are identifiable with a leaf of some subtree in $\Gamma(x)$, and $\mathfrak{M}(x_{l_\rho}) = \mathfrak{M}(x_{j_\rho})$ $(\rho = 1, \ldots, n)$.*

Proof. Choose cycles (not necessarily proper cycles) in the graph $\Gamma(y)$ in such a way that any subtree occurring in a cycle occurs in exactly one of the distinguished cycles. Using these cycles, construct new, improper cycles, repeating each occurrence of an arc in the original cycle several times. The exact number of repetitions will not be specified, but we shall assume that it is always sufficient for the following constructions to be valid. (That this may always be achieved will be obvious.) All subtrees occurring in the new cycles are assumed distinct, denoted by y'_i and apportioned among classes $\mathfrak{Y}_i$: $y'_j \in \mathfrak{Y}_i$ if and only if the original notation for the subtree in question was y_i. Label the arcs of the subtrees in the cycles by letters of $\mathfrak{A}$. The subtree obtained from y'_j by this assignment of labels will be denoted by x_j. Now divide the subtrees x_j into classes $\mathfrak{X}_i$: $x_j \in \mathfrak{X}_i$ if and only if $y'_j \in \mathfrak{Y}_i$. Because of our assumption concerning the construction of the new cycles, we may stipulate that, for any admissible assignment of labels to the arcs of a subtree y_j occurring in some cycle, there exists a subtree $x_k \in \mathfrak{X}_j$ in which this assignment is actually made. Label the arcs of the cycles by letters of $\mathfrak{A}$. The assignment of letters to the arcs of the cycles and of the subtrees may be carried out in such a way that each cycle yields a semi-admissible input graph.

We construct the graph $\Gamma(x)$ in steps. At each step of the construction the graph will be built up from the cycles described above.

Let $y_{i_1}, \ldots, y_{i_n}$ be an arbitrary set of subtrees whose roots are identified with a leaf of a subtree y_i; consider an admissible assignment, not yet used in construction of $\Gamma(x)$, of letters to the arcs of $y_{i_1}, \ldots, y_{i_n}$.

Form the graph $T(y_i, \Gamma(y), N)$. The subtrees $y_{i_1}, \ldots, y_{i_n}$ are leaves of this graph. Let $T'(y_i, N)$ be the graph obtained from $T(y_i, \Gamma(y), N)$ by deleting all leaves other than y_{i_j} $(j = 1, \ldots, n)$ and all vertices from which there are no paths to these leaves. Assign letters of $\mathfrak{A}$ to the vertices of the subtrees in $T'(y_i, N)$ in such a way that the subtrees $x_{i_1}, \ldots, x_{i_n}$ of the resulting graph

$T'(x_i, N)$ with root x_i are isomorphic to the subtrees $x_{j_1}, \ldots, x_{j_n}$ obtained from $y_{i_1}, \ldots, y_{i_n}$ by the given assignment, and in such a way that the graph $T'(x_i, N)$ is semi-admissible. The subtrees of $T'(x_i, N)$ are assumed to be distinct from one another and from all subtrees of $\Gamma(x)$ constructed at previous steps. Now divide the subtrees of $T'(x_i, N)$ into classes $\mathfrak{Y}'_i$: $x_j \in \mathfrak{Y}'_p$ if and only if x_j is obtained from a subtree $y_j \in \mathfrak{Z}_i(y_p)$ of the graph $T(y_i, \Gamma(y), N)$.

Suppose that (at the present step of the construction) the graph $\Gamma(x)$ contains a subtree $x_\lambda \in \mathfrak{X}_i$ isomorphic to a subtree $x_i \in \mathfrak{Y}'_i$, and that x_λ has not yet originated as described above from some other set $y_{k_1}, \ldots, y_{k_n}$ or some other assignment of labels to the subtrees $y_{i_1}, \ldots, y_{i_n}$. This requirement may always be met, thanks to our assumption that each cycle contains enough repetitions. The subtree x_λ will correspond to the subtree x_i. If y_i does not occur in any cycle of $\Gamma(y)$, we let x_i be a subtree of $\Gamma(x)$ and x_i will correspond to itself, $x_i \in \mathfrak{X}_i$.

Suppose that at the present step the graph $\Gamma(x)$ has vertices $x_{j_1}, \ldots, x_{j_m}$ corresponding to j-th level vertices $x_{k_1}, \ldots, x_{k_m}$ of the graph $T'(x_i, N)$. Suppose there are arcs from x_{k_1} to subtrees $x_{\lambda_1}, \ldots, x_{\lambda_\nu}$, $x_{\lambda_j} \in \mathfrak{Y}'_{r_j}$. Let us assume that for some of these subtrees, say $x_{\lambda_1}, \ldots, x_{\lambda_\mu}$, we can already select isomorphic subtrees $x_{\rho_1}, \ldots, x_{\rho_\mu}$ in $\Gamma(x)$, $x_{\rho_j} \in \mathfrak{X}_{r_j}$, not previously selected in this way. Our correspondence will then match the subtrees x_{λ_i} and x_{ρ_i} $(i = 1, \ldots, \mu)$. Suppose that some of the subtrees x_{ρ_j} $(j = 1, \ldots, \mu)$ occur in a cycle together with x_{j_1}. We may then stipulate that the cycle contains an arc from x_{j_1} to one of these subtrees. But if a subtree x_{ρ_j} $(j = 1, \ldots, \mu)$ does not occur in any of the cycles containing x_{j_1}, we stipulate an arc from x_{j_1} to x_{ρ_j}. For each of the remaining subtrees x_{ρ_j} $(j = 1, \ldots, \mu)$, we introduce a new subtree $x_{\lambda_j} \in \mathfrak{X}_{r_j}$ and let arcs go from x_{j_1} to all these new subtrees. Similarly, we introduce new subtrees $x_{\lambda_{\mu+1}}, \ldots, x_{\lambda_\nu}$ in $\Gamma(x)$ and construct the appropriate arcs. The new subtrees x_{λ_i} of $\Gamma(x)$ will correspond to the subtrees x_{λ_i} of $T'(x_i, N)$. If a subtree x_{π_j} of $\Gamma(x)$ corresponds to a subtree x_{λ_j} of $T'(x_i, N)$ and the arc from x_{k_1} to x_{λ_j} is labeled a_m, the arc from x_{j_1} to x_{π_j} in $\Gamma(x)$ is assigned the same label, unless this arc has already been labeled. At this stage of the construction, the graph $\Gamma(x)$ is semi-admissible. The procedure is analogous as regards the vertices $x_{j_2}, \ldots, x_{j_m}$.

The construction of $\Gamma(x)$ now continues similarly, examining the vertices on level $j+1$ of the graph $T'(x_i, N)$.

The graph $\Gamma(x)$ obtained after examination of level $N-1$ of the graph $T'(x_i, N)$ satisfies condition 6 for the set $y_{i_1}, \ldots, y_{i_n}$ and the specified assignment of labels.

Once level $N-1$ of the graph $T'(x_i, N)$ has been dealt with, we proceed either to a different set of subtrees $y_{j_1}, \ldots, y_{j_m}$ or to another assignment of letters to the arcs of the same subtrees. The procedure is repeated until all sets of subtrees and all assignments have been exhausted.

The resulting graph $\Gamma(x)$ is semi-admissible.

At this stage of the construction, there may be subtrees $y_\varkappa$ for which the sets $\mathfrak{X}_\varkappa$ are empty. Of these subtrees, select those which are not ends of any arc in $\Gamma(y)$, and label their arcs by letters of $\mathfrak{A}$ in such a way as to obtain an admissible input tree. Suppose this gives subtrees $x_{j_1} \in \mathfrak{X}_{k_1}, \ldots, x_{j_l} \in \mathfrak{X}_{k_l}$. For all these subtrees, we proceed as follows. Suppose that $\Gamma(y)$ contains arcs from y_{k_ν} to $y_{l_1}, \ldots, y_{l_r}$. Suppose that some of the sets $\mathfrak{X}_{l_1}, \ldots, \mathfrak{X}_{l_r}$, say $\mathfrak{X}_{l_1}, \ldots, \mathfrak{X}_{l_j}$, have the property that for any $x_l \in \mathfrak{X}_{l_\nu}$ $(\nu = 1, \ldots, j)$ there is no admissible graph containing an arc from x_{j_ν} to x_l. Then we add subtrees to the sets $\mathfrak{X}_{l_1}, \ldots, \mathfrak{X}_{l_j}$ in such a way as to make such arcs possible. An arc is introduced between the corresponding subtrees, the vertices are identified in any admissible way, and the arc is labeled in such a way that condition 3 of Definition 19 is not violated.

This procedure is repeated for all newly introduced subtrees. It is clear that the introduction of new subtrees must break off at some stage.

The graph $\Gamma(x)$ may now contain subtrees $x_j \in \mathfrak{X}_i$ from which emanate fewer arcs than from y_i in $\Gamma(y)$. In that case, we add the missing arcs in the following manner.

Suppose that $\Gamma(y)$ contains arcs from y_i to subtrees $y_{i_1}, \ldots, y_{i_l}$, and at this stage of the construction $\Gamma(x)$ contains arcs from $x_j \in \mathfrak{X}_i$ to subtrees $x_{j_1} \in \mathfrak{X}_{i_1}, \ldots, x_{j_n} \in \mathfrak{X}_{i_n}$ $(1 \leqslant n < l)$. Moreover, all arcs in the subtrees $x_{j_1}, \ldots, x_{j_n}$ that issue from $(N-1)$-th level vertices identifiable with the same N-th level vertex of x_j have different labels. Suppose that (in $\Gamma(y)$) the subtrees $y_{i_{n+1}}, \ldots, y_{i_m}$ occur in cycles, but $y_{i_{m+1}}, \ldots, y_{i_l}$ do not. We may stipulate that each set $\mathfrak{X}_{i_j}$ $(j = n+1, \ldots, m)$ contains all subtrees x_f that may be obtained by an arbitrary admissible assignment of letters from $\mathfrak{A}$ to the arcs of the subtree y_{i_j}; also that there is a subtree $x_g \in \mathfrak{X}_{i_j}$ $(j = n+1, \ldots, m)$ to which an arc may be drawn from x_j in such a way that the vertices of x_j and x_g can be identified and a letter of $\mathfrak{A}$ attached to the arc without violating condition 3 of Definition 19.

If some of the sets $\mathfrak{X}_{i_j}$ $(j = m+1, \ldots, l)$ do not contain a subtree permitting arcs to be introduced subject to the conditions of Definition 19, we enlarge the graph $\Gamma(x)$ by adding a new subtree x_λ, as an element of $\mathfrak{X}_{i_j}$, with an arc going from x_j to x_λ.

Since the set of all subtrees of $\Gamma(y)$ is finite, as is the alphabet $\mathfrak{A}$, the procedure of adding new subtrees must break off at some stage.

That conditions $1-3$ are satisfied follows in an obvious manner from the construction of $\Gamma(x)$.

Now let $\Gamma(y)$ contain a cycle in which there are subtrees $y_{i_1}, \ldots, y_{i_n}$, with an arc going from y_{i_n} to y_{i_1}; suppose that the distinguished cycles (see the beginning of the proof) contain paths passing through the subtrees $y_{i_1}, \ldots, y_{i_m}$; $y_{i_{m+1}}, \ldots, y_{i_l}$; $\ldots$; $y_{i_r}, \ldots, y_{i_n}$. (The semicolon separates subtrees occurring in distinct distinguished cycles.) Select any two subtrees of $\Gamma(x)$, $x_{l_\varkappa} \in \mathfrak{X}_{i_\varkappa}$ and $x_{l_\lambda} \in \mathfrak{X}_{i_\lambda}$ $(\varkappa < \lambda)$. Consider an arbitrary subtree $x_{j_1} \in \mathfrak{X}_{i_1}$. From x_{j_1} there is a path to some subtree $x_{j_m} \in \mathfrak{X}_{i_m}$, and from x_{j_m} an arc to some subtree $x_{j_{m+1}} \in \mathfrak{X}_{i_{m+1}}$. Continuing in this way, we see that $\Gamma(x)$ contains a path passing through the subtrees $x_{j_1}, \ldots, x_{j_n}$, and an arc from x_{j_n} to x_{j_1}. Now suppose that subtrees $x_{l_\varkappa}$ and x_{l_λ} occur in the distinguished cycles. Then the above path may be so chosen that it also contains the subtrees $x_{l_\varkappa}$ and x_{l_λ}.

Suppose that $x_{l_\varkappa}$ does not occur in any distinguished cycle. There exists a subtree x_k in one of the distinguished cycles, from which there is a path to $x_{l_\varkappa}$. Moreover, there is a subtree x_l in the same or another distinguished cycle, such that a path leads from $x_{l_\varkappa}$ to x_l. Since x_k and x_l occur in cycles, it follows from the previous arguments that the cycle may be so chosen that it contains the subtree $x_{i_\varkappa}$.

The case that the subtree x_{l_λ} or both subtrees $x_{l_\varkappa}$ and x_{l_λ} do not occur in distinguished cycles is handled similarly. Thus condition 4 is satisfied.

Suppose now that there is a cycle in $\Gamma(x)$ containing subtrees $x_{i_1},\ldots,x_{i_n}$, with an arc from x_{i_n} to x_{i_1}. There is an arc from x_{i_k} to $x_{i_{k+1}}$ only if $x_{i_k}\in\mathfrak{X}_{j_k}$ and $x_{i_{k+1}}\in\mathfrak{X}_{j_{k+1}}$ and there is an arc in $\Gamma(y)$ from y_{j_k} to $y_{j_{k+1}}$. This implies condition 5 of the theorem.

Condition 6 was disposed of during the construction of $\Gamma(x)$.

This completes the proof of Theorem 30.

Theorem 31. Consider an admissible graph with subtrees $x_1,\ldots,x_I$. We can construct an admissible graph $\Gamma(t)$ satisfying the following condition.

The set of subtrees of $\Gamma(t)$ may be partitioned into disjoint subsets $\mathfrak{T}_1,\ldots,\mathfrak{T}_I$, corresponding in one-to-one fashion with $x_1,\ldots,x_I$, so that the following conditions hold:

(1) Each subtree $t_j\in\mathfrak{T}_n$ is isomorphic to x_n.

(2) If $\Gamma(x)$ contains an arc from x_j to x_i, there exist subtrees $t_{j_1}\in\mathfrak{T}_j$ and $t_{i_1}\in\mathfrak{T}_i$ such that $\Gamma(t)$ contains an arc from t_{j_1} to t_{i_1}.

(3) If there exist subtrees $t_i\in\mathfrak{T}_{i_1}$ and $t_j\in\mathfrak{T}_{j_1}$ such that $\Gamma(t)$ contains an arc from t_i to t_j, then $\Gamma(x)$ contains an arc from x_{i_1} to x_{j_1}.

(4) If x_i and x_j occur in a cycle in $\Gamma(x)$, then any subtrees $t_{i_1}\in\mathfrak{T}_i$ and $t_{j_1}\in\mathfrak{T}_j$ occur in a cycle in $\Gamma(t)$.

(5) If t_i and t_j occur in a cycle in $\Gamma(t)$ and $t_i\in\mathfrak{T}_{i_1}$, $t_j\in\mathfrak{T}_{j_1}$, then x_{i_1} and x_{j_1} occur in a cycle in $\Gamma(x)$.

(6) Let $x_{i_1},\ldots,x_{i_n}$ be any given set of subtrees whose roots are identifiable with a leaf of some subtree in $\Gamma(x)$; for any admissible assignment of words of length N over $\mathfrak{B}$ to these subtrees, producing subtrees $t_{l_1},\ldots,t_{l_n}$, there is a set of subtrees $t_{j_1},\ldots,t_{j_n}$ of $\Gamma(t)$ such that $t_{j_k}\in\mathfrak{T}_{i_k}$ $(k=1,\ldots,n)$, the roots of these subtrees are identifiable with a leaf of some subtree in $\Gamma(t)$, $\mathfrak{M}(t_{j_\rho})=\mathfrak{M}(x_{i_\rho})$, and the subtrees t_{j_ρ} and t_{l_ρ} define the same word over $\mathfrak{B}$.

The proof of this theorem is similar to that of Theorem 30 and is therefore omitted.

We have already defined the type of a state of an IL-I-N automaton (see Definition 16). For the next definition, we remark that sets of subtrees may be introduced and their vertices identified without reference to automata.

Definition 24. A *type* is a set of subtrees $y_{i_1},\ldots,y_{i_n}$ of type (K, N), whose vertices are identified in such a way that (1) in any complete tree y_k of type (K,N), we can specify disjoint sets of leaves $\mathfrak{Y}_{i_1},\ldots,\mathfrak{Y}_{i_n}$ such that the subtree $y_{\varkappa_j}$ obtained from y_k by discarding all leaves not in $\mathfrak{Y}_{i_j}$ and all vertices from which there are no paths leading to vertices in $\mathfrak{Y}_{i_j}$ is isomorphic to y_{i_j} $(j=1,\ldots,n)$; (2) vertices are identifiable in the subtrees $y_{i_1},\ldots,y_{i_n}$ if and only if they correspond to vertices of $y_{\varkappa_1},\ldots,y_{\varkappa_n}$ originating in the same vertex of the tree y_k.

Figure 12 illustrates a set of subtrees $\{y_1, y_2\}$ with identifiable vertices (indicated by identical numbers), and the formation of isomorphic subtrees from a complete tree (the numeral 1 or 2 indicates the leaves of the complete tree used to form a subtree isomorphic to y_1 or y_2, respectively).

It follows from Theorems 24, 27 and 30 that for any type we can construct an automaton $B(\mathrm{I}, N)$, having a type I standard inverse A with delay N in which there is a state of the required type, provided there exists an admissible graph $\Gamma(y)$ containing subtrees isomorphic to the subtrees of the type, whose roots are identifiable with some leaf and whose only identifiable vertices are those corresponding to the identifiable vertices in the type.

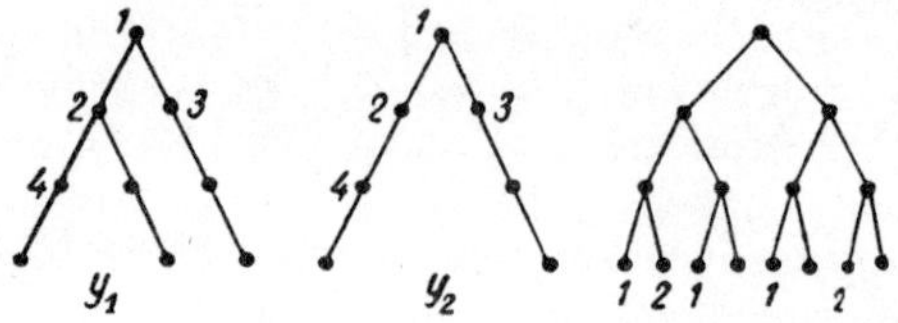

FIGURE 12.

If the automata B and A are not required to be complete, and certain inessential restrictions are imposed on $|\mathfrak{B}|$, one can always construct a graph $\Gamma(y)$ with the above-mentioned properties, whatever the number of sets of subtrees specifying the types and the number of admissible assignments of labels to their arcs; one can even demand that the graph $\Gamma(y)$ be strongly connected. (This statement will be proved later.) Henceforth, therefore, whenever discussing construction of the automata A and B we shall assume from the start that a suitable graph $\Gamma(y)$ is indeed available. Not only can we prescribe the types of the states of A (including several states of each type), but we may even demand that the states s_i of these types define arbitrary sets of words $\mathfrak{M}_{\mathrm{I}}(s_i, \beta_{i_j})$ $(j=1, \ldots, n_i;$ β_{i_j} are the words the automaton A can produce when in state s_i) obtained by an admissible assignment of letters from $\mathfrak{A}$ to the arcs of the subtrees $y_{i_1}, \ldots, y_{i_n}$ defining the type. There may also be several states $s_{i_1}, \ldots, s_{i_l}$ of the same type but with different sets $\mathfrak{M}(s_{i_\lambda}, \beta_{i_j\lambda})$ $(j=1, \ldots, n,\ \lambda=1, \ldots, l)$. The only upper bound on the number l is due to the possible number of distinct admissible assignments.

It follows from Theorems 23, 26 and 31 that we can construct an automaton $B(\mathrm{I}, N)$ and for it a type I standard inverse A with delay N having states $s_{i_1}, \ldots, s_{i_l}$ of prescribed types with prescribed sets $\mathfrak{M}(s_{i_j}, \beta_{i_j\lambda})$, such that even the words $\beta_{i_j\lambda}$ may all be assigned in advance. The only restriction on the choice of words β_{i_j} for a state s_{i_j} is that they constitute an admissible assignment of words to the subtrees $x_{i_j 1}, \ldots, x_{i_j\lambda}$ with identifiable roots defining the set $\mathfrak{M}(s_{i_\lambda}, \beta_{i_j\lambda})$.

Conditions 3 and 4 of Theorems 30 and 31 govern the connectivity properties of the automaton A and its underlying graph $\Gamma(y)$. In particular, if $\Gamma(y)$ is strongly connected, the automaton A is also strongly connected.

Let us devote closer attention to the case of a strongly connected automaton A. As follows from Theorems 23, 24, 26 and 27, the numbers M and L such that the automaton B defined by the appropriate graph $\Gamma(t)$ (or $\Gamma(x)$ and $\Gamma(tx)$) and its standard inverse A are ILS-I-M and ILS-I-L, respectively, are not entirely arbitrary but depend on the sets of subtrees with identifiable vertices used for the construction (see condition 6 in Theorems 30 and 31). Thus, if these sets contain only panicles of types (K, N, L_ν), $L_\nu \leqslant L$, and at least one panicle of type (K, N, L), then A may be ILS-I-R only if $R \geqslant L$. Similarly, if any two subtrees in the same set may have identifiable vertices only on level M_ν, $M_\nu < M$, and at least one set contains two subtrees with identifiable vertices on level $M-1$, then the automaton B defined by the resulting graph $\Gamma(t)$ (or $\Gamma(x)$ and $\Gamma(tx)$) may be ILS-I-P only if $P \geqslant M$. The following theorem will show that, if $|\mathfrak{B}|$ is sufficiently large, one can construct a strongly connected graph $\Gamma(t)$ (or $\Gamma(x)$ and $\Gamma(tx)$) such that the automata A and B that it defines are ILS-I-R and ILS-I-M, respectively, where R and M depend on the properties of the types and are defined in the theorem.

Before stating the theorem we introduce a new definition.

Definition 25. Let $\mathfrak{A}_0$ be an arbitrary set. We shall say that sets $\mathfrak{A}_1, \ldots, \mathfrak{A}_m$ of disjoint subsets of $\mathfrak{A}_0$ form an imbedded sequence of partitions of $\mathfrak{A}_0$ if, for each $n=1, \ldots, m$, any element of $\mathfrak{A}_n$ is the union of elements of $\mathfrak{A}_{n-1}$. The number m will be called the level of the imbedded sequence. The order of the imbedded sequence is defined to be the largest number r such that some $\mathfrak{A}_j$ $(1 \leqslant j \leqslant m)$ contains a set which is the union of exactly r elements of $\mathfrak{A}_{j-1}$.

Theorem 32. Let $|\mathfrak{B}| \geqslant K$ and let $y_{11}, \ldots, y_{1M_1}; \ldots; y_{k1}, \ldots, y_{kM_k}$ be given types, satisfying the following conditions:

(i) *Each subtree y_{ij} is a panicle of type $(K, N, \varkappa)$, where $\varkappa \leqslant R$.*

(ii) *In the sets of subtrees defining the types, only vertices on levels M_ν, $M_\nu < M$, may be identified.*

(iii) *For any type $y_{i1}, \ldots, y_{iM_i}$, treated as a set $\mathfrak{A}_0$, there exists an imbedded sequence of partitions $\mathfrak{A}_1, \ldots, \mathfrak{A}_N$ of order at most $|\mathfrak{B}|$ such that no two distinct subsets p_i and p_j of a partition $\mathfrak{A}_\nu$ $(\nu=1, \ldots, N)$ can contain subtrees (one in each subset) with identifiable $(M-\nu)$-th level vertices.*

(iv) *No subset of a partition $\mathfrak{A}_\nu$ $(\nu=1, \ldots, N)$ contains two subtrees with identifiable R_ν-the level vertices, where $R_\nu > N-R-\nu$.*

(v) *One of the types has the following property: either it contains two subtrees with two identifiable $(M-1)$-th level vertices, or some partition $\mathfrak{A}_\nu$ of its set of subtrees contains two subsets in which there are subtrees with identifiable $(M-1-\nu)$-th level vertices.*

(vi) *At least one of the types has the following property: either it contains a panicle of type (K, N, R), or some partition $\mathfrak{A}_\nu$ of its set of subtrees contains a subset in which there are two subtrees with identifiable $(N-R-\nu)$-th level vertices.*

Then we can construct a strongly connected graph $\Gamma(y)$ with the following properties:

(1) *$\Gamma(y)$ contains the subtrees $y_{11}, \ldots, y_{1M_1}; \ldots; y_{k_1}, \ldots, y_{kM_k}$.*

(2) *The only vertices of the subtrees $y_{i_1}, \ldots, y_{iM_i}$ identifiable in $\Gamma(y)$ are those identifiable in the type.*

(3) *The graph contains panicles only of types (K, N, R_ν), $R_\nu \leqslant R$.*

(4) *The graph contains a panicle of type (K, N, R).*

(5) *The graph $\Gamma(y)$ does not contain three subtrees y_i, y_{i_1}, y_{i_2} with arcs from y_i to y_{i_1} and y_{i_2} such that each of the subtrees y_{i_1}, y_{i_2} contains an M_ν-th level vertex identifiable with an $(M_\nu+1)$-th level vertex of y_i, $M_\nu \geqslant M$.*

(6) *The graph $\Gamma(y)$ contains three subtrees y_j, y_{j_1}, y_{j_2} with arcs from y_j to y_{j_1} and y_{j_2} such that each of the subtrees y_{j_1}, y_{j_2} contains an $(M-1)$-th level vertex identifiable with the same M-th level vertex of y_j.*

(7) *The number of arcs emanating from each subtree of $\Gamma(y)$ is at most $|\mathfrak{B}|$.*

Proof. Let $y_{i_1},\ldots,y_{iM_i}$ be any one of the given types; treating it as the set $\mathfrak{A}_0$ of Definition 25, construct an imbedded sequence of partitions $\mathfrak{A}_0,\ldots,\mathfrak{A}_N$ of order at most $|\mathfrak{B}|$, satisfying conditions (iii) — (vi). Recall that each subtree in the type determines a set of leaves in the complete tree of type (K, N). For each class of a partition in the sequence, consider the sets of leaves of all subtrees in the class, and for each of these sets of leaves construct a subtree of the complete tree y_k of type (K, N) by discarding all vertices which are either not in the set or have no paths leading from them to a vertex of the selected set.

Considering all subtrees obtained from a partition $\mathfrak{A}_j$, discard all vertices of levels $N-j+1,\ldots,N$. Thus the partition $\mathfrak{A}_j$ produces subtrees of type $(K, N-j)$. (For the partition $\mathfrak{A}_N$, we obtain a subtree containing only one vertex.) Join the resulting subtrees by arcs as follows. Suppose that p_j is a class of $\mathfrak{A}_j$, the union of classes $p_{i_1},\ldots,p_{i_n}$ of $\mathfrak{A}_{j-1}$. Let arcs lead from the subtree corresponding to p_j to the subtrees corresponding to $p_{i_1},\ldots,p_{i_n}$. By condition (iii), there are at most $|\mathfrak{B}|$ arcs emanating from each subtree. In adjacent subtrees of the resulting graph, identify the vertices that correspond to the same vertex of y_k. Finally, attach each tree of type $(K, N-j)$ $(j\geqslant 1)$ to the leaf of a subtree of type (K, j) with only $(j+1)$ vertices. In the newly constructed portions of the subtrees, identify the single vertices so as to obtain a semi-admissible graph. This is clearly always possible.

Proceeding in this manner for all the given types, we obtain a graph $\Gamma(y)$.

It follows from conditions (ii) and (iii) that the graph $\Gamma(y)$ has property 5. Conditions (i) and (iv) imply that $\Gamma(y)$ possesses property 3. Similarly, conditions (v) and (vi) imply that $\Gamma(y)$ has properties 4 and 6.

That $\Gamma(y)$ possesses properties 1, 2 and 7 follows directly from the construction.

The rest of the construction also preserves the validity of properties 1 through 7.

For any subtree from which no arcs emanate, we construct new subtrees as follows.

Let y_j be a subtree with this property; suppose that there are $\varkappa$ arcs from one of its L-th level vertices $(L=N-R)$ to vertices $\xi_{j,L+1,1},\ldots,\xi_{j,L+1,\varkappa}$. Obviously, $\varkappa\leqslant K\leqslant|\mathfrak{B}|$. We form $\varkappa$ subtrees as follows. Take $\varkappa$ subtrees isomorphic to those attached to the vertices $\xi_{j,L+1,1},\ldots,\xi_{j,L+1,\varkappa}$; attach these subtrees to the leaves of $\varkappa$ subtrees of type $(K, L-1)$ with L vertices. Identify each of these leaves with the corresponding vertex $\xi_{j,L+1,\nu}$, and the vertices of the newly formed subtrees (in the attached sections) with the corresponding vertices of the subtree y_j. Since y_j is a panicle of type (K, N, R_ν) with $R_\nu\leqslant R$, it is clear that one can identify a unique vertex on each level below $L+1$ in y_j with a unique vertex on each level below L in the newly formed subtrees. For each leaf on level $N-1$ in one of the newly introduced subtrees, add an N-th level vertex and an arc from the corresponding $(N-1)$-th level vertex. Finally, draw (at most K) arcs from the subtree y_j to all the new subtrees. This construction of new subtrees for all subtrees from which no arcs emanate is now repeated $N-1$ times.

The parts of the graph thus constructed are trees satisfying the following condition: their roots and leaves have the property that from every vertex which is not a leaf exactly one arc emanates. We can therefore build up an admissible strongly connected graph from these connected graphs. It is sufficient, for example, to order all the connected graphs and add arcs leading from the leaves of the subtrees of the preceding graph to the root of the next graph, one arc from each leaf (and also arcs leading from the leaves of the last graph to the root of the first).

This completes the proof of Theorem 32.

The results of the next sections will show that Theorem 32 fails to hold if the automata A and B are complete.

Example 11. Figure 13, a illustrates a type with $|\mathfrak{A}|=|\mathfrak{B}|=2$ (the identified vertices are indicated by the dashed curve). Requiring that the automaton A have a state s_i with sets $\mathfrak{M}(s_i, \beta_1)=\{000, 001\}$ and $\mathfrak{M}(s_i, \beta_2)=$ $=\{110, 111\}$, we can construct the graph $\Gamma(y)$ (Figure 13,b) and the corresponding graph $\Gamma(x)$ (Figure 13,c); by Theorem 30, this last graph implies the existence of an automaton A with the desired properties. Assigning letters of $\mathfrak{B}$ to the arcs of $\Gamma(x)$ in an arbitrary manner (the only restriction being that distinct arcs issuing from the same subtree should not be labeled by the same letter of $\mathfrak{B}$), we obtain the required automaton B.

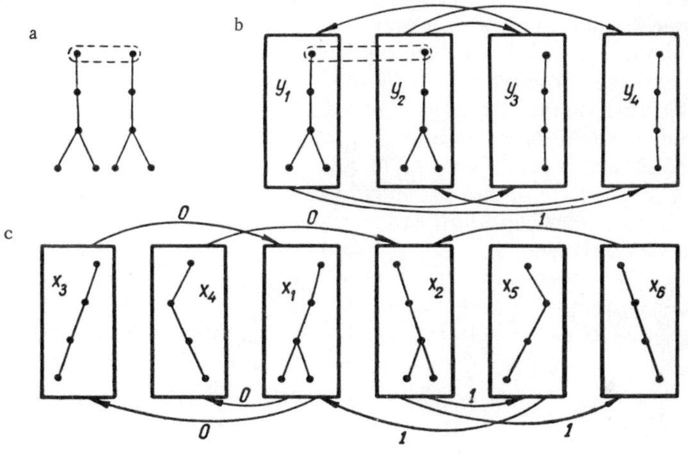

FIGURE 13.

It is evident from this example that the actual construction of the graphs $\Gamma(y)$, $\Gamma(x)$ and $\Gamma(t)$ may be considerably simpler than envisaged in the proofs of Theorems 30—32. In the example, however, we could take the individual features of the problem into account, which is of course impossible in a general proof.

The results of the last sections were presented in part in /7/.

§6. SIMPLEST PROPERTIES OF NORMAL AUTOMATA

Of special interest in automata theory are strongly connected complete automata. Because of strong connectivity, an automaton with this property can never reach a state in which it behaves like an automaton with fewer states. Furthermore, there is no point in studying incomplete IL-I-N or IL-II-N automata unless the only reason that the functions λ and may be undefined for some "state — input" pair is that the restrictions imposed on input words and initial states prevent the pair in question from ever appearing (for more details on this point, see below). To simplify the subsequent exposition, we therefore introduce a new concept.

Definition 26. An automaton is said to be **normal** if it is strongly connected, IL-I-N for some N, complete, and the principal part of any type I inverse with delay N is also complete.

It follows from Corollary 3I that if an automaton is normal any of its inverses may be identified with the principal part of a standard inverse.

Theorem 33. An automaton may be normal only if $|\mathfrak{A}| = |\mathfrak{B}|$.

Proof. Let B be an inverse of a normal automaton A. Suppose that $M > K$, where $|\mathfrak{A}| = K$, $|\mathfrak{B}| = M$.

Let $t_k = (s_j, \beta_1) \in \mathfrak{T}_1$ be a state such that $|\mathfrak{M}(s_j, \beta_1)| = \min_{(s_i, \beta)} |\mathfrak{M}(s_i, \beta)| = n$.

Since A is complete, the total number of arcs emanating from those of its $(N-1)$-th level vertices which are identifiable with some N-th level vertex is K. Thus all subtrees which are ends of arcs from t_k have all in all Kn leaves. Since B is complete, we have M subtrees $t_{l_1}, \ldots, t_{l_M}$ which are ends of arcs from t_k. Consequently, $|\mathfrak{M}(t_{l_1})| + \ldots |\mathfrak{M}(t_{l_M})| = Kn$. Since $|\mathfrak{M}(t_{l_j})| \geqslant n$ $(j = 1, \ldots, M)$, this cannot be true if $M > K$.

By Theorem 16, we may view A as an inverse of B; thus it follows that $M < K$ is also impossible, and so $M = K$.

Theorem 34. Let the prime factors of K $(K = |\mathfrak{A}|)$ *be* $p_{i_1}, \ldots, p_{i_l}$. *Then for any normal automaton* A *we have* $|\mathfrak{M}(s_i, \beta)| = p_{i_1}^{j_1} \cdot \ldots \cdot p_{i_l}^{j_l}$, *where* $j_\lambda \geqslant 0$ *are fixed numbers.*

Proof. We first show that the sets $\mathfrak{M}(s_i, \beta)$ all contain the same number of elements.

Suppose this is false. Let $t_k = (s_i, \beta_1)$ be a state of the inverse B such that

$$|\mathfrak{M}(s_i, \beta_1)| = \max_{(s_j, \beta)} |\mathfrak{M}(s_j, \beta)| = n$$

and there is an arc from t_k to a subtree t_l such that $|\mathfrak{M}(t_l)| < |\mathfrak{M}(t_k)|$. Such subtrees exist by our assumption that the numbers $|\mathfrak{M}(s_j, \beta)|$ are not all the same. As in the proof of Theorem 33, we see that if $t_{l_1}, \ldots, t_{l_K}$ are subtrees to which lead arcs from t_k, then necessarily $|\mathfrak{M}(t_{l_1})| + \ldots + |\mathfrak{M}(t_{l_K})| = Kn$. Since $|\mathfrak{M}(t_{l_j})| \leqslant n$ for all subtrees $t_{l\,j}$, and for one at least, say $t_{l\,j_0}$, $|\mathfrak{M}(t_{l\,j_0})| < n$, this equality is impossible.

Suppose that the graph $\Gamma(B)$ contains a subtree of type (K, N). Since A is normal, the root of any subtree in $\Gamma(B)$ is identifiable with some leaf of a subtree. The total number of leaves of all subtrees whose roots are identifiable with some leaf is K^N. To complete the proof, it remains only to divide the number K^N into equal parts.

It follows from our results up to now that any automaton B may be characterized by two numbers M and L satisfying the following condition: B is an ILS-I-L automaton, and any standard inverse of B with delay N is ILS-I-M. It follows from Theorem 34 that a normal automaton B is characterized by yet another parameter — the weight of the roots of the subtrees in the graph $\Gamma(B)$. We shall therefore sometimes write B(SI, M, L, x) to mean that the numbers M and L have the properties mentioned above, and x is the weight of the roots of the subtrees in $\Gamma(B)$. This number will henceforth be called the weight of the graph $\Gamma(B)$, denoted by $|\Gamma(B)|$.

Proceeding in the same way as for $\Gamma(B)$, we may construct a graph $\Gamma(A)$ for the inverse automaton A. The relation between the weights of $\Gamma(B)$ and $\Gamma(A)$, where A has delay N, is given by the following

Theorem 35. $|\Gamma(B)|\cdot|\Gamma(A)|=K^N$

Proof. Consider an arbitrary word $\alpha\in\mathfrak{M}(t_l)$, where t_l is some subtree in $\Gamma(B)$. We have $\mu(t_l, \beta)=\alpha$ if and only if $\varepsilon(t_l, \beta)=t_m$ and the root of t_m is identifiable with the vertex $\tau_{lN\alpha}$. The number of words β satisfying this condition is $K^N/|\Gamma(B)|$, since this is precisely the number of subtrees whose roots are identifiable with the vertex $\tau_{lN\alpha}$. But the number of such words is $|\mathfrak{M}(t_l, \alpha)|$, and this completes the proof.

Theorem 36. If A is strongly connected, complete and IL-I-N, and $|\mathfrak{A}|=|\mathfrak{B}|=K$, then A is normal.

Proof. Suppose that the inverse B is not complete. Let t_k be any subtree from which there are less than K arcs in the graph $\Gamma(B)$. Then at least one of the subtrees which are the ends of the arcs from t_k, say t_{k_1}, must be such that $|\mathfrak{M}(t_{k_1})|>|\mathfrak{M}(t_k)|$, since (by the completeness of A) the number of leaves of these subtrees is $K\cdot|\mathfrak{M}(t_k)|$ and these leaves must be divided among $M<K$ subtrees. Since A is strongly connected, so is B (Theorem 14); there is a path from t_{k_1} to t_k. If this path is an arc from t_{k_1} to t_k, at least one of the subtrees $t_{l_1}, \ldots, t_{l_R}$ which are ends of arcs from t_{k_1} must have the property $|\mathfrak{M}(t_{l_j})|>|\mathfrak{M}(t_{k_1})|$, since (as before) $K\cdot|\mathfrak{M}(t_{k_1})|$ leaves must be divided among $R\leqslant K$ subtrees, one of which has less than $|\mathfrak{M}(t_{k_1})|$ leaves. Suppose now that there is no arc from t_{k_1} to t_k. Consider an arbitrary path from t_{k_1} to t_k, passing through vertices $t_{k_1}=t_{\nu_1}, t_{\nu_2}, \ldots, t_{\nu_m}=t_k$. If $|\mathfrak{M}(t_{\nu_2})|<|\mathfrak{M}(t_{\nu_1})|$, there must be a subtree t_m such that $|\mathfrak{M}(t_m)|>|\mathfrak{M}(t_{k_1})|$. If $|\mathfrak{M}(t_{\nu_2})|>|\mathfrak{M}(t_{\nu_1})|$, there is also a subtree whose root has weight greater than $|t_{k_1}|$. Let $|\mathfrak{M}(t_{\nu_2})|=|\mathfrak{M}(t_{\nu_1})|$. Repeating the preceding argument if necessary for all pairs of these subtrees up to $t_{\nu_{m-1}}$ and t_{ν_m}, we finally see that there exists a subtree t_l such that $|\mathfrak{M}(t_l)|>|\mathfrak{M}(t_{k_1})|$. Now the graph $\Gamma(B)$ contains a path from t_l to t_k. Repeating the above argument, one shows that there exists a subtree t_m with $|\mathfrak{M}(t_m)|>|\mathfrak{M}(t_l)|$. Thus the assumption that B is not complete implies that the graph $\Gamma(B)$ must contain subtrees with roots of arbitrarily large weight, which is of course impossible. This completes the proof.

Following Berge /13/, we shall use the term outgoing degree for the number of arcs emanating from a vertex.

The next definition will prove useful for our further constructions.

Definition 27. A cleavage* of rank n of a subtree z_j is a semi-admissible graph $\Gamma(z)$ which is a subtree of type (M, n) with root z_j. A cleavage $\Gamma(z)$ is said to be normal if there are exactly K arcs emanating from each subtree of $\Gamma(z)$, the sum of outgoing degrees of the identifiable vertices on the $(N-1)$-th level of the subtrees is K, and the weights of the roots of all subtrees are equal.

* [The Russian word used here is apparently a coinage of the author, meaning something formed by splitting. Our "cleavage" has been used in graph theory (see /18/) but in a different sense. — Trans.]

Certain properties and existence conditions for IL-I-N automata are conveniently expressed in terms of the weights of vertices of subtrees. We therefore consider graphs of type $\Gamma(y)$.

Theorem 37. Let the subtree y_i be a panicle of type (K, N, n), such that the subgraphs attached to its $(N-l)$-th level vertices are complete trees of type (K, l); suppose that y_i has a normal cleavage of rank m satisfying the condition: all subtrees of the cleavage are panicles of one of the types $(K, N, \varkappa)$ $(\varkappa=m_1, \ldots, n_1 \leqslant N)$ and the subgraphs attached to their $(N-l_1)$-th level vertices are complete trees of type (K, l_1) $(l_1 \leqslant l)$. Then the product of the weight of any vertex of y_i on level $N-n_1+\nu$ and the number K^ν $(\nu=0, 1, \ldots, m \leqslant n_1-l_1)$ is a multiple of $|y_i|$.

Proof. Discard all vertices of levels $0, 1, \ldots, N-n_1-1, N-l_1+1, \ldots, N$ from the subtree y_i and from all subtrees of the cleavage whose existence is assumed. Denote the subtree thus obtained from y_i by y_μ. It is clear that the subtrees obtained from the j-th level subtrees of the cleavage of y_i are j-th level subtrees of a cleavage of rank m of y_μ, and the ρ-th level vertices of the subtrees of the cleavage at y_i $(\rho=N-n_1, \ldots, N-l_1)$ become $(\rho-N+n_1)$-th level vertices of the subtrees of the cleavage of y_μ. It will therefore suffice to prove the following assertion: the product of the weight of any σ-th level vertex of y_μ $(\sigma=0, 1, \ldots, m \leqslant n_1-l_1)$ and the number K^σ is a multiple of $|y_\mu|$. Consider an arbitrary vertex $\xi_{\mu\sigma k}$ on the σ-th level of y_μ; let $|\xi_{\mu\sigma k}|=M$. Since the cleavage is normal, the sum of weights of all roots of subtrees on its σ-th level which are identifiable with $\xi_{\mu\sigma k}$ is $K^\sigma M$. If this number is not a multiple of $|y_\mu|$, the cleavage cannot be normal, since the weights of all roots of the subtrees of the cleavage cannot be equal.

As a corollary of this theorem, we deduce the following theorem characterizing the subtrees of a normal automaton B.

Theorem 38. Let $B(SI, M, L, F)$ be a normal automaton. Then the product of the weight of any σ-th level vertex of a subtree in $\Gamma(B)$ and the number K^σ is a multiple of F.

Proof. For each subtree t_l in the graph $\Gamma(B)$, construct the tree $T(t_l, \Gamma(B), N)$ (see p. 61). This tree is a cleavage of rank N of t_l. By Theorem 34 and the fact that B is normal, this cleavage is normal. The conclusion of our theorem now follows from Theorem 37.

§7. PROPERTIES OF SUBTREES WHICH MAY BE VERTICES OF NORMAL GRAPHS

Our next results relate to the problem of specifying types of states for normal automata. We shall first prove a converse of Theorem 37. Before stating the theorem, we need a new definition.

Definition 28. A subtree of type (K, N) is said to be critical if it satisfies the following conditions: 1) the prime factors of the weight of its root are prime factors of K; 2) vertices on the same level have equal outgoing degrees; 3) if K contains a prime factor p to the n-th power and the outgoing degree of the ν-th level vertices is divisible by p, then the outgoing degree of the μ-th level vertices, $\mu>\nu$, is divisible by p^n.

A complete panicle is a special case of a critical subtree. If K is a prime, any critical subtree is a complete panicle. But if K is not a prime there are critical subtrees which are not complete panicles (see Figure 14, where $K=12$ and the weight of the root is 18).

FIGURE 14.

Suppose we are concerned with subtrees of type (K, N). The numbers K and N and the weight of the root of a critical subtree must satisfy certain restrictions.

Definition 29. The number M is said to be critical for K and F if a critical subtree with root of weight F is a panicle of type (K, N, M).

In the above example, $M=2$.

Theorem 39. If M is critical for K and F, then M is the smallest number such that K^M is divisible by F.

Proof. Let $F=p_{i_1}^{j_1}p_{i_2}^{j_2}\cdot\ldots\cdot p_{i_n}^{j_n}$, $j_1\geqslant j_2\geqslant\ldots\geqslant j_n$, and $K=p_{i_1}^{k_1}p_{i_2}^{k_2}\cdot\ldots\cdot p_{i_n}^{k_n}$. It follows from Definition 28 that all vertices on any one level of a critical subtree have equal weights. The weight of any $(N-1)$-th level vertex of a critical subtree is $E_{N-1}=p_{i_1}^{l_1}\cdot\ldots\cdot p_{i_n}^{l_n}$, where $l_\nu=\min(k_\nu, j_\nu)$ $(\nu=1,\ldots,n)$. If we discard all leaves of the original critical subtree, we obtain a new critical subtree of type $(K, N-1)$, whose root has weight $F_1=p_{i_1}^{m_1}\cdot p_{i_2}^{m_2}\cdot\ldots\cdot p_{i_n}^{m_n}$, where $m_\nu=j_\nu-l_\nu=j_\nu\dot{-}k_\nu$* $(\nu=1,2,\ldots,n)$. If all the exponents m_ν vanish, then $M=1$, $k_\nu\geqslant j_\nu$, and K is divisible by F.

Suppose that not all the m_ν vanish. Then $M>1$ and K is not divisible by F. We then repeat the above reasoning for the new critical subtree. Discarding the leaves, we get a subtree of type $(K, N-2)$ whose root has weight $F_2=p_{i_1}^{r_1}p_{i_2}^{r_2}\cdot\ldots\cdot p_{i_n}^{r_n}$, where $r_\nu=m_\nu-\min(k_\nu, m_\nu)=j_\nu\dot{-}2k_\nu$ $(\nu=1,\ldots,n)$. If all the r_ν vanish, we have $M=2$ and K^2 is divisible by F. Repeating the argument sufficiently many times, we obtain the desired conclusion.

Theorem 40. Let the subtree y_i be a panicle of type (K, N, n) such that the subgraphs attached to all its $(N-l)$-th level vertices are complete trees of type (K, l), and the product of the weight of any of its $(N-n_1+\nu)$-th level vertices $(N\geqslant n_1>0)$ and the number K^ν $(\nu=0, 1,\ldots,n_1-1)$ is a multiple of $|y_i|$.

Then there exists a normal cleavage of rank M, where M is the critical number for K and $|y_i|$, satisfying the conditions:

(1) *the subtrees of the cleavage are panicles of one of the types $(K, N, \varkappa)$ where $\varkappa\leqslant\max(n, n_1)$;*

(2) *all subtrees on the M-th level of the cleavage are critical.*

Proof. As in the proof of Theorem 37, we shall simplify matters by assuming that the subgraphs attached to the $(N-1)$-th level of vertices of y_i are not all complete trees and moreover $\max(n, n_1)=N$. That any given subtree may be reduced to a subtree satisfying this condition was shown in the proof of Theorem 37.

* $a\dot{-}b=\max(a-b, 0)$.

The rather tedious proof of the theorem will be divided into several steps.

Step 1.

Lemma 6. Let a_0 be a number whose prime divisors are all prime devisors of K, and define numbers A_n, B_n ($n=1, 2, \ldots$) as follows. A_1 is the greatest common divisor (g.c.d.) of a_0 and K; A_{n+1} is the g.c.d. of $a_0/A_1\cdot\ldots\cdot A_n$ and K. is the g.c.d. of a_0 and K^n. Then $B_n=A_1\cdot\ldots\cdot A_n$.

Proof. We first assume that the numbers a_0 and K are divisible by exactly one prime, $a_0=p^r$, $K=p^m$. Then $A_n=p^m$ for all $n=1, 2, \ldots$ such that $nm\leqslant r$. If n_0 is the number such that $(n_0-1)m<r\leqslant n_0m$, then $A_n=p^{r\dot{-}(n-1)m}$ for $n\geqslant n_0$. $B_n=p^{r_n}$, where $r_n=\min(nm, r)$. The assertion is obvious for $n\leqslant n_0-1$. We have $B_{n_0}=p^r$ and $A_1\cdot\ldots\cdot A_{n_0}= p^{(n_0-1)m}\cdot p^{r-(n_0-1)m}=p^r$. Since $A_n=1$ for $n>n_0$, the conclusion also holds for $n>n_0$.

If K has more than one prime divisor, similar arguments hold for each prime divisor separately.

Lemma 7. If $m>k$, then A_k is divisible by A_m.

Proof. If K has only one prime divisor, the conclusion follows directly from the explicit expressions for A_k derived in Lemma 6. If K has more than one prime divisor, the proof follows from the fact that the exponents of the various primes in the numbers $A_1, A_2, \ldots, A_m$ cannot increase.

Step 2. We are going to construct a cleavage of rank M for the subtree y_i, satisfying the following conditions:

(i) The weight of the root of any ν-th level subtree in the cleavage ($\nu=1, \ldots, M$) is $|y_i|/A_M A_{M-1}\ldots A_{M+1-\nu}$, where A_j and B_j are defined as in Lemma 6 with $a_0=|y_i|$.

(ii) The product of the weight of any ν-th level vertex of any subtree and the number K^ν is divisible by the weight of the root.

(iii) All the subtrees are panicles of one of the types $(K, N, \varkappa)$, where $\varkappa\leqslant\max(n, n_1)$.

(iv) For any leaf of a j-th level subtree of the cleavage the sum of weights of the $(N-1)$-th level vertices of the $(j+1)$-th level subtrees identifiable with this leaf ($j=0, 1, \ldots, M-1$) is K/A_{M-j}.

We shall construct the required cleavage level by level.

1-st level of the cleavage. To each vertex ξ_{ijk} we shall assign a number which we call its residual weight. The residual weights will be readjusted in the course of the construction. Their initial values are $|\xi_{ijk}|\cdot K/A_M$. Let ξ_{i1k} be any first level vertex of the subtree y_i. Consider the subtree attached to y_i at ξ_{i1k}, together with the residual weights of its vertices. To each leaf of this subtree we attach a subtree of type $(K, 1)$ containing K/A_M arcs. This makes the residual weights of the vertices equal to their weights in the newly formed subtree, which is denoted by y_k. For convenience, we retain the same notation for the vertices of this subtree as in y_i; the new leaves will be denoted by $\xi_{i,N+1,\nu}$. Since $K\cdot|\xi_{i1k}|$ is divisible by $|y_i|$, it follows that $|\xi_{i1k}|\cdot K/A_M$ is divisible by $|y_i|/A_M$. Setting $(|\xi_{i1k}|\cdot K/A_M)/(|y_i|/A_M)=r$, we shall now define r subtrees of the cleavage, identifying their roots with the vertex ξ_{i1k} of y_i. These subtrees, denoted by $y_{j_1}, \ldots, y_{j_r}$, will be constructed level by level. In the process, we shall assign certain numbers to the vertices of the subtrees, which we call conditional weights. The notation for conditional weights will be the same as for weights.

Construction of level 0. We start with the roots of the subtrees $y_{j_1}, \ldots, y_{j_r}$, which are identified with the vertex ξ_{i1k} of y_i. The conditional weight of each root is $|y_i|/A_M$. The vertex ξ_{i1k} is assigned a new residual weight 0. It is clear that (a) the number $K^0 \cdot |\xi_{j_k 01}|$ $(k=1,\ldots,r)$ is divisible by $|y_i|/A_M$; (b) the sum of conditional weights of all 0-th level vertices of our subtrees, which we have identified with ξ_{i1k}, is equal to the sum of residual weights of the second level vertices of y_i which are ends of arcs from ξ_{i1k}.

Construction of level $n+1$ $(n=0,1,\ldots,N-1)$. Suppose the following conditions hold: (a) for any n-th level vertex $\xi_{j_\rho nk}$ of the subtrees under construction, the number $K^n \cdot |\xi_{j_\rho nk}|$ is divisible by $|y_i|/A_M$; (b) the sum of conditional weights of all the n-th level vertices of these subtrees identifiable with the same $(n+1)$-th level vertex of y_i, say $\xi_{i,n+1,\nu}$, is equal to the sum of residual weights of the $(n+2)$-th level vertices of y_i which are ends of arcs from $\xi_{i,n+1,\nu}$. Let $\xi_{j_\rho n\mu}$ be a vertex in one of the subtrees which is identifiable with the vertex $\xi_{i,n+1,\nu}$. Take any vertices $\xi_{i,n+2,\mu_\sigma}$ $(\sigma=1,\ldots,\Xi)$ which are ends of arcs from $\xi_{i,n+1,\nu}$, such that the sum of residual weights of the selected vertices in the subtree y_k is not less than the conditional weight of $\xi_{j_\rho n\mu}$. Subtract from the residual weights of the vertices $\xi_{i,n+2,\mu_\sigma}$ in y_k numbers λ_σ $(\sigma=1,\ldots,\Xi)$ such that $K^{n+1}\cdot\lambda_\sigma$ is divisible by $|y_i|/A_M$ and $\lambda_1+\ldots+\lambda_\Xi=|\xi_{j_\rho n,\mu}|$. The number $K^{n+2}\cdot|\xi_{i,n+2,\mu_\sigma}|$ is divisible by $|y_i|$ by assumption, and so the number $K^{n+1}\cdot|\xi_{i,n+2,\mu_\sigma}|\cdot K/A_M$, i. e., the product of K^{n+1} and the residual weight of $\xi_{i,n+2,\mu_\sigma}$, is divisible by $|y_i|/A_M$. Since $K^n\cdot|\xi_{j_\rho n,\mu}|$ is also divisible by this number by condition (a), the numbers λ_σ may be chosen so that condition (b) is satisfied. We now build up the $(n+1)$-th level of the subtree y_{j_ρ}, letting it contain as many vertices as there are nonzero numbers λ_σ and identifying each of these vertices with one of the vertices $\xi_{i,n+2,\mu_\sigma}$ corresponding to nonzero λ_σ; each of these new vertices is assigned the appropriate conditional weight λ_σ. Now add arcs going from $\xi_{j_\rho,n,\mu}$ to each of the new vertices. The residual weights of the $(n+1)$-th level vertices of y_k will now satisfy the condition: the product of the residual weight and the number K^{n+1} is divisible by $|y_i|/A_M$.

Analogous constructions are now applied to the other vertices of the subtrees identified with $\xi_{i,n+1,\nu}$. Following the same pattern, we build up the $(n+1)$-th levels of our subtrees for all other $(n+1)$-th level vertices of y_i. It is clear that the $(n+1)$-th level vertices satisfy the required conditions (a) and (b), and if $n+1 < N-1$ the $(n+2)$-th levels of the subtrees $y_{j_1}, \ldots, y_{j_r}$ may be constructed in similar fashion.

The subtrees in the first level of our cleavage, constructed as described, satisfy the appropriate conditions in Definition 27.

$(n+1)$-th level of the cleavage $(n=0,1,\ldots,M-1)$. Let the weight of each root of a subtree in the n-th level of the cleavage be a_n. We then construct the first level of a cleavage for each of these subtrees, imitating the construction of the first level of the cleavage for y_i. The weight of each root of a subtree on the $(n+1)$-th level of the cleavage is a_n/A_{M-n}.

Step 3. We now construct M cleavages of rank M, satisfying the following conditions:

(a) The weight of a subtree on the ν-th level of the μ-th cleavage ($\mu=1,\dots,M$) is $|y_i|$ if $\nu=0, 1,\dots,\mu$ and $|y_i|/A_{M-\mu}\cdot A_{M-\mu-1}\cdot\dots\cdot A_{M-\mu-(\nu-1)}$ if $\nu=\mu+1,\dots,M$.

(b) For any leaf of a subtree on the ν-th level of the μ-th cleavage, the sum of weights of the $(N-1)$-th level vertices on the $(\nu+1)$-th level of the cleavage which are identifiable with this leaf is K if $\nu=0, 1,\dots,\mu-1$ and $K/A_{M-\nu}$ if $\nu=\mu,\dots,M-1$.

(c) In the subtrees on the k-th level ($k=j,\dots,M$) of the j-th cleavage, the outgoing degree of any l-th level vertex ($N-k\leqslant l\leqslant\min(N-1,\ N-k+(j-1))$) is divisible by $A_{N+M-l-k}$.

The 0-th cleavage will be that constructed in Step 2 above; it clearly satisfies conditions (a) — (c).

Assuming that the μ-th cleavage ($\mu=0,\ 1,\dots,M-1$) has been constructed, we construct the $(\mu+1)$-th as follows. For $\nu=0,\ 1,\dots,\mu$, the ν-th level of the new cleavage coincides with the ν-th level of the μ-th cleavage. The subtrees on the $(\mu+\varkappa)$-th level are obtained from those of the $(\mu+\varkappa)$-th level ($\varkappa=1,\ 2,\dots,\ M-\mu$) of the μ-th cleavage as follows. Consider an arbitrary subtree on level $\mu+\varkappa$ of the μ-th cleavage. For each arc issuing from an $(N-\varkappa)$-th level vertex of the subtree, add $A_{M-\mu}-1$ more arcs going from the same vertex to a new vertex on level $N-\varkappa+1$. Each of the new groups of arcs issuing from one vertex is associated with exactly one arc issuing from the same vertex in the original subtree. To each new vertex, attach a graph isomorphic to the attached graph of the vertex at the end of the arc associated with the new arcs. The arcs between the new subtrees follow the same pattern as in the μ-th cleavage; specifically: if the μ-th cleavage contains an arc from y_i to y_k and these subtrees yield new subtrees y_l and y_m, respectively, the $(\mu+1)$-th cleavage will contain an arc from y_l to y_m. The fact that an admissible identification of the vertices of the new levels in subtrees of the $(\mu+1)$-th cleavage is possible follows by isomorphism from the fact that there is such an identification for vertices of subtrees in the μ-th cleavage. Now, for any leaf of a subtree on the μ-th level of the μ-th cleavage, the sum of weights of all $(N-1)$-th level vertices of subtrees on level $\mu+1$ of the cleavage which are identifiable with the leaf is $K/A_{M-\mu}$; it follows that in the new cleavage this sum is K and conditions (a) and (b) are satisfied for $\nu=1, 2,\dots,\mu+1$. The details of the construction show that these conditions are also valid for $\nu>\mu+1$. Finally, condition (c) follows from the fact that the arcs of the corresponding levels in the 0-th cleavage are duplicated A_ρ times, where ρ is suitably chosen.

Step 4. We now show that all subtrees on the M-th level of the M-th cleavage are critical. The outgoing degree of any $(N-M+j)$-th level vertex ($j=0,\ 1,\dots,M-1$) in these subtrees is A_{M-j}. By Lemma 6, we have $A_1\cdot A_2\cdot\dots\cdot A_M=B_M=|y_i|$. Thus condition 2 of Definition 28 is satisfied. Condition 3 of the definition follows from Lemma 7, and condition 1 from the assumptions of Theorem 40 and the properties of the M-th cleavage.

This completes the proof of Theorem 40.

Theorems 37 and 40, taken together, furnish necessary and sufficient conditions for a subtree to have a normal cleavage.

Figure 15 illustrates a type in which each subtree satisfies the conditions of Theorem 40, but there is no normal automaton with a state of this type, since condition 3 of Theorem 32 does not hold.

It is difficult to find necessary and sufficient conditions on sets of subtrees, ensuring that a unique vertex on some level be identifiable with one vertex of a subtree in a normal cleavage.

For the sequel, however, Theorem 41 (see below) will suffice.

Definition 30. A subtree of type (K, N) with root of weight C will be called a *decomposition subtree* if each of its levels contains at most one vertex to which no complete tree is attached, and moreover it is a panicle of type (K, N, N_1), where $N_1=[C/K^m]+\operatorname{sgn}(C-K^m)$, $K^{m+1}> C\geqslant K^m$.

The following properties of a decomposition subtree are immediate consequences of the definition. Suppose that the representation of the number C with base K is $C=a_mK^m+a_{m-1}K^{m-1}+\ldots+a_0K^0$. Then the subtree has a_j vertices on level $N-j$, not occurring in any complete tree of type $(K, \varkappa_j)$ with $\varkappa_j>j$, whose attached subgraphs are complete trees of type (K, j) $(j=0, 1, \ldots, m$; by a complete tree of type $(K, 0)$ we mean a single vertex). It follows readily from this property that for every $C\leqslant K^N$ there exists a decomposition subtree of type (K, N), with root of weight C.

Figure 16 illustrates a decomposition subtree with $K=12$, $C=18$.

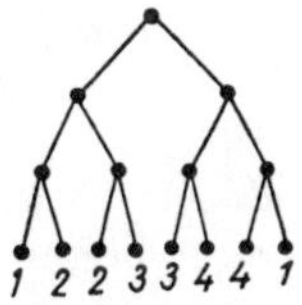

FIGURE 15.

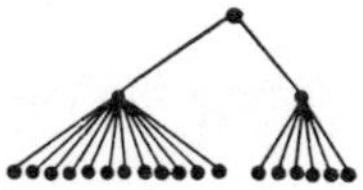

FIGURE 16.

Theorem 41. Suppose that the $(N-l)$-th level of a normal cleavage of rank $N-l$ for some subtree y_k contains subtrees $y_{i_1}, \ldots, y_{i_n}$ such that the following conditions hold:

(1) The roots of $y_{i_1}, \ldots, y_{i_n}$ are identifiable with the same $(N-l)$-th level vertex of y_k.

(2) The subgraphs attached to the $(N-l)$-th level vertices of any subtree in the cleavage are complete trees of type (K, l).

(3) Each subtree in the cleavage is a panicle of one of the types $(K, N, \varkappa)$, $\varkappa=1, 2, \ldots, N-M$.

(4) The weight of the root of any subtree in the cleavage is C.

(5) The product of the weight of any $(M+j)$-th level vertex of any subtree in the cleavage and the number K^j $(j=1, \ldots, N-M)$ is divisible by C.

Then any decomposition tree of type (K, N) with root of weight C has a normal cleavage of rank $N-1$ such that the following conditions are satisfied:

(6) The $(N-l)$-th level of the cleavage contains subtrees $y_{j_1}, \ldots, y_{j_n}$ isomorphic to $y_{i_1}, \ldots, y_{i_n}$, respectively, such that the isomorphism preserves all relations of identification between vertices.

(7) The subgraphs attached to the $(N-l)$-th level vertices of any subtree in the cleavage are complete trees of type (K, l).

(8) Each subtree in the cleavage is a panicle of one of the types $(K, N, \varkappa)$, $\varkappa=1, \ldots, N-M$.

(9) The weight of the root of any subtree in the cleavage is C.

(10) *The product of any $(M+j)$-th level vertex of any subtree in the cleavage and the number K^j is divisible by C $(j=1,\dots,N-M)$.*

Proof. As before, we confine attention to the slightly simpler case $l=0$.

Denote the decomposition subtree in question by y_j. The proof splits up into several steps.

Step 1. Properties of the weights of subtrees in a cleavage of y_j.

Let $K=p_{i_1}^{j_1}p_{i_2}^{j_2}\cdot\ldots\cdot p_{i_\varkappa}^{j_\varkappa}$ and $C=p_{i_1}^{l_1j_1+k_1}p_{i_2}^{l_2j_2+k_2}\cdot\ldots\cdot p_{i_\varkappa}^{l_\varkappa j_\varkappa+k}$, where $l_1\leqslant l_2\leqslant\ldots\leqslant l_\varkappa$ and $0\leqslant k_\mu<j_\mu$ for $\mu=1,\dots,\varkappa$. Define numbers c_j as follows: for $j=0, 1,\dots,M$, we put $c_j=C$; for $j=M+1,\dots,N$,

$$c_j=p_{i_1}^{(l_1j_1+k_1)-(j-M)j_1}\cdot p_{i_2}^{(l_2j_2+k_2)-(j-M)j_2}\cdot\ldots\cdot p_{i_\varkappa}^{(l_\varkappa j_\varkappa+k_\varkappa)-(j-M)j_\varkappa}.$$

Let d_j be any number such that $d_j\cdot K^{j-M}$ is divisible by C. It is clear that c_j is the smallest possible number d_j, $j=M+1,\dots,N$.

Lemma 8. The number Kc_j is divisible by c_{j-1} for $j=M+1,\dots,N$.

Proof. One verifies directly that the exponent of each prime divisor of Kc_j is at least the exponent of the same prime in c_{j-1}.

Lemma 9. The weight of any j-th level vertex of a subtree y_l with root of weight C which satisfies condition 5 may be expressed as a sum of terms equal to c_j.

Proof. c_j divides any number d_j such that $d_j\cdot K^{j-M}$, $j=M+1,\dots,N$, is divisible by C. This follows from the fact that the exponent of any prime in the standard form of d_j cannot be less than the exponent of the same prime in c_j. The assertion of the lemma now follows.

Let us say that the weights of the vertices of a subtree are in special form if the weight of each j-th level vertex is a sum of terms c_j.

Lemma 10. If the weights of the vertices of a subtree y_l with root of weight C may be expressed in special form, the subtree y_l satisfies condition 10.

This follows from the properties of the numbers c_j.

Step 2. Existence of a cleavage satisfying conditions 6—10 for a subtree $y_\varkappa$ with vertices whose weights satisfy certain conditions.

Lemma 11. Let y_μ and y_ν be two subtrees of type (K, N) with roots of weight C, such that the subtrees attached to vertices $\xi_{\mu j\rho}$ and $\xi_{\nu j\sigma}$ $(M+1\leqslant j\leqslant N)$ are isomorphic and the special forms of the weights of the subtrees y_μ and y_ν satisfy the condition: for any vertices $\xi_{\mu i\rho_i}$ and $\xi_{\nu i\sigma_i}$ $(0\leqslant i\leqslant j)$ which lie on the paths from ξ_μ to $\xi_{\mu j\rho}$ and from ξ_ν to $\xi_{\nu j\sigma}$, respectively, the special form of the weight of $\xi_{\nu i\sigma_i}$ has at least as many terms as that of the weight of $\xi_{\mu i\rho_i}$. Suppose we have a cleavage of rank 1 of y_μ, satisfying the condition: the weights of the vertices of the subtrees in the cleavage may be expressed in special form. Then there exists a cleavage of rank 1 of y_ν, satisfying the following conditions:

(1) The weights of the vertices of the subtrees in the cleavage may be expressed in special form.

(2) There is a one-to-one correspondence between certain subtrees $y_{i_1},\dots,y_{i_n}$ in the cleavage of y_μ and certain subtrees $y_{j_1},\dots,y_{j_n}$ in the cleavage of y_ν, such that: (a) each of the subtrees $y_{i_1},\dots,y_{i_n}$ has a vertex, $\xi_{i_\lambda,j-1,\rho_\lambda}$ say, identifiable with the vertex $\xi_{\mu j\rho}$, and each of the subtrees $y_{j_1},\dots,y_{j_n}$ has a vertex, $\xi_{i_\lambda,j-1,\sigma_\lambda}$ say, identifiable with the vertex $\xi_{\nu j\sigma}$;

(b) the subtree attached to $\xi_{j_\lambda,j-1,\sigma_\lambda}$ *is isomorphic to that attached to* $\xi_{i_\lambda,j-1,\rho_\lambda}$ $(\lambda=1,\dots,n)$; *(c) if vertices* ξ_{i_λ,m,ρ_m} *and* $\xi_{j_\lambda,m,\sigma_m}$ *lie on the paths from* ξ_{i_λ} *to* $\xi_{i_\lambda,j-1,\rho_\lambda}$ *and from* ξ_{j_λ} *to* $\xi_{j_\lambda,j-1,\sigma_\lambda}$, *respectively, then the special form of the weight of* $\xi_{j_\lambda,m,\sigma_\lambda}$ *contains at least as many terms as the special form of the weight of* $\xi_{i_\lambda,m,\rho_\lambda}$ $(\lambda=1,\dots,n,\ m=0,1,\dots,\ j-1)$.

Proof. We proceed to construct the required cleavage of y_ν.

Attach a complete tree of type $(K,\ 1)$ to each leaf of y_ν, and denote the resulting subtree by y_π. The vertices of y_π are assigned residual weights, which will be continually readjusted in the course of the proof. The initial values of the residual weights are the weights of the vertices. The residual weight of a j-th level vertex $(j=1,\dots,N)$ is expressed as a sum of terms c_{j-1}. That this is possible follows from Lemma 8.

Take n distinct subtrees $y_{k_1},\dots,y_{k_n}$, all isomorphic to y_π, and identify corresponding vertices of the subtrees $y_\nu, y_\pi, y_{k_1},\dots,y_{k_n}$. We are going to discard certain vertices and arcs of the subtrees $y_{k_1},\dots,y_{k_n}$, to obtain new subtrees $y_{j_1},\dots,y_{j_n}$. During the construction the vertices of the subtrees $y_{k_1},\dots,y_{k_n}$ will be assigned conditional weights in the form of sums; the initial conditional weights are 0.

Consider the subtree y_{i_p} $(p=1,\dots,n)$. Discard vertices and arcs from the subtree y_{k_p} in such a way that the subtree that remains attached to the vertex $\xi_{k_p,j,\sigma}$ identified with $\xi_{\nu j\sigma}$ is isomorphic to the subtree in y_{i_p} attached to the vertex identified with $\xi_{\mu j\rho}$. It is clear that the weights of the $\varkappa$-th level vertices of the attached subtrees may be expressed as sums of terms $c_{\varkappa-1}$ $(\varkappa=j,j+1,\dots,N)$. As conditional weights of the $\varkappa$-th level vertices of the subtrees attached to $\xi_{k_p,j,\sigma}$ we take simply their weights in the form of sums of terms $c_{\varkappa-1}$; the residual weights of the corresponding vertices of y_π are diminished by the terms just assigned as conditional weights. It is clear that after this the following vertices of y_π will have residual weight zero: (i) vertices identifiable with $\xi_{\nu j\sigma}$; (ii) all vertices which are ends of paths from a vertex of type (i).

Let ξ_{k_p,m,σ_m} be a vertex on the path from the root of y_{k_p} to $\xi_{k_p,j,\sigma}$ $(m=0,1,\dots,j-1,p=1,\dots,n)$. The conditional weight assigned to any such vertex ξ_{k_p,m,σ_m} will be a sum of terms c_{m-1} equal to the weight of the vertex $\xi_{i_p,m-1,\rho_{m-1}}$ on the path from the root of y_{i_p} to the vertex of the latter subtree that is identified with the vertex $\xi_{\mu j\rho}$ of y_μ. Simultaneously, the same sum of terms is subtracted from the residual weight of the corresponding identified vertex of the subtree y_π (this operation will henceforth be taken for granted and not mentioned explicitly). The assumptions of the lemma ensure that the residual weights do not thereby become negative.

At this stage of the construction, the following condition holds:

Condition A. The sum of the residual weight of any vertex $\xi_{\pi j\varkappa}$ of y_π and the conditional weights of the vertices $\xi_{k_p,j,\varkappa_p}$ identified with $\xi_{\pi j\varkappa}$ is equal to the weight of $\xi_{\pi j\varkappa}$. (This follows from the initial values of the residual and conditional weights and the way in which they are adjusted.)

Now consider some subtree y_{k_p} and any of its vertices, say $\xi_{k_p m\varkappa}$, whose conditional weight is not equal to the sum of conditional weights of the vertices which are ends of arcs from $\xi_{k_p m\varkappa}$. Let these vertices be

$\xi_{k_p,m+1,\varkappa_1}, \ldots, \xi_{k_p,m+1,\varkappa_l}$. Denoting the conditional weight of a vertex ξ_{ijm} by $\|\xi_{ijm}\|$, we set

$$X = \|\xi_{k_p m\varkappa}\| - \sum_{j=1}^{l} \|\xi_{k_p,m+1,\varkappa_j}\|$$

Obviously, $X = dc_m$, where d is some integer. Consider the set of vertices of y_π identifiable with $\xi_{k_p,m+1,\varkappa_1}, \ldots, \xi_{k_p,m+1,\varkappa_l}$; select sufficiently many of these vertices of y_π to make the sum of their residual weights at least X. (That this may indeed be done will be proved below.) Now add numbers, sums of terms c_m, to the conditional weights of the vertices $\xi_{k_p,m+1,\varkappa_1}, \ldots, \xi_{k_p,m+1,\varkappa_l}$, in such a way that the sum of the added numbers is equal to X and in no case is the number added to the conditional weight of a vertex greater than the residual weight of the vertex of y_π identifiable with it.

Continue this procedure until the subtrees $y_{k_1}, \ldots, y_{k_n}$ satisfy the following condition: the conditional weight of any given vertex is equal to the sum of conditional weights of the vertices which are ends of arcs emanating from it. It is clear that condition A remains valid after each adjustment of residual and conditional weights.

We have to show that vertices of y_π may indeed by selected as required above. If not, there will be a first stage of the construction at which the following situation occurs.

We have a subtree y_{k_λ} and a vertex $\xi_{k_\lambda,m,\varkappa}$ such that

$$\|\xi_{k_\lambda,m,\varkappa}\| - \sum_{j=1}^{l} \|\xi_{k_\lambda,m+1,\varkappa_j}\| = X > 0,$$

where $\xi_{k_\lambda,m+1,\varkappa_j}$ are the vertices which are ends of arcs from $\xi_{k_\lambda,m,\varkappa}$. Let $\xi_{\pi m\gamma}$ be identifiable with $\xi_{k_\lambda m\varkappa}$ and the vertices $\xi_{\pi,m+1,\lambda_j}$ with the vertices $\xi_{k_\lambda,m+1,\varkappa_j}$, respectively; suppose that

$$\sum_{j=1}^{l} |\xi_{\pi,m+1,\lambda_j}| < X,$$

where $|\xi_{ijm}|$ denotes the residual weight of ξ_{ijm}. Then

$$\|\xi_{k_\lambda m\varkappa}\| > \sum_{j=1}^{l} (\|\xi_{k_\lambda,m+1,\varkappa_j}\| + |\xi_{\pi,m+1,\lambda_j}|).$$

For all subtrees $y_{k_1}, \ldots, y_{k_n}$ except y_{k_λ}, we have

$$\|\xi_{k_l m\varkappa_j}\| \geqslant \sum_{j=1}^{n} \|\xi_{k_l,m+1,\gamma_j}\|,$$

where $\xi_{k_l,m,\varkappa_j}$ is identifiable with $\xi_{\pi m\gamma}$, and $\xi_{k_l,m+1,\gamma_j}$ is identifiable with $\xi_{\pi,m+1,\lambda_j}$.

It follows from condition A that

$$|\xi_{\pi m\gamma}| + \sum_{r=1}^{n} \|\xi_{k_r m\varkappa_r}\| = \sum_{j=1}^{K} (|\xi_{\pi,m+1,\lambda_j}| + \sum_{r=1}^{n} \|\xi_{k_r,m+1,\gamma_j}\|).$$

In view of the preceding inequalities, this may be true only provided $|\xi_{\pi m\gamma}|<0$, but this is impossible, so that the situation described above cannot arise and our assertion is proved.

Let $n<K$. Then we add new subtrees $y_{k_{n+1}},\ldots,y_{k_K}$ isomorphic to y_π, assigning all their vertices except those on the first level conditional weight 0. The first level vertices are assigned conditional weight C. Proceeding as before, we adjust the conditional weights of the other levels of $y_{k_{n+1}},\ldots,y_{k_K}$ in such a way that the sum of conditional weights of all vertices which are ends of arcs from another vertex is equal to the conditional weight of the latter. That this can be done is verified in the same way as for the conditional weights of $y_{k_1},\ldots,y_{k_n}$.

Now discard vertices and arcs from the subtrees $y_{k_1},\ldots,y_{k_K}$ until the conditional weights of the vertices of the transformed subtrees become equal to their weights. Discard also the roots of the subtrees $y_{k_1},\ldots,y_{k_K}$ and all arcs issuing from the roots. Denote the subtree obtained from y_{k_l} by y_{j_l} $(l=1,\ldots,K)$. The vertices of the subtrees $y_{j_1},\ldots,y_{j_K}$ are now identified with those of y_ν: $\xi_{j_l,m-1,\rho}$ is identifiable with $\xi_{\nu mr}$ if and only if $\xi_{j_l,m-1,\rho}$ originates in a vertex $\xi_{k_l,m,p}$ identifiable with $\xi_{\nu mr}$.

Condition 1 is satisfied, because the conditional weights of the vertices of $y_{k_1},\ldots,y_{k_K}$ had the form of sums at each stage of the construction. Condition 2 follows from the special construction of the subtrees attached to the vertices $\xi_{k_p,j,\sigma}$ and from the way in which conditional weights were assigned to the vertices ξ_{k_p,m,σ_m}. This completes the proof of Lemma 11.

Step 3. Comparison of the weights of vertices of a decomposition subtree and any other subtree whose root has the same weight.

Lemma 12. *Let y_j be an arbitrary subtree of type (K, N) the weights of whose vertices are expressed in special form. Then the weights of the vertices of a decomposition subtree of type (K, N) whose root has the same weight may be expressed in special form in such a way that the following conditions hold:*

(1) *The weights of vertices on corresponding levels of the subtrees have the same terms.*

(2) *There exists a leaf of the decomposition subtree such that the weights of the vertices on the path from the root of this leaf have at least as many terms as the weight of any vertex on the corresponding level of y_j.*

Proof. Let $C=a_mK^m+\ldots+a_0K^0$. Denote the decomposition subtree by y_μ. If $j=0,1,\ldots,M$, where $M=N-(m+\operatorname{sgn}(C-K^m))$, the decomposition subtree has only one j-th level vertex, whose weight is C. A direct check shows that C is divisible by c_j, $j=0,1,\ldots,N$. Let $j>M$, and suppose first that the number $N-M$ is critical for C and K. Then the weights of the j-th level vertices whose attached subgraphs are complete trees of type $(K, N-j)$ may be expressed as sums of terms $c_\varkappa$, $\varkappa=j-M, j-M+1,\ldots,N-M$, since the number $K^\varkappa\cdot K^{N-j}$ is divisible by C. But then the same form may be given to the weight of the unique j-th level vertex of the decomposition tree whose attached subgraph is not a complete tree, since its weight is $d_j=C-a_mK^m-a_{m-1}K^{m-1}-\ldots-a_{m+M-j+1}K^{m+M-j+1}$ and the number $K^\varkappa\cdot d_j$ is divisible by $c_\varkappa$, $\varkappa=j-M,\ldots,N-M$.

If $N-M$ is not critical for C and K, the weights of the vertices of the decomposition subtree are to be expressed as sums of terms which divide the terms of the special forms of weights in the preceding case. This proves part 1 of the lemma.

We now go on to part 2. Choose any leaf of the decomposition tree, belonging to a complete tree of type (K, m) attached to $\xi_{\mu,N-m,\rho}$. It is clear that the weight of any vertex y_μ to which there is a path from $\xi_{\mu,N-m,\rho}$ cannot be less than the weight of any vertex on the same level of any other subtree of type (K, N). For $i=0, 1, \ldots, M$, the weight of any i-th level vertex of the decomposition subtree is C, and is therefore $\geqslant$ the weight of any vertex on this level of a subtree y_j. Thus the weight of any i-th level vertex $(i=0, 1, \ldots, N-1)$ of y_j contains at most as many equal terms as does the weight of a vertex on the same level of y_μ on the path from ξ_μ to the above-mentioned leaf. This completes the proof.

Step 4. We now consolidate the results of the previous steps. Let the roots of subtrees $y_{i_1}, \ldots, y_{i_n}$ be identifiable with a vertex ξ_{kNi}. With this vertex we associate a leaf ξ_{jNk} of y_j (the decomposition subtree in the statement of the theorem) which is contained in a complete tree of type (K, m). The subgraphs attached to these two vertices are isomorphic subtrees of type $(K, 0)$. By Lemma 9, the weights of the vertices of y_k may be expressed in special form. By Lemma 12, the special forms of the weights of vertices on the paths from the roots to the respective vertices ξ_{kNi} and ξ_{jNk} satisfy the assumptions of Lemma 11. Suppose that the first level of the given cleavage of y_k contains subtrees $y_{k_1}, \ldots, y_{k_m}$ having vertices $\xi_{k_1,N-1,i_1}, \ldots, \xi_{k_m,N-1,i_m}$ identifiable with ξ_{kNi}. By Lemma 11, there is a cleavage of y_j whose first level contains subtrees $y_{j_1}, \ldots, y_{j_m}$ having vertices $\xi_{j_1,N-1,l_1}, \ldots, \xi_{j_m,N-1,l_m}$ identifiable with ξ_{jNk}, such that the subtree attached to each vertex $\xi_{j_r,N-1,l_r}$ is isomorphic to the subtree attached to $\xi_{k_r,N-1,i_r}$ $(r=1, \ldots, m)$. In addition, the special form of the weight of any vertex of y_{j_r} on the path from the root to $\xi_{j_r,N-1,l_r}$ contains at least as many terms as the special form of any vertex on the same level of y_{k_r} on the path from the root to $\xi_{k_r,N-1,i_r}$. If the cleavage contains subtrees other than $y_{j_1}, \ldots, y_{j_m}$, their weights may also be expressed in special form. We now associate each subtree y_{k_r} with y_{j_r} $(r=1, \ldots, m)$.

Suppose we have constructed the l-th level of the required cleavage of y_j $(l=1, \ldots, N-1)$ and for each subtree y_{k_1} on the l-th level of the cleavage of y_k, having an $(N-l)$-th level vertex $\xi_{k,N-l,r}$ identifiable with ξ_{kNi}, the l-th level of the cleavage of y_j contains the subtree y_{j_1} associated with y_{k_1} as stipulated above, such that the following conditions hold:

(a) y_{j_1} contains a vertex $\xi_{j_1,N-l,p}$ identifiable with ξ_{jNk}, and the subtree attached to this vertex is isomorphic to the subtree attached to $\xi_{k_1,N-l,r}$ in y_{k_1}.

(b) The special forms of the weights of vertices of y_{j_1} on the path from the root to $\xi_{j_1,N-l,p}$ contain at least as many terms as for the vertices on the same levels of y_{k_1} on the path from the root to $\xi_{k_1,N-l,r}$. If the l-th level of the cleavage of y_j contains additional subtrees, not associated as above with any subtree of the cleavage of y_k, the weights of their vertices may be expressed in special form.

Proceeding as in the construction of the first level of the cleavage of y_j, one can show that there is a cleavage of rank 1 of y_{j_1} with the property: for every subtree y_{j_2} on the first level of the cleavage of y_{j_1} that has an $(N-l-1)$-th level vertex $\xi_{j_2,N-l-1,p_1}$ identifiable with $\xi_{j_1,N-l,p}$, the cleavage of y_{k_1} contains a subtree y_{k_2} which may be associated in one-to-one fashion with y_{j_2} in such a way that conditions (a) and (b) above are satisfied. Moreover, this cleavage of y_{j_1} is such that the weights of the vertices of all its subtrees not associated with first level subtrees of the cleavage of y_{k_1} may be expressed in special form. For subtrees on the l-th level of the cleavage of y_j not associated with any l-th level subtree of the cleavage of y_k, one can construct a cleavage of rank 1 such that the weights of all its subtrees may be expressed in special form. The construction of a cleavage satisfying these conditions is described in the proof of Theorem 40.

We thus have cleavages of rank 1 for all the subtrees on the l-th level of the cleavage of y_j; from these cleavages we now build up the $(l+1)$-th level of the cleavage.

Proceeding in this way, we construct a cleavage of rank N for the subtree y_j. The construction ensures the validity of condition 6. The weights of any subtree of the cleavage are expressible in special form. By the choice of the numbers $c_\varkappa$, this implies that conditions 8 through 10 are satisfied.

As to condition 7, if $l \neq 0$, everything may be reduced to the case just considered by discarding from the cleavage of y_k all vertices of subtrees on levels $N-l+1, \ldots, N$. After constructing the required cleavage of y_j, we attach complete trees of type (K, l) to the leaves of its subtrees, thus obtaining a cleavage satisfying condition 7.*

This completes the proof of Theorem 41.

§8. EXISTENCE OF NORMAL AUTOMATA WITH PRESCRIBED PROPERTIES HAVING A STATE OF PRESCRIBED TYPE

In principle, Theorem 32 establishes the existence of automata having states of a prescribed type. Moreover, one may also demand that certain other conditions be satisfied, concerning assignment of labels to the arcs of subtrees (Theorems 30 and 31), and also regarding the numbers M and L for which the automaton and its standard inverse are ILS-I-M and ILS-I-L, respectively.

Despite the fact that the normality condition seems to be quite restrictive, an analog of Theorem 32 may be proved for normal automata as well. A restriction is nevertheless imposed on the specification of types for the states — they must also be specified by means of some normal automaton. The restriction embodied in Theorem 34 must of course also be observed. We first prove an auxiliary proposition.

Theorem 42. *Suppose we have a critical subtree which is a panicle of type (K, N, M) with root of weight C, such that the subgraphs attached to its $(N-1)$-th level vertices are complete trees; suppose moreover that M is a critical number for K and C. Then there exists a normal cleavage of rank N_1 $(N_1 \leqslant N)$ with the following properties:*

(1) *Each subtree of the cleavage is a panicle of one of the types $(K, N, \varkappa)$, $\varkappa \leqslant M$.*

(2) *The N_1-th level of the cleavage contains a decomposition subtree.*

* The transformations applied in this case alter the numbers $c_\varkappa$ and C, but the other conditions remain valid in the process.

(3) *The product of the weight of any j-th level vertex $j=N-M+1,\ldots,N$ and the number K^{j-N+M} is divisible by C.*

(4) *The subgraphs attached to all $(N-l)$-th level vertices of the subtrees in the cleavage are complete trees.*

Proof. We may assume without loss of generality that $l=0$, for otherwise we simply drop the vertices of the last l levels in the original critical subtree.

We adopt the same notation for the standard form (prime number representation) of K and C as in the proof of Theorem 41. Set $c_j=C$ for $j=0,1,\ldots,N-M$, and define c_j for $j=N-M+1,\ldots,N-1$ as done in Theorem 41 for $j=M+1,\ldots,N$.

Level 1 of cleavage. Denote the given critical subtree by y_j. Attach complete trees of type $(K, 1)$ to the leaves of y_j, to obtain a subtree y_ρ. Let $y_{\rho_1},\ldots, y_{\rho_K}$ be K subtrees isomorphic to y_ρ. As in previous proofs, we shall assign the vertices of y_ρ residual weights, initially equal to their weights. The vertices of the subtrees $y_{\rho_1},\ldots,y_{\rho_K}$ will be assigned conditional weights, initially all 0. Identify corresponding vertices of $y_j, y_\rho, y_{\rho_1},\ldots,y_{\rho_K}$. It is easy to see that the weights of the vertices of the critical subtree may be expressed in special form with terms c_j for the j-th level vertices. Using the expressions for K, C and c_j, we may express the weights of the $(j+1)$-th level vertices of y_ρ in special form with terms c_j $(j=0, 1,\ldots, N)$ (see Lemma 8). The conditional and residual weights of the subtrees $y_\rho, y_{\rho_1},\ldots,y_{\rho_K}$ will be assumed to be in special form with the terms mentioned above. The vertices of y_{ρ_1} are assigned conditional weights in special form, in such a way that at least one $(N-l_1)$-th level vertex of y_{ρ_1} whose attached subgraph is a complete tree of type (K, l_1+1) has its own weight as conditional weight. Any number added to the conditional weight of a vertex is at the same time subtracted from the residual weight of the vertex identified with it in y_ρ. This is clearly possible if $K^{l_1+1}\leqslant C$. If $K^{l_1+1}>C$, we can construct a subtree of the complete tree of type (K, l_1+1), with root of weight C, which is a decomposition subtree. The conditional weights are then assigned in such a way that they coincide with the weights of the vertices after construction of this decomposition subtree. By Lemma 12, the conditional weights may be expressed in special form in this case too. Moreover, the conditional weights assigned to the vertices of y_{ρ_1} must also satisfy the following condition: the sum of conditional weights of vertices which are ends of arcs from some other vertex is equal to the conditional weight of the latter. Once this has been done, the residual weights of y_ρ are also expressible in special form. Following the same lines as in the proof of Lemma 11, one can assign conditional weights in special form to the subtrees $y_{\rho_2},\ldots,y_{\rho_K}$, observing the above condition for the sums of conditional weights, in such a way that all residual weights of the subtree y_ρ vanish. Now delete arcs and vertices from $y_{\rho_1},\ldots,y_{\rho_K}$ in such a way that the conditional weights become ordinary weights. The subtrees thus constructed comprise the first level of the required cleavage. Conditions 1 and 3 hold by virtue of the details of the construction. If $K^{l_1+1}>C$, condition 2 is also satisfied and the proof is complete.

Level $n+1$ of cleavage. Let $K^{l_1+n}<C$, and suppose that the n-th level of the cleavage contains a subtree y_μ with an $N-(l_1+n)$-th level vertex whose attached subgraph is a complete tree of type (K, l_1+n), and conditions 1 and 3 hold for all subtrees of this level. For all n-th level subtrees except y_μ, construct arbitrary normal cleavages satisfying conditions 1 and 3 (that this is possible follows from Theorem 40). For y_μ, on the other hand, construct a normal cleavage in the same way as for the first level of the cleavage of y_j. There are two cases:

Case I. $K^{l_1+n+1}\geqslant C$. We can then construct a cleavage of y_μ which contains a decomposition subtree.

Case II. $K^{l_1+n+1}<C$. We can then construct a cleavage of y_μ containing a subtree y_{μ_1} such that the subgraph attached to some vertex on level $N-(l_1+n+1)$ is a complete tree of type (K, l_1+n+1). In either case the cleavage may be so constructed that conditions 1 and 3 are satisfied. In Case I condition 2 is also satisfied.

We have $K^N\geqslant C$, and so for some $N_1\leqslant N$ the N_1-th level will contain a decomposition subtree and condition 2 holds.

If $l\neq 0$, we attach complete trees of type $N-l$ to all leaves of the subtrees in the cleavage, and then condition 4 will also be satisfied.

This completes the proof.

Theorem 43. Let $A_1, A_2, \ldots, A_n$ be normal IL-I-N automata which are respectively ILS-I-R_i; let the principal parts B_i of standard inverses of A_i with delay N be ILS-I-M_i automata, and suppose that the weights of all subtrees in the graphs $\Gamma(B_i)$ are the same and equal to C $(i=1,\ldots,n)$. Let $\mathfrak{N}_1,\ldots,\mathfrak{N}_L$ be types consisting of subtrees of type (K, N), such that at least one of the automata A_i $(1\leqslant i\leqslant n)$ has a state of type $\mathfrak{N}_j$ $(j=1,\ldots,L)$.

Then there exists a normal automaton A satisfying the following conditions:

(1) *$A(SI, R)$, where $R=\max\limits_i R_i$.*

(2) *The principal part of a standard inverse constructed for A with delay N is an ILS-I-M automaton, where $M=\max M_i$.*

(3) *For any type $\mathfrak{N}_i$ and any admissible assignment of labels from $\mathfrak{A}$ and $\mathfrak{B}$ to the arcs of the subtrees in the type, producing subtrees $t_{i_1},\ldots,t_{i_p}$ which define words $\beta_1,\ldots,\beta_p$, respectively, the automaton A has a state s_k in which its only possible outputs in response to arbitrary input words of length N are the words β_j $(j=1,\ldots,p)$, and $\mathfrak{M}_{\mathrm{I}}(s_k, \beta_j)=\mathfrak{M}(t_{i_j})$.*

Proof. Let $c_{\nu j}$ denote the numbers defined as follows: $c_{\nu j}=C$ for $\nu=0,\ldots,N-R_j$, while for $\nu=N-R_j+1,\ldots,N-1$ the number $c_{\nu j}$ is the smallest possible number $d_{\nu j}$ such that $d_{\nu j}\cdot K^{\nu+R_j-N}$ is divisible by C. It is clear from the explicit expressions for C, K and $c_{\nu j}$ derived in the proof of Theorem 41 that $c_{\nu j}$ is divisible by $c_{\nu k}$ whenever $R_k\geqslant R_j$. We may assume without loss of generality that one of the subtrees in the given types is a panicle of type (K, N, R) and another subtree has the property that none of the subgraphs attached to its $(M-1)$-th level vertices is a complete tree; if these conditions are not satisfied, we need only add suitable new types.

Let us construct the graph $\Gamma(y)$. Take a number of critical subtrees which are panicles of type (K, N, F) with root of weight C, where F is critical for K and C, sufficiently many to allow construction of normal cleavages with the following properties: (a) the last levels of the cleavages contain at least L decomposition subtrees; (b) the weights of the vertices of all subtrees in the cleavages may be expressed in special form with terms $c_{\nu j}$ for any $1 \leqslant j \leqslant n$; (c) the subgraphs attached to all M-th level vertices of each subtree are complete trees. That this is possible follows from Theorem 42 and the fact that the numbers c_ν (Theorem 41) are divisible by $c_{\nu j}$.

At this stage of the construction, we let $\Gamma(y)$ consist of the above cleavages. Taking L of the decomposition subtrees obtained, construct normal cleavages such that (1) for each type $\mathfrak{N}_l$ $(1 \leqslant l \leqslant L)$, the last level of one of the cleavages contains subtrees isomorphic to the subtrees of type $\mathfrak{N}_l$, with corresponding vertices identified; (2) the weights of all vertices of the cleavages are expressible in special form with terms $c_{\nu j}$; (3) the subgraphs attached to all M-th level vertices of all subtrees in the cleavages are complete trees. This is possible by Theorem 41.

The graph $\Gamma(y)$ now consists of several parts — subtrees whose vertices are subtrees. Their roots are critical subtrees, in fact panicles of type (K, N, F), and their leaves are subtrees the weights of whose vertices may be expressed in special form with terms $c_{\nu j}$ for some j; the subgraphs attached to all vertices of each subtree are complete trees. By virtue of the above property of the numbers $c_{\nu j}$, the weights of all subtrees which are leaves of the trees composing $\Gamma(y)$ may be expressed in special form with terms $c_{\nu k}$, where $R_k = R$. Thus it follows from Theoreom 40 that for all leaves one can construct normal cleavages, which will serve as the next levels of the cleavages already constructed, such that all subtrees on the last level are panicles of type (K, N, F) (and therefore critical), the weights of the vertices of all subtrees are expressible in special form with terms $c_{\mu j}$, and the subgraphs attached to all M-th level vertices are complete trees.

Since $c_{N-R,k} = C$, all the subtrees are panicles of one of the types $(K, N, \varkappa)$, $\varkappa \leqslant R$.

We now use these parts to build up a strongly connected graph. Denote the parts by $\Gamma_1, \ldots, \Gamma_P$. Let arcs go from the leaves of the subtrees of Γ_i to K different critical subtrees in Γ_{i+1} $(\Gamma_{P+1} = \Gamma_1)$, in such a way that one arc from each subtree reaches the root of Γ_{i+1}. The vertices in $\Gamma_1, \ldots, \Gamma_P$ may be identified in such a manner that the parts become semi-admissible graphs. Now, given any complete tree of type $(K, 1)$ whose vertices are critical subtrees of type (K, N), one can always identify vertices of subtrees in such a way as to obtain a semi-admissible graph; in constructing the strongly connected graph, then, one can identify vertices of critical subtrees connected by arcs so as to obtain an admissible graph.

By Theorems 30 and 31, there exists a strongly connected admissible graph $\Gamma(t)$ satisfying the following condition. For every type $\mathfrak{N}_p$ and any given admissible assignment of labels from $\mathfrak{A}$ and $\mathfrak{B}$ to the arcs of the subtrees in the type, producing subtrees $t_{i_1}, \ldots, t_{i_l}$ that define words $\beta_1, \ldots, \beta_l$, respectively, there exists a set of subtrees in $\Gamma(t)$, $t_{j_1}, \ldots, t_{j_l}$ say, such that t_{j_ν} and t_{i_ν} $(\nu = 1, \ldots, l)$ are isomorphic, the subtrees define words $\beta_1, \ldots, \beta_l$, respectively, and the roots of the subtrees $t_{j_1}, \ldots, t_{j_l}$ are identifiable. Then, by Theorem 26, the principal part A of an inverse constructed with delay N for the automaton defined by $\Gamma(t)$ has a state s_k such that when in this state A can produce the output words $\beta_1, \ldots, \beta_l$ only, and moreover $\mathfrak{M}_\mathrm{I}(s_k, \beta_\nu) = \mathfrak{M}(t_{j_\nu})$ $(\nu = 1, \ldots, l)$. All subtrees of $\Gamma(t)$ are panicles of one of the types

$(K, N, \varkappa)$, $\varkappa \leqslant R$, and at least one subtree is a panicle of type (K, N, R). By Theorem 28, A is an ILS-I-R automaton.

Now let B' be the principal part of a standard inverse with delay N for A. Then the set of subtrees of the graph $\Gamma(B')$ comprises only subtrees which have isomorphic counterparts in $\Gamma(t)$. Since the subgraphs attached to all M-th level vertices in subtrees of $\Gamma(t)$ are complete trees and at least one subtree of $\Gamma(t)$ is such that (at least) one of its $(M-1)$-th level vertices has an attached subgraph which is not a complete tree, it follows that B' is an ILS-I-M automaton.

The outgoing degree of each subtree in $\Gamma(y)$, hence also in $\Gamma(t)$, is K. Thus, by Theorem 25, the automaton B defined by $\Gamma(t)$ is complete. By Theorem 33 and the fact that the automata A_i $(i=1,\ldots,n)$ are normal, we have $|\mathfrak{A}|=|\mathfrak{B}|$. Hence, by Theorem 36 and the fact that $B(\mathrm{I}, N)$, the automaton A is also complete. Analogous reasoning shows that B is also complete; thus A is a normal automaton and the proof is complete.

An alternative interpretation of Theorem 43 is that any given number of states of different normal IL-I-N automata, such that the sets $\mathfrak{M}_{\mathrm{I}}(s_j, \beta)$ (where $|\beta|=N$ and s_j is a state of any given automaton) have the same cardinality, may be combined in a single normal IL-I-N automaton. The operation of "combination" mentioned here is defined as follows: If one of the given automata has a state s in which it can produce words $\beta_1,\ldots,\beta_P$ of length N, then the automaton in which the states are to be combined (call it A) has a state s' such that $\mathfrak{M}_{\mathrm{I}}(s', \beta_p)=\mathfrak{M}_{\mathrm{I}}(s, \beta_p)$ for all $p=1,\ldots,P$. This automaton A is ILS-I R, where R is the greatest of the numbers R_i such that the given automata are ILS-I-R_i, and the principal part of a standard inverse constructed with delay N for A is ILS-I-M, where M is the greatest of the numbers M_i such that the principal parts of the standard inverses of the given automata with delay N are ILD-I-M_i automata.

The results of §§6—8 were published in a less complete form in /9/.

§9. SELF-ADJUSTING TYPE I INVERSE AUTOMATA

It is important to investigate the functioning of inverse automata subject to distortion of the input. If a change in one letter of an input word is liable to alter the output word of the inverse automaton at an arbitrarily large distance from the position of the changed letter, the automaton is evidently of little use. It is therefore desirable to construct inverse automata for which a random error in the input word may affect the output only up to a limited distance from the error position.

Definition 31. A set of admissible errors, or simply error set, is any set of unordered pairs of distinct letters of $\mathfrak{B}$. Any pair in an error set will be called an admissible error.

Definition 32. An automaton B is said to be self-adjusting relative to a specified error set, with adjustment time M (in symbols: SA-M) if, for any admissible error (b_k, b_l), any initial state t_i of B, any word β of length M, and any words β_1, β_2,

$$\mu(\varepsilon(t_i, \beta_1 b_k \beta), \beta_2)=\mu(\varepsilon(t_i, \beta_1 b_l \beta), \beta_2).$$

The first question to be considered here is the existence of a procedure deciding whether a given automaton is self-adjusting.*

Given an error set and an automaton B. The algorithm we now describe produces a set of unordered pairs which we denote by $\mathfrak{N}(B)$.

Algorithm 4.

Step 1. For each pair (b_k, b_l) in the error set and each state t_i of the automaton B, the set $\mathfrak{N}(B)$ will contain the pair $(\varepsilon(t_i, b_k), \varepsilon(t_i, b_l))$. (If $\varepsilon(t_i, b_n)$ is undefined, its position is filled by a dash.)

Step $n+1$. Suppose that the pairs introduced at Step n are $(t_{i_1}, t_{j_1}), \ldots, (t_{i_n}, t_{j_n})$, where the states are distinct. Then, for any $b_m \in \mathfrak{B}$, the set $\mathfrak{N}(B)$ will contain all pairs $(\varepsilon(t_{i_1}, b_m), \varepsilon(t_{j_1}, b_m)), \ldots, (\varepsilon(t_{i_n}, b_m), \varepsilon(t_{j_n}, b_m))$ not yet included at previous steps.

Algorithm 4 halts when no new pair of states appears. Since the state set of B is finite, there is a finite step at which this occurs.

We now construct a graph $G_s(B)$ with vertex set $\mathfrak{N}(B)$. For any vertex (t_i, t_j) of $G_s(B)$, $t_i \neq t_j$, and any letter $b_l \in \mathfrak{B}$, the graph contains an arc from (t_i, t_j) to $(\varepsilon(t_i, b_l), \varepsilon(t_j, b_l))$.

Theorem 44. If the automaton B has no equivalent states, it is SA-M for some M if and only if the graph $G_s(B)$ contains no cycles and no vertices of the form $(t_i, -)$. If B is SA-M, then M is at most the maximum length of a path in $G_s(B)$.

Proof. Suppose that B is not SA-M for any M. Then for any M there exist an admissible error (b_k, b_l), an initial state t_i, a word β of length M and words β_1, β_2 such that

$$\mu(\varepsilon(t_i, \beta_1 b_k \beta), \beta_2) \neq \mu(\varepsilon(t_i, \beta_1 b_l \beta), \beta_2) .$$

Let N be the number of states in B. Let $M \geqslant N(N-1)/2$ and set $\varepsilon(t_i, \beta_1) = t_j$. Then

$$\mu(\varepsilon(t_j, b_k \beta), \beta_2) \neq \mu(\varepsilon(t_j, b_l \beta), \beta_2).$$

There are two possibilities.

Case I. $\mu(\varepsilon(t_j, b_k\beta), \beta_2)$ is defined but $\mu(\varepsilon(t_j, b_l\beta), \beta_2)$ is not. Equivalently, $\varepsilon(t_j, b_k\beta\beta_2)$ is defined but $\varepsilon(t_j, b_l\beta\beta_2)$ is not. Set $\beta\beta_2 = b_{i_1} b_{i_2} \ldots b_{i_m}$. It is clear that there is a number $0 \leqslant \nu \leqslant m$ for which $\varepsilon(t_j, b_k b_{i_1} \ldots b_{i_\nu})$ is defined but $\varepsilon(t_j, b_l b_{i_1} \ldots b_{i_\nu})$ is not, $\varepsilon(t_j, b_k b_{i_1} \ldots, b_{i_\mu}) \neq \varepsilon(t_j, b_l b_{i_1} \ldots b_{i_\mu})$, $\mu = 0, 1, \ldots, \nu-1$** (both values defined). But then the graph $G_s(B)$ has vertices $(\varepsilon(t_j, b_k), \varepsilon(t_j, b_l))$ and $(\varepsilon(t_j, b_k b_{i_1} \ldots b_{i_\mu}), \varepsilon(t_j, b_l b_{i_1} \ldots b_{i_\mu}))$ for $\mu = 1, \ldots, \nu-1$, and a vertex $(\varepsilon(t_j, b_k b_{i_1} \ldots b_{i_\nu}), -)$.

Case II. $\mu(\varepsilon(t_j, b_k\beta), \beta_2)$ and $\mu(\varepsilon(t_j, b_l\beta), \beta_2)$ are both defined. Using the previous notation, we have $\varepsilon(t_j, b_k) \neq \varepsilon(t_j, b_l)$, $(\varepsilon(t_j, b_k b_{i_1} \ldots b_{i_\mu}) \neq \neq \varepsilon(t_j, b_l b_{i_1} \ldots, b_{i_\mu})$, the graph $G_s(B)$ contains vertices $(\varepsilon(t_j, b_k), \varepsilon(t_j, \beta_l))$ and $(\varepsilon(t_j, b_k b_{i_1} \ldots b_{i_\mu}), \varepsilon(t_j, b_l b_{i_1} \ldots b_{i_\mu}))$, $\mu = 1, \ldots, m$; there are arcs from the vertex $(\varepsilon(t_j, b_k), \varepsilon(t_j, b_l))$ to the vertex $(\varepsilon(t_j, b_k b_{i_1}), \varepsilon(t_j, b_l b_{i_1}))$, and from $(\varepsilon(t_j, b_k b_{i_1} \ldots b_{i_\mu}), \varepsilon(t_j, b_l b_{i_1} \ldots b_{i_\mu}))$ to $(\varepsilon(t_j, b_k b_{i_1} \ldots b_{i_{\mu+1}}), \varepsilon(t_j, b_l b_{i_1} \ldots b_{i_{\mu+1}}))$, $\mu = 1, \ldots, m-1$. Since $m \geqslant N(N-1)/2$ and there are at most $N(N-1)/2$ pairs of different states, some of the above vertices must reappear, so that $G_s(B)$ contains a cycle.

* Definition 32 is meaningful for arbitrary automata, and not only IL-I-N automata.

**If $\mu = 0$, $b_{i_1} \ldots b_{i_\mu}$ is the empty word.

Conversely, suppose that $G_s(B)$ contains no vertices $(t_j, -)$ and no cycles. Then the length of all paths is bounded by some number M. Let (t_i, t_j) be any vertex of the graph introduced at Step 1 of Algorithm 4. Then for any word β of length M such that either $\varepsilon(t_i, \beta)$ or $\varepsilon(t_j, \beta)$ is defined, there exist words β_1 and β_2 (one of which may be empty) such that $\beta = \beta_1\beta_2$ and $\varepsilon(t_i, \beta_1) = \varepsilon(t_j, \beta_1)$. This means that $G_s(B)$ contains the vertex $(\varepsilon(t_i, \beta_1), \varepsilon(t_j, \beta_1))$, since otherwise it would contain a path of length greater than M. But then $\varepsilon(t_i, \beta) = \varepsilon(t_j, \beta)$ and for any word β' such that $\varepsilon(t_i, \beta\beta')$ or $\varepsilon(t_j, \beta\beta')$ is defined we have $\mu(\varepsilon(t_i, \beta), \beta') = \mu(\varepsilon(t_j, \beta), \beta')$.

Since the vertex (t_i, t_j) and the word β are arbitrary, this implies that the automaton is SA-M.

If M_1 is the maximum length of a path in $G_s(B)$, it is evident from the construction that a word β of length M_1 will suffice, i. e., B is SA-M_1.

Since B does not contain equivalent states, it follows that for any two states t_i, t_j $(t_i \neq t_j)$ there is a word β_1 such that $\mu(t_i, \beta_1) \neq \mu(t_j, \beta_1)$. Thus it cannot be true that $G_s(B)$ contains a cycle and B is an SA-M automaton.

This completes the proof.

The next theorem shows that SA-M automata possess a far stronger property than that following directly from Definition 32.

Theorem 45. If B is an SA-M automaton relative to an error set $\mathfrak{N}$, $(b_{i_\varkappa}, b_{j_\varkappa}) \in \mathfrak{N}$, $\varkappa = 1, 2, \ldots, N$, *where N is an arbitrary integer,* $\beta_0, \beta_1, \ldots, \beta_N$ *are (possibly empty) words of arbitrary length, and β a word of length N, then for any initial state t_λ*

$$\mu(\varepsilon(t_\lambda, \beta_0 b_{i_1}\beta_1 b_{i_2}\beta_2 \ldots b_{i_N}\beta), \beta_N) = \mu(\varepsilon(t_\lambda, \beta_0 b_{j_1}\beta_1 b_{j_2}\beta_2 \ldots b_{j_N}\beta), \beta_N).$$

Proof. Consider the following sequence of values of the next-state function:

$$\mu(\varepsilon(t_\lambda, \beta_0 b_{i_1}\beta_1 b_{i_2}\beta_2 \ldots b_{i_N}\beta), \beta_N), \mu(\varepsilon(t_\lambda, \beta_0 b_{i_1} \ldots b_{i_{N-1}}\beta_{N-1} b_{j_N}\beta), \beta_N),$$

$$\ldots, \mu(\varepsilon(t_\lambda, \beta_0 b_{i_1}\beta_1 b_{j_2} \ldots b_{j_N}\beta), \beta_N), \mu(\varepsilon(t_\lambda, \beta_0 b_{j_1}\beta_1 b_{j_2} \ldots b_{j_N}\beta), \beta_N).$$

In any two adjacent members of this sequence, the function arguments have the form $\beta' b_k \beta''$ and $\beta' b_l \beta''$, where $(b_k, b_l) \in \mathfrak{N}$, $|\beta''| \geqslant M$; thus the corresponding values of the next-state function are equal, since B is SA-M relative to the error set $\mathfrak{N}$. But the equality of the first and last members of the sequence is precisely what we have to prove.

Example 12. Consider the noninitialized automata A and B given by Tables 20 and 21, respectively, and let the error set be $(0, 1)$.

TABLE 20.

	0	1
s_1	s_3, 0	s_4, 0
s_2	s_4, 1	s_3, 1
s_3	s_1, 0	s_2, 1
s_4	s_2, 0	s_1, 1

TABLE 21.

	0	1		0	1
t_1	t_5, 0	t_7, 1	t_5	t_1, 0	t_2, 0
t_2	t_8, 1	t_6, 0	t_6	t_3, 1	t_4, 1
t_3	t_5, 1	t_7, 0	t_7	t_3, 0	t_4, 0
t_4	t_8, 0	t_6, 1	t_8	t_1, 1	t_2, 1

Figures 17 and 18 illustrate the graphs $G_s(A)$ and $G_s(B)$, respectively; it is clear from them that A is not SA-M for any M, while B is SA-2.

It is also readily verified that both automata are ILS-I-2 and each is an inverse of the other. Thus the inverse of an SA-M automaton need not be SA-M, and vice-versa.

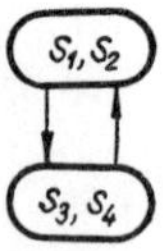

FIGURE 17.

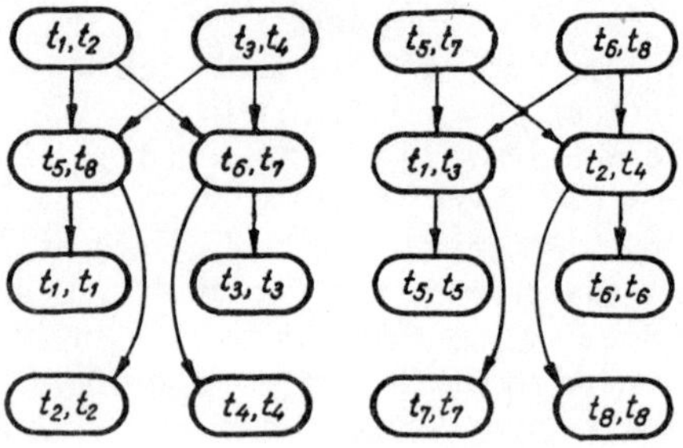

FIGURE 18.

Of special interest are automata which are at one and the same time IL-I-N and SA-M. We first establish a relationship between the numerical parameters of such automata.

Theorem 46. Let K, N, L, R, M be numbers such that $N \geqslant 2$, $K \geqslant 2$, $R \leqslant N$, $L \leqslant N$, $L+R \geqslant N+2$, $M \geqslant N-R+1$. Let $\mathfrak{A}$ and $\mathfrak{B}$ be K-letter alphabets. Then for any given error set there exists a normal automaton $A\,(SI, R)$ having an inverse B with delay N which is ILS-I-L, SA-M relative to the given error set, but not SA-$M-1$.

Proof. Step 1. We begin with the case $R = L = N$. Then $M \geqslant 1$. The proof proceeds by induction.

Let $N=2$. Define input trees $x_1, \ldots, x_P$, where $P = M_1K$, as follows. The subtrees $x_{\mu K+1}, \ldots, x_{\mu K+K}$ $(\mu = 1, 2, \ldots, M_1-1)$ will be complete panicles of type $(K, 2, 1)$, forming a partition of a complete tree of type $(K, 2)$. The other subtrees define the following sets of words:

$$\mathfrak{M}(x_1) = \{a_1a_1, a_2a_2, \ldots, a_Ka_K\},$$
$$\mathfrak{M}(x_2) = \{a_1a_2, a_2a_3, \ldots, a_{K-1}a_K, a_Ka_1\}, \ldots,$$
$$\mathfrak{M}(x_K) = \{a_1a_K, a_2a_1, \ldots, a_Ka_{K-1}\}.$$

Now let arcs go from each of the subtrees x_j, $j = \varkappa K + l$ $(j = mK+1, \ldots$ $\ldots, (m+1)K$, $m = 0, 1, \ldots, M_1-2)$, to all subtrees x_n $(n = (m+1)K+1,$ $(m+1)K+2, \ldots, (m+2)K)$, and from each subtree x_i $(i = (M_1-1)K+1,$ $(M_1-1)K+2, \ldots, M_1K)$ to all subtrees $x_1, \ldots, x_K$. Consider any two subtrees x_i, x_j connected by an arc from x_i to x_j. Construct a set $\mathfrak{F}(x_i, x_j)$ as follows. Let x_i be a panicle of type $(K, 2, 1)$ and χ_{i1a_l} its unique first level vertex. Then $(\chi_{i1a_l}, \chi_j) \in \mathfrak{F}(x_i, x_j)$ and for each letter $a_m \in \mathfrak{A}$ we put $(\chi_{i,2,a_la_m}, \chi_{j1a_m}) \in$ $\in \mathfrak{F}(x_i, x_j)$. Let x_j be a panicle of type $(K, 2, 1)$, χ_{j1a_m} its unique first level vertex, and suppose that x_i is not a panicle of type $(K, 2, 1)$. Then x_i has a vertex χ_{i1a_n} such that an arc emanating from it is labeled a_m. Set

$(\chi_{i1a_n}, \chi_j) \in \mathfrak{F}(x_i, x_j)$ and $(\chi_{i,2,a_n a_m}, \chi_{j1a_m}) \in \mathfrak{F}(x_i, x_j)$. It is clear that for any subtree x_i the set $\mathfrak{G}(x_i) = \mathfrak{F}(x_i, x_{j_1}) \cup \ldots \cup \mathfrak{F}(x_i, x_{j_v})$ (the union extending over all subtrees which are ends of arcs from x_i) is admissible, i. e., satisfies condition 1 of Definition 19. Condition 2 follows directly from the assumptions of our theorem. We now label the arc from x_i to x_j by a letter of $\mathfrak{A}$ in such a way that condition 3 also holds: if the set $\mathfrak{F}(x_i, x_j)$ contains the pair (χ_{i1a_l}, χ_j) (this pair is unique), the arc is labeled a_l. Thus we obtain an admissible graph $\Gamma(x)$.

Let $M=1$ and $M_1=M+1$. Set up one-to-one correspondences between the sets $x_1, \ldots, x_K$ and $x_{K+1}, \ldots, x_{2K}$, on the one hand, and the alphabet $\mathfrak{B}$ on the other. Label each arc leading to one of these subtrees by the corresponding letter. The result is a graph $\Gamma(tx)$ in which, by the construction of arcs in $\Gamma(x)$, all arcs emanating from the same subtree have pairwise distinct labels from $\mathfrak{B}$. By Definition 21, $\Gamma(tx)$ is an admissible graph. By Theorem 24, $\Gamma(tx)$ defines an automaton B (SI, 2), since the special construction of the sets $\mathfrak{G}(x_i)$ ensures satisfaction of condition 2 of that theorem with $M=2$. The graph $\Gamma(x)$ is strongly connected, and hence so are the graph $\Gamma(tx)$ and the automaton B. By Theorem 14, the principal part A of a standard inverse with delay 2 for B is also strongly connected. By the construction of $\Gamma(x)$ and Theorems 25 and 29, both automata B and A are complete, and by Theorem 28 we have A(SI, 2). By Theorem 16, the automaton B is an inverse for A, with delay 2.

For any two letters b_k, b_l $(b_k \neq b_l)$, $\varepsilon(x_i, b_k) \neq \varepsilon(x_i, b_l)$, but the states $\varepsilon(x_i, b_k)$ and $\varepsilon(x_i, b_l)$ are in the same set $x_1, \ldots, x_K$ or $x_{K+1}, \ldots, x_{2K}$. It is readily seen that, for any two distinct states $x_\varkappa$ and x_λ of the automaton B in the same one of the above-specified sets, and any letter b_μ, we have $\mu(x_\varkappa, b_\mu) \neq \mu(x_\lambda, b_\mu)$. Thus B cannot be SA-0 for any error set. For the same states $x_\varkappa$ and x_λ and any letter b_μ, we have $\varepsilon(x_\varkappa, b_\mu) = \varepsilon(x_\lambda, b_\mu)$. Hence B is an SA-1 automaton for any error set.

Now let $M>1$ and $M_1=M$. The arcs leading to the subtrees $x_1, \ldots, x_K$ are assigned labels in the same way as in the case $M=1$. Arcs emanating from the subtrees x_j, $j=1, \ldots, (M_1-1)K$ are labeled as follows. Let $j=nK+l$ $(1 \leqslant l \leqslant K)$. Then the arcs from x_j to x_i, $i=(n+1)K+\lambda$, are labeled $b_{\lambda+l-1}$ if $\lambda+l \leqslant K+1$ and $b_{\lambda+l-K-1}$ if $\lambda+l>K+1$. The result is an admissible graph $\Gamma(tx)$, and so all the previous statements concerning the delays of B and A remain valid. For any state x_i $((M_1-1)K+1 \leqslant i)$ and any two letters b_k, b_l, we have $\varepsilon(x_i, b_k) \neq \varepsilon(x_i, b_l)$ and both states are in the set $\{x_1, \ldots, x_K\}$. For any two states x_i, x_j, $i=nK+l$, $j=nK+\lambda$ $(1 \leqslant l, \lambda \leqslant K,\ n=0, \ldots, M_1-2)$, and any letter b_μ, we have $\varepsilon(x_i, b_\mu) \neq \varepsilon(x_j, b_\mu)$ and both states are in the set $\{x_{(n+1)K+1}, \ldots, x_{(n+2)K}\}$. Since no two states of the automaton B are equivalent, it is easy to see that B cannot be SA-$M-1$ for any error set. For any two states x_i, x_j $((M_1-1)K+1 \leqslant i, j \leqslant M_1K)$ and any letter b_μ, $\varepsilon(x_i, b_\mu) = \varepsilon(x_j, b_\mu)$. Therefore B is an SA-M automaton for any given error set.

Suppose we have a normal automaton B(SI, N) which is not SA-$M-1$ but is SA-M, has a standard inverse with delay N whose principal part is ILS-I-N, and moreover has no pairs of equivalent states. Let B be defined by a graph $\Gamma(tx)$ having M_1K subtrees which are divided into groups as in the previous construction; the subtrees $x_{(M_1-1)K+1}, \ldots, x_{M_1K}$ are complete panicles of type $(K, N, N-1)$, and the subtrees $x_1, \ldots, x_K$ panicles of type (K, N, N) such that the subgraphs attached to their $(N-1)$-th level vertices are not complete trees of type $(K, 1)$. Suppose moreover that for any two subtrees x_i, x_j in the set $\{x_{(M_1-1)K+1}, \ldots, x_{M_1K}\}$ and any letter b_μ we have $\varepsilon(x_i, b_\mu) = \varepsilon(x_j, b_\mu)$.

We now construct an admissible graph $\Gamma'(tx)$ with $(M_1+1)K$ subtrees of type $(K, N+1)$. Take K complete input trees of type $(K, 1)$, say $x''_1, \ldots, x''_K$. Construct input subtrees $x'_{M_1K+1}, x'_{M_1K+2}, \ldots, x'_{(M_1+1)K}$ as follows: the subtree x'_{M_1K+j} $(j=1, \ldots, K)$ is the result of attaching to the vertices χ''_{j1a_m} subtrees isomorphic to x_{m-j+1} for $m \geqslant j$ and to $x_{K+m-j+1}$ for $m < j$ $(m=1, \ldots, K)$. Now attach complete input trees of type $(K, 1)$ to all the leaves of $\Gamma(tx)$, retaining the previous notation. The arcs in $\Gamma(tx)$ emanating from the subtrees $x_{(M_1-1)K+1}, \ldots, x_{M_1K}$ are deleted, and new arcs added from each of these subtrees to each of the newly formed subtrees. In addition, we stipulate arcs going from each of the new subtrees to each of $x_1, \ldots, x_K$. Vertices are now identified so as to obtain an admissible graph $\Gamma(x)$ (excluding the letters of $\mathfrak{B}$ from consideration); this is done in the same way as for $N=2$. Set up a one-to-one correspondence between the new subtrees and the letters of $\mathfrak{B}$, and label the arcs leading to them by the corresponding letters. A similar procedure is adopted to label the arcs leading to $x_1, \ldots, x_K$ by letters of $\mathfrak{B}$. To differentiate between subtrees of $\Gamma(tx)$ and $\Gamma'(tx)$ we shall use primes.

By the properties of the subtrees $x_1, \ldots, x_K$ and the construction of $x'_{M_1K+1}, \ldots, x'_{(M_1+1)K}$, we may state that the automaton B' defined by $\Gamma'(tx)$ and the corresponding standard inverse with delay $N+1$ are ILS-I-$N+1$ automata. Both automata are also strongly connected, and B' has no pairs of equivalent states.

Suppose that B' is SA-$M-1$, i.e., for any state x'_i, any pair (b_l, b_r) in the error set, any word β of length $M-1$ and any word β'

$$\mu'(\varepsilon'(x'_i, b_l\beta), \beta') = \mu'(\varepsilon'(x'_i, b_r\beta), \beta') .$$

Now suppose that for some prefix β'' of β $(\beta'' \neq \beta)$ the states $\varepsilon'(x'_i, b_l\beta'')$ and $\varepsilon'(x'_i, b_r\beta'')$ belong to the set $x'_{(M_1-1)K+1}, \ldots, x'_{M_1K}$; then the states $\varepsilon(x_i, b_l\beta'')$ and $\varepsilon(x_i, b_r\beta'')$ are in the set $x_{(M_1-1)K+1}, \ldots, x_{M_1K}$, whence it follows that

$$\varepsilon(x_i, b_l\beta) = \varepsilon(x_i, b_r\beta)$$

and

$$\mu(\varepsilon(x_i, b_l\beta), \beta') = \mu(\varepsilon(x_i, b_r\beta), \beta') .$$

But if there is no word β'' with the above property, we must have $\varepsilon(x_i, b_l\beta) = \varepsilon(x_i, b_r\beta)$, since application of inputs $b_l\beta$ and $b_r\beta$ in states x'_i and x_i passes the automata B' and B into identically indexed states. Thus B is SA-$M-1$, contrary to assumption.

Let β be a word of length M. If there is some prefix β'' of β $(\beta'' \neq \beta)$ such that the states $\varepsilon(x_i, b_r\beta'')$ and $\varepsilon(x_i, b_l\beta'')$ belong to the set $x_{(M_1-1)K+1}, \ldots, x_{M_1K}$, then the states $\varepsilon'(x'_i, b_l\beta'')$ and $\varepsilon'(x'_i, b_r\beta'')$ are in the set $x'_{(M_1-1)K+1}, \ldots, x'_{M_1K}$, so that

$$\varepsilon'(x'_i, b_r\beta) = \varepsilon'(x'_i, b_l\beta)$$

and

$$\mu'(\varepsilon'(x'_i, b_r\beta), \beta') = \mu'(\varepsilon'(x'_i, b_l\beta), \beta').$$

But if application of inputs $b_r\beta$ and $b_l\beta$ in state x_i does not pass B through states in the set $x_{(M_1-1)K+1}, \ldots, x_{M_1K}$ then, as before, we must have $\varepsilon'(x'_i, b_r\beta) = \varepsilon'(x'_i, b_l\beta)$. Hence B' is an SA-M automaton. Before going on to the next step, we apply a "cyclic shift" operation with period K to the indices of the subtrees of our graph. Figure 19 illustrates the graph $\Gamma(tx)$ for $K=3$, $L=N=R=2$, $M=2$, with the convention that arcs / are labeled a_1, arcs | a_2, and arcs \ a_3. Figure 20 shows the graph $\Gamma'(tx)$ derived from $\Gamma(tx)$ $(N=3)$.

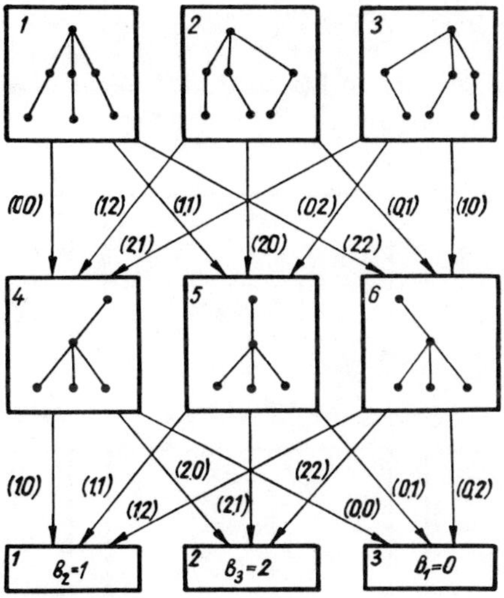

FIGURE 19.

Step 2. Let $B(\mathrm{SI}, L)$ be a normal automaton which is not SA-$M-1$ but is SA-M, having a standard inverse with delay N which is ILS-I-R. We shall construct an automaton $B'(\mathrm{SI}, L+1)$ which is not SA-M but is SA-$M+1$, having a standard inverse with delay $N+1$ which is ILS-I-R.

Suppose that B has states $t_1, \ldots, t_P$. The states of B' will be $\{(t_j, a_m)\}$, $j=1, \ldots, P$, $m=1, \ldots, K$. For any state (t_j, a_m) and any letter $b_r \in \mathfrak{B}$, we define

$$\varepsilon'((t_j, a_m), b_r) = (\varepsilon(t_j, b_r), \mu(t_j, b_r)),$$
$$\mu'((t_j, a_m), b_r) = a_m.$$

It follows from these definitions that the automaton B' may pass from state (t_j, a_m) only into states for which the sets of output words are precisely those of the automaton B for state t_j. When in state (t_j, a_m), B' may emit only the letter a_m. Hence, for every input subtree x_j of type (K, N) in $\Gamma(Bx)$ there is a subtree x'_i in the graph $\Gamma(B'x)$ which may be obtained by attaching an input subtree isomorphic to x_j to a leaf of some input subtree of type $(K, 1)$ containing only one arc. By $\Gamma(B'x)$ we mean a graph whose vertices, in one-to-one correspondence with the states of B', are automaton subtrees of type $(K, N+1)$ such that each subtree x'_i represents the set of words that B' can produce in the corresponding state. In $\Gamma(B'x)$, there is an arc from x'_i to x'_j if and only if there is a letter b_μ such that $\varepsilon'(t'_i, b_\mu) = t'_j$, where t'_i and t'_j are the states corresponding to x'_i and x'_j. Thanks to the relationship between the subtrees of $\Gamma(Bx)$ and $\Gamma(B'x)$ and the pattern of arcs in $\Gamma(B'x)$, we can identify vertices of adjacent subtrees in $\Gamma(B'x)$ in such a way that condition 1 of Definition 19 is satisfied. Condition 2 follows from the construction of the automaton B' and the graph $\Gamma(B'x)$, while condition 3 is fulfilled if we label all arcs emanating from each subtree by the letter labeling the arc emanating from the root of the subtree. The graph $\Gamma(B'x)$ is then admissible, and for any assignment of letters from $\mathfrak{B}$ to its arcs, producing an admissible graph $\Gamma(x't)$, it defines an IL-I-$N+1$ automaton B''.

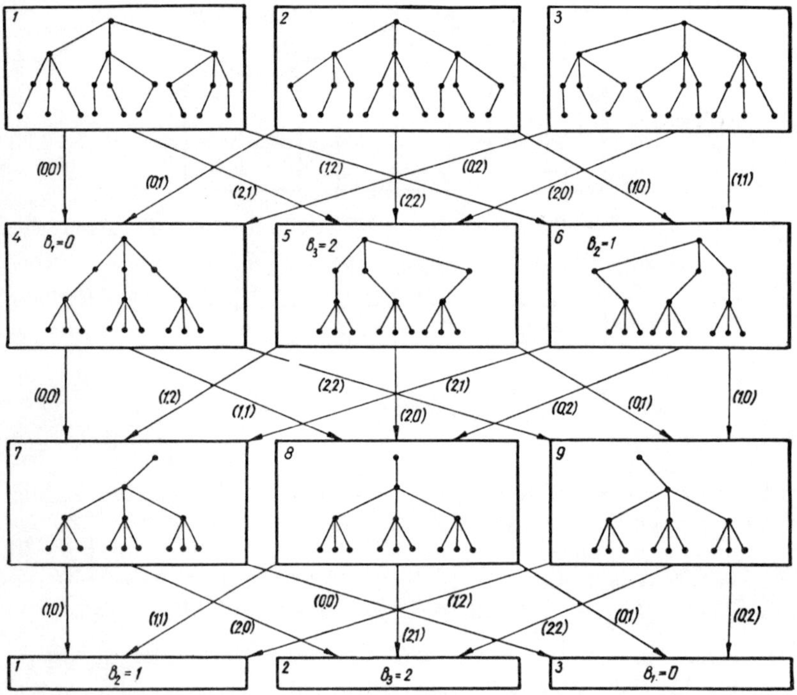

FIGURE 20.

Because of the relationship between the subtrees of $\Gamma(Bx)$ and $\Gamma(B'x)$, and also by virtue of Theorems 19, 21, 24 and 28, B'' is an ILS-I-$L+1$ automaton, and has an ILS-I-R standard inverse with delay $N+1$. In particular, letters of $\mathfrak{B}$ may be assigned to the arcs of $\Gamma(B'x)$ in such a way that the result is the automaton B'. Thus all we have said of B'' is also true of B'.

We claim that B' is SA-$M+1$ but not SA-M.

Using induction, one readily proves that for any word βb_μ and any state (t_j, a_m),

$$\varepsilon'((t_j, a_m), \beta b_\mu) = (\varepsilon(t_j, \beta b_\mu), \mu(\varepsilon(t_j, \beta), b_\mu)),\ \mu'((t_j, a_m), \beta b_\mu) = a_m \mu(t_j, \beta).$$

For any pair (b_r, b_l) in the error set, any word βb_μ and any state (t_j, a_m),

$$\varepsilon'((t_j, a_m), b_r \beta b_\mu) = (t_{j_r}, a_{\mu_r}),\ \varepsilon'((t_j, a_m), b_l \beta b_\mu) = (t_{j_l}, a_{\mu_l}),$$

where

$$t_{j_r} = \varepsilon(t_j, b_r \beta b_\mu),\ t_{j_l} = \varepsilon(t_j, b_l \beta b_\mu),$$
$$a_{\mu_r} = \mu(\varepsilon(t_j, b_r\beta), b_\mu),\ a_{\mu_l} = \mu(\varepsilon(t_j, b_l \beta), b_\mu).$$

For any word $\beta' b_\nu$,

$$\mu'((t_{j_r}, a_{\mu_r}), \beta' b_\nu) = a_{\mu_r} \mu(t_{j_r}, \beta'),$$
$$\mu'((t_{j_l}, a_{\mu_l}), \beta' b_\nu) = a_{\mu_l} \mu(t_{j_l}, \beta').$$

Let $|\beta b_\mu| = M+1$. Since B is SA-M, it follows from the above equalities that $a_{\mu_r} = a_{\mu_l}$, and the states t_{j_l} and t_{j_r} have the property that $\mu(t_{j_r}, \beta') = \mu(t_{j_l}, \beta')$ for any word β'. Thus B' is SA-$M+1$.

Since B is not SA-$M-1$, we may select a state t_j, a pair (b_r, b_l), a word β of length $M-1$, a letter b_μ and a word β' such that either $a_{\mu_r} \neq a_{\mu_l}$ or $\mu(t_{j_r}, \beta') \neq \mu(t_{j_l}, \beta')$. Hence it follows that B' is not SA-M.

Step 3. Suppose we have constructed a normal automaton B which is SA-M and ILS-I-L and whose standard inverse with delay N is ILS-I-R. By attaching complete trees of type $(K, 1)$ to all leaves of $\Gamma(Bx)$, we form a new graph, from which, by appropriate labeling with letters of $\mathfrak{B}$, we can obtain the same automaton B. It follows from the properties of the new graph that a standard inverse with delay $N+1$ is an ILS-I-$R+1$ automaton.

Step 4. Given numbers K, N, L, R and M, we can use Step 1 to construct a normal SA-M and ILS-I-$L+R-N$ automaton whose standard inverse with delay $L+R-N$ is also ILS-I-$L+R-N$. If $L=R=N=L+R-N$, this is the required automaton.

Let $R<N$. Then, as shown in Step 2, we start from the SA-M_1 automaton constructed above, where $M_1 = M-(N-R) \geqslant 1$, and construct an SA-$M$ and ILS-I-L automaton whose standard inverse with delay L is ILS-I-$L+R-N$. If $L=N$, we are done.

Suppose, then, that $L<N$. As above, we construct an ILS-I-L and SA-M automaton B whose standard inverse with delay L is ILS-I-$R-(N-L)$. It follows from Step 3 that the standard inverse of B with delay N is ILS-I-R.

In none of the cases considered is any of the automata SA-$M-1$.

This completes the proof.

Theorem 47. Let K, N, L, R and M be nonnegative numbers such that $N \geqslant 1$, $K \geqslant 2$, $R+L=N$, $M \geqslant N-R$, and $\mathfrak{A}$, $\mathfrak{B}$ K-letter alphabets. Then for any given error set there exists a normal automaton $A(SI, R)$ having an *inverse B (SI, L) with delay N which is an SA-M automaton but is not SA-$M-1$.*

Proof. Case I: $N=L=1$. Construct a graph $\Gamma(x)$ with subtrees $x_1, \ldots, x_P$ of type $(K, 1)$ containing only one arc ($P=M_1K$). Divide this set of subtrees into groups, each containing K subtrees, so that for every letter of $\mathfrak{A}$ there is a subtree in each group representing it. Number the groups from 1 to M_1. From each subtree in the j-th group ($j=1, \ldots, M_1-1$) we let arcs go to all subtrees of the $(j+1)$-th group, and from each subtree of the M_1-th group to all subtrees of the first. It is obvious that the graph $\Gamma(x)$ may be made admissible.

To form a graph $\Gamma(tx)$, we assign letters from $\mathfrak{B}$ to the arcs of $\Gamma(x)$, in the same way as in Step 1 of the proof of Theorem 46 for $N=2$.

Hence it is clear that we can construct an automaton B(SI, 1) which is not SA-$M-1$ but is SA-M, for any given M satisfying the assumptions of the theorem, and in such a way that a standard inverse of B with delay 1 is ILS-I-0.

Case II: $N=R=1$. If $M=0$, the automaton B has only one state — a complete input tree of type $(K, 1)$.

If $M \geqslant 1$ the construction of B is the same as in Step 1 of the proof of Theorem 46 for $N=2$. All the subtrees of $\Gamma(x)$ are complete input trees of type $(K, 1)$.

If $M>1$, the vertex χ_i in $\Gamma(x)$ is identified with $\chi_{j,1,a_{\lambda+l-1}}$ for $\lambda+l \leqslant K+1$, and with $\chi_{j,1,a_{\lambda+l-K-1}}$ for $\lambda+l>K+1$ ($j=nK+l$, $i=(n+1)K+\lambda$, $n=0, 1, \ldots, M_1$ or $j=(M_1-1)K+\lambda$, $i=l$, $1 \leqslant \lambda \leqslant K$, $1 \leqslant l \leqslant K$).

If $M=1$, the vertices of the subtrees x_j and x_i, $j=l$, $i=K+\lambda$ ($1 \leqslant l \leqslant K$, $1 \leqslant \lambda \leqslant K$) are identified for $M>1$. For $j=K+l$ and $i=\lambda$, we identify the vertex χ_i with $\chi_{j,1,a_{K-\lambda-l+2}}$ if $\lambda+l \leqslant K+1$, and with $\chi_{j,1,a_{2K-\lambda-l+2}}$ if $\lambda+l>K+1$. In construction of the graph $\Gamma(tx)$, the subtree x_{nK+l} ($n=0, 1$; $1 \leqslant l \leqslant K$) is associated with the letter b_l.

For other parameters N, R and L, the required automaton is constructed along the lines of Step 4 in the proof of Theorem 46.

This completes the proof.

The following theorem shows that in a certain sense Theorems 46 and 47 exhaust all possibilities.

Theorem 48. Given numbers K, N, L, R and M satisfying the conditions: $N \geqslant 2$, $K \geqslant 2$, $R \leqslant N$, $L \leqslant N$, $L+R \geqslant N+2$, $0 \leqslant M < N-R+1$, and K-letter alphabets $\mathfrak{A}$ and $\mathfrak{B}$, there exists an error set for which there is no automaton A (SI, R) having an inverse B (SI, L) with delay N which is SA-M.

Proof. The error set will consist of all unordered pairs of letters of $\mathfrak{B}$.

Let $R \leqslant N$, $M=0$ and let A (SI, R) be any automaton having an ILS-I-N standard inverse B with delay N. Since B is not IL-I-0, there exist a state t_j of B and distinct letters b_k, b_l such that $\mu(t_j, b_k)=\mu(t_j, b_l)$. The states $\varepsilon(t_j, b_k)$ and $\varepsilon(t_j, b_l)$ cannot be equivalent, since then B would not be IL-I-N. The pair (b_k, b_l) is in the error set, so that B cannot be SA-0. It is clear that any two complete automata one of which is a simplification of the other are either both SA-M or both not SA-M (for any M). Hence, by Theorem 8, no other inverse of A with delay N may be SA-0.

Now let $R<N$, $M\leqslant N-R$. Construct two standard inverses for A: B' with delay $N-1$ and B'' with delay N. Denote the states of B' by $(s_i, \beta)'$, those of B'' by $(s_i, \beta)''$.

Let $(s_i, \beta)'$ be any state of B'. For any state s_i, there exist a state s_k and a letter a_j such that $\delta(s_k, a_j)=s_i$; therefore, for any state $(s_i, \beta)'$ of B', there exists a state $(s_k, b_l\beta)''$ such that $b_l=\lambda(s_k, \mu''((s_k, b_l\beta)'', b_m))$ and $s_i=\delta(s_k, \mu''((s_k, b_l\beta)'', b_m)$, where b_m is an arbitrary letter of $\mathfrak{B}$. Hence, for any word $\beta_1 b_\lambda$,

$$\mu''((s_k, b_l\beta)'', \beta_1 b_\lambda)=a_j\mu'((s_i, \beta)', \beta_1).$$

Set

$$\mu''((s_k, b_l\beta)'', b_{\nu_1}\beta'\beta''b_\lambda)=a_m\alpha'\alpha'',$$
$$\mu''((s_k, b_l\beta)''\ b_{\nu_2}\beta'\beta''b_\lambda)=a_m\alpha'_1\alpha''_1,$$

where $b_{\nu_1}\neq b_{\nu_2}$ and β', α', α'_1 are words of length M. Let B'' be SA-M relative to the given error set; then $\alpha''=\alpha''_1$ and

$$\mu'((s_i, \beta)', b_{\nu_1}\beta'\beta'')=\alpha'\alpha'',\ \mu'((s_i, \beta)', b_{\nu_2}\beta'\beta'')=\alpha'_1\alpha''.$$

Using Theorem 8 as before, we see that if A has an inverse B'' with delay N which is SA-M it also has an inverse B' with delay $N-1$ which is SA-$M-1$.

Repeating the argument, we finally deduce that A has an inverse which is SA-0. But as shown above this is impossible, and the proof is complete.

Theorem 49. *Given numbers K, N, L, R and M such that $N\geqslant 1$, $K\geqslant 2$, $R+L=N$, $M<N-R$, and K-letter alphabets $\mathfrak{A}$ and $\mathfrak{B}$, there exists an error set for which there is no automaton A(SI, R) having an inverse B (SI, L) which is SA-M.*

Proof. The error set will be the same as in Theorem 48. Given an arbitrary automaton A(SI, R), let B be a standard inverse with delay N. All subtrees of $\Gamma(B)$ will be panicles of type (K, N, R). But then for any two words $b_l\beta$, $b_k\beta$ of length $N-R$ and any state t_j we have $\mu(t_j, b_l\beta)=\mu(t_j, b_k\beta)$. The states $\varepsilon(t_j, b_l\beta)$ and $\varepsilon(t_j, b_k\beta)$ cannot be equivalent, for then B would not be IL-I-N. Hence the conclusion of the theorem.

If K is a prime number, Theorems 46 through 49 exhaust all possibilities for the numbers R, L, N, since in that case we cannot have $R+L=N+1$. This is proved as follows. Let A (SI, R) be an automaton and B (SI, L) an inverse of A with delay N, where $L=N-R+1$, both automata being complete. By Theorem 37, the weight of any $(N-R)$-th level vertex in any subtree of the graph $\Gamma(B)$ is a multiple of K^ν for some integer ν. By Theorem 20, the subgraphs attached to all L-th level vertices of $\Gamma(B)$ are complete trees of type $(K, N-L)$, i. e., the weights of the $(N-R+1)$-th level vertices of all its subtrees are equal to K^{N-L}. There exists a subtree in $\Gamma(B)$ such that the outgoing degree of its $(N-R)$-th level vertices is >1. But all these conditions are compatible only if $K^\nu=K\cdot K^{N-L}$, i. e., the outgoing degree of all $(N-R)$-th level vertices of the subtrees of $\Gamma(B)$ is K or, in view of the properties of the $(N-R+1)$-th level vertices, the subgraphs attached to the $(N-R)$-th level vertices of the subtrees in $\Gamma(B)$ are complete trees and B is ILS-I-$N-R$, i. e., $L\neq N-R+1$.

Theorem 50. Let $K>2$ be nonprime, N, L, R and M numbers such that $N \geqslant 1$, $R+L \geqslant N+1$, $M \geqslant N-R+1$, $R \leqslant N$, $L \leqslant N$, $\mathfrak{A}$ and $\mathfrak{B}$ K-letter alphabets. There exists a normal automaton $A(SI, R)$ having an inverse $B(SI, L)$ with delay N which is SA-M, but not SA-$M-1$, relative to any error set.

Proof. Of all the possibilities, we shall discuss only two: (1) $N=1$, (2) $N \geqslant 2$, $R+L=N+1$. The other cases were examined in Theorem 46.

Let $N=1$, and let $p<K$ be a divisor of K. We construct a graph $\Gamma(x)$ consisting of M_1K/p subtrees of type $(K, 1)$, such that

$$\mathfrak{M}(x_{jK/p+i}) = \{a_{(i-1)p+1}, \ldots, a_{ip}\} \quad (i=1, \ldots, K/p,\ j=0,\ 1, \ldots, M_1-1).$$

We let p arcs lead from each subtree x_i $(i=jK/p+l,\ j=0, 1, \ldots, M_1-2,\ 1 \leqslant l \leqslant K/p)$ to each of the subtrees x_m, $m=(j+1)K/p+n$, $n=1, \ldots, K/p$. From each subtree x_i $(i=(M_1-1)K/p+1, \ldots, M_1K/p)$ we let p arcs go to each subtree x_j $(j=1, \ldots$ $\ldots, K/p)$. In adjacent subtrees, each leaf of a subtree from which there are arcs emanating is identified with the roots of the subtrees to which the arcs lead. We obtain an admissible graph $\Gamma(x)$.

Let $M=1$; then $M_1=2$. With each subtree $x_{jK/p+i}$ we associate the letters $\{b_{(i-1)p+1}, \ldots, b_{ip}\}$, and label each arc leading to a subtree by one of the letters associated in this way with the subtree, in such a way that no two arcs issuing from the same subtree have the same label. The properties of the automata A and B are verified as in the proof of Theorem 46 for $N=2$, $M=1$.

If $M>1$, we take $M_1=M$. The arcs leading to the first K/p subtrees are labeled as in the case $M=1$. Now let $j=nK/p+l$ $(n=1, \ldots, M-1,\ 1 \leqslant l \leqslant K/p)$. Each of the arcs leading to a subtree x_i, $i=(n+1)K/p+\lambda$, is assigned one of the letters $b_{\nu K/p+\lambda+l-1}$ if $\lambda+l \leqslant K/p+1$ or $b_{\nu K/p+\lambda+l-K/p-1}$ if $\lambda+l>K/p+1$ $(\nu=$ $=0,\ 1, \ldots, p-1)$. The properties of the automata A and B are verified as in Theorem 46 for $N=2$, $M>1$.

Let $N \geqslant 2$, $R+L=N+1$. Using the automata constructed for $N=1$ and following the lines laid down in Steps 2 and 3 of the proof of Theorem 46, we get the required automata.

Theorems 48 and 49 do not preclude the existence of error sets for which there is an automaton $A(\mathrm{SI}, R)$ having an inverse $B(\mathrm{SI}, L)$ with delay N which is SA-M for $M=N-R$. These cases are taken care of in the following theorems.

Theorem 51. Let K, N, L and R be as in Theorem 50, $M=N-R$, p $(p \neq K)$ a divisor of K maximizing the expression $K/p \cdot \dfrac{p!}{2!(p-2)!}$, $\mathfrak{A}$ and $\mathfrak{B}$ K-letter alphabets. Then there exists an automaton $A(SI, L)$ having an inverse $B(SI, R)$ with delay N for which there exists an error set, containing $I=K/p \cdot \dfrac{p!}{2!(p-2)!}$ elements, relative to which B is SA-M but not SA-$M-1$.

Proof. Let $N=R=1$. Let B be the automaton constructed in the proof of Theorem 50 for $N=R=1$, $M=1$. To form the graph $\Gamma(tx)$, the set $\{b_1, \ldots, b_K\}$ is divided into K/p subsets, each with p elements, and the letters designating all arcs connecting two given subtrees are so chosen that they belong to the same subset. If the error set consists only of pairs of letters from the same subset, then B is SA-0. The maximum number of pairs in the error set is I.

Let $N=R>1$; assume that there is an automaton of the desired type with $N_1=R_1=N-1$, satisfying the conditions: (1) $\Gamma(tx)$ contains N_1K/p subtrees, divided into groups each containing K/p subtrees; (2) the subtrees $x_{(N_1-1)K/p+1},\ldots,x_{N_1K/p}$ are such that the subgraphs attached to their first level vertices are complete trees of type (K,N_1-1); (3) the subgraphs attached to the (N_1-1)-th level vertices of the subtrees $x_1,\ldots,x_{K/p}$ are not complete trees of type $(K,1)$.

Form K/p new subtrees by attaching subtrees isomorphic to $x_1,\ldots,x_K/_p$ to the leaves of a complete tree of type $(K,1)$, according to the rule: let x be a subtree in $\Gamma(tx)$ which is the end of an arc from $x_{N_1K/p}$ labeled $b_{m-\nu+1}$ $m\geqslant\nu$ or $b_{K+m-\nu+1}(m<\nu)$; attach a subtree isomorphic to x to each vertex which is the end of an arc labeled a_m; the resulting subtree will be $x_{N_1K/p+\nu}$ $(1\leqslant\nu\leqslant K/p)$. Now attach complete trees of type $(K,1)$ to all leaves of the graph $\Gamma(tx)$, delete the arcs emanating from the subtrees $x_{(N_1-1)K/p+1},\ldots,x_{N_1K/p}$ and replace them by arcs going to the newly formed subtrees, p arcs from each subtree. Finally, let p arcs issue from each new subtree to each of the first K/p subtrees of $\Gamma(tx)$. It is clear that vertices may be identified in the new graph so as to obtain an admissible graph $\Gamma_1(x)$.

To form the graph $\Gamma_1(tx)$, arcs between subtrees which have identically indexed counterparts in $\Gamma(tx)$, also connected by arcs, are assigned the same letters of $\mathfrak{B}$ as the corresponding arcs in $\Gamma(tx)$. With each subtree $x_{N_1K/p+i}$ and x_i $(i=1,\ldots,K/p)$ we associate the letters $\{b_{(i-1)p+1},\ldots,b_{ip}\}$, and label the arcs leading to these subtrees by one of these letters. The rest of the proof is the same as for $N=1$.

Before going on to the next step, we apply a "cyclic shift" transformation with period K/p to the indices of the subtrees.

Let $N>R$. The proof then follows the lines of the second step in the proof of Theorem 46, using the existence of an automaton A (SI, R) having an inverse B (SI, 1) with delay R which is SA-0 relative to the given error set.

This completes the proof of Theorem 51.

There may also exist ILS-I-R automata having ILS-I-L inverses with delay N which are at the same time SA-$N-R$ relative to a suitable error set, even when K is a prime.

Theorem 52. Let K be a prime expressible as $K=pq+r$, where $p<r$, $p<q$, $pr\leqslant K$, and let N,L,R satisfy the conditions $N\geqslant2$, $R+L=N+2$, $R\leqslant N$, $L\leqslant N$; let $\mathfrak{A}$ and $\mathfrak{B}$ be K-letter alphabets. Then there exists an automaton A(SI, R) having an inverse B(SI, L) with delay N, which is SA-$N-R$ relative to a certain error set containing $I=p\dfrac{p!}{2!(p-2)!}$ elements.

Proof. Let $N=R=L=2$. We shall construct an admissible graph $\Gamma(x)$ containing $(r+q)p+r^2$ subtrees if $r\geqslant q$ and $2pq+r$ subtrees if $r<q$.

In either case, the subtees x_i $(i=1,\ldots,2pq)$ are identical. Consider the subtrees x_{jq+i} $(j=0,1,\ldots,p-1,\ i=1,\ldots,q)$. The arcs emanating from the root of x_{jq+i} are labeled a_{jq+l} $(l=1,\ldots,q)$. The arcs emanating from each first level vertex are labeled $a_{(i-1)p+m}$ $(m=1,\ldots,p)$. In addition, arcs emanate from the vertex $\chi_{jq+i,1,a_{jq+i}}$ with labels $a_{pq+1},\ldots,a_K$.

The subtrees $x_{pq+jp+i}$ $(j=0,\ 1,\ldots,\max(r-1,q-1),\ i=1,\ldots,p)$ are constructed similarly. The arcs from the root of $x_{jp+i+pq}$ are labeled a_{jp+l} $(l=1,\ldots,p)$. The arcs from each first level vertex are labeled

$a_{(i-1)q+m}$ $(m=1,\ldots,q)$. In addition, arcs emanate from the vertex $\chi_{pq+jp+i,1,a_{jp+i}}$ with labels $a_{pq+1},\ldots,a_K$.

Let $r \geqslant q$. The subtrees $x_{(r+q)p+ir+j}$ $(i=0,\ 1,\ldots,\ r-1,\ j=1,\ldots,r)$ are formed as follows. Take subtrees with r arcs issuing from the root, labeled as follows:

$$\begin{aligned} &\text{for} \quad i=0,1,\ldots,q: \quad a_{ip+1},\ldots,a_{ip+(r-q)p},a_{rp+1},\ldots,a_K, \\ &\text{for} \quad i=q+1,\ldots,r-1: \quad a_1,a_2,\ldots,a_{(i-q)p},a_{ip+1},\ldots,a_K. \end{aligned} \tag{1}$$

To simplify the description of the arcs emanating from the first level vertices, number the arcs from the root arbitrarily from 1 to r. The labels of the next-level arcs for the subtrees $x_{(r+q)p+ir+j}$ are the same for all i but depend on j. For all $j=1,\ldots,r-q$, the arcs emanating from each of the first level vertices numbered $j+1,\ldots,j+q$ are labeled $a_{(j-1)p+1},\ldots,a_{jp}$. For $j=r-q+1,\ldots,r$, the arcs emanating from the vertices numbered $1,\ldots,j-(r-q)$, $j+1\ldots,r$ are labeled $a_{(j-1)p+1},\ldots,a_{jp}$. In addition, arcs are introduced going from the j-th first level vertex of $x_{(r+q)p+ir+j}$ with labels (1) for $j=i+1$.

Arcs leading to first level vertices for which we have not specified outgoing arcs are deleted.

Let $r<q$. In the subtrees x_{2pq+j} $(j=1,\ldots,r)$, arcs issue from the roots, labeled $a_{pq+1},\ldots,a_K$. Arcs issue from the first level vertices with labels $a_{(j-1)p+1},\ldots,a_{jp}$, and in addition there are arcs from the vertex $\chi_{2pq+j,1,a_{pq+j}}$ labeled $a_{rp+1},\ldots,a_K$.

This system of subtrees has the property that, for every subtree attached to a first level vertex which has l leaves and defines a set of words $\mathfrak{A}_1$, the system contains l subtrees, defining disjoint sets of words; for each of these subtrees the set of words defined by the arcs issuing from the root is a subset of $\mathfrak{A}_1$. It follows that we can construct an admissible graph $\Gamma(x)$. This graph $\Gamma(x)$ has the property that for any subtree x_i there are p subtrees $x_{j_1},\ldots,x_{j_p}$ such that the number of arcs from x_i to x_{j_ρ} $(\rho=1,\ldots,p)$ is p.

Thus we can construct an admissible graph $\Gamma(tx)$ such that the p arcs reaching some subtree x_{j_ρ} from x_i are labeled by letters from the same set $\{b_1,\ldots,b_p\}$, $\{b_{p+1},\ldots,b_{2p}\},\ldots,\{b_{(p-1)p+1},\ldots,b_{p^2}\}$. It is clear that if the error set contains only pairs of letters belonging to the same set in this list, then B is an SA-0 automaton. There are all in all I pairs of letters satisfying this condition.

For $N>2$, the proof uses the automaton just constructed and the arguments of the proof of Theorem 46. This completes the proof.

One can also construct automata whose numerical parameters satisfy all the assumptions of Theorem 52, except $R+L=N+2$, which is replaced by the condition $R+L>N+2$. In this case, however, the construction is extraordinarily complicated.

The main results of this section were originally presented in /12/.

§10. CONSTRUCTION OF ILS-I-N AND ILS-II-N AUTOMATA

Consider the question: how can we construct an ILS-I-R automaton having a standard inverse with delay N which is ILS-I-L? If no restrictions are adopted concerning the types of the states, the simplest solution is achieved by means of graphs $\Gamma(x)$ and $\Gamma(tx)$. It is very easy to construct an admissible graph $\Gamma(x)$, even if we require it to be a normal graph and stipulate that all its subtrees be panicles of one of the types $(K, N, \varkappa)$, $\varkappa \leqslant L$, with complete trees attached to all R-th level vertices, and moreover that the graph contain a subtree such that the subgraph attached to one of its $(R-1)$-th level vertices is not a complete tree. It is preferable to replace the last two conditions by the following: the subgraphs attached to the vertices of the penultimate level of each subtree are not all complete trees of type $(K, 1)$; N is replaced by and $\varkappa$ by $\varkappa-(N-R)$.

Consider an arbitrary input subtree which is a panicle of type $(K, N, \varkappa)$ with root of weight C divisible only by prime divisors of K, such that the product of the weight of any ν-th level vertex and the number $K^{\nu-N+\varkappa}$ is divisible by C. Construct a normal cleavage of this subtree all of whose subtrees satisfy the same conditions, then form cleavages of the new subtrees, and so on. This should be done in such a way that certain subtrees on the last levels of the cleavages are isomorphic to previously constructed subtrees. In such cases arcs are drawn from the previous level of the cleavages to isomorphic subtrees already present in the graph. Figure 21 illustrates the construction of a graph $\Gamma(x)$ such that the graph $\Gamma(tx)$ defines a normal automaton $B(\mathrm{SI}, 3)$ having an inverse A with delay 4 which is ILS-I-3. The graph $\Gamma(tx)$ is derived from $\Gamma(x)$ by simply labeling the arcs with letters of $\mathfrak{B}$ in such a way that no two arcs issuing from the same subtree are given the same label.

One can also construct graphs $\Gamma(x)$ such that B is SA-M for a prescribed M. Some devices to this end may be found in the proofs of the theorems in §9. These devices, however, do not cover the construction of an arbitrary normal automaton with these properties.

In SA-M automata, main significance attaches to the transitions rather than the outputs. Therefore, when trying to construct an SA-M and ILS-I-R automaton one may proceed as follows. Construct an acceptor (i.e., automaton without output) B_1 such that the graph $G_s(B_1)$ contains neither cycles nor vertices of the type $(t_j, -)$. Then replace the vertices in the diagram of B_1 by input subtrees so that the arcs of the resulting graph may be labeled by letters of $\mathfrak{A}$ to obtain an admissible graph $\Gamma(tx)$.

Example. Let B_1 be the automaton defined by Table 22 (for simplicity's sake, the outputs are not specified and the diagram is not given).

TABLE 22.

	0	1		0	1		0	1
t_1	t_9	t_{10}	t_5	t_1	t_2	t_9	t_5	t_6
t_2	t_{10}	t_9	t_6	t_3	t_4	t_{10}	t_7	t_8
t_3	t_{11}	t_{12}	t_7	t_1	t_2	t_{11}	t_5	t_6
t_4	t_{12}	t_{11}	t_8	t_3	t_4	t_{12}	t_7	t_8

The vertices in the diagram of this automaton may be replaced by input subtrees of type (2,1), all defining the set of words $\{0, 1\}$. The table of the automaton $B(\mathrm{SI}, 0)$ may be obtained by arbitrarily assigning outputs 0 and 1 in Table 22 (one output to each row).

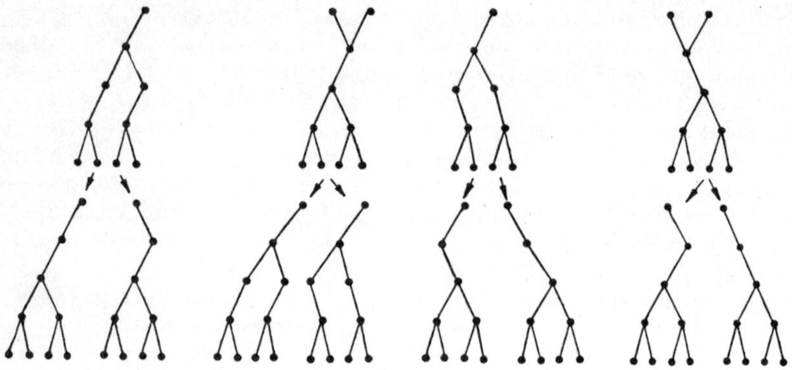

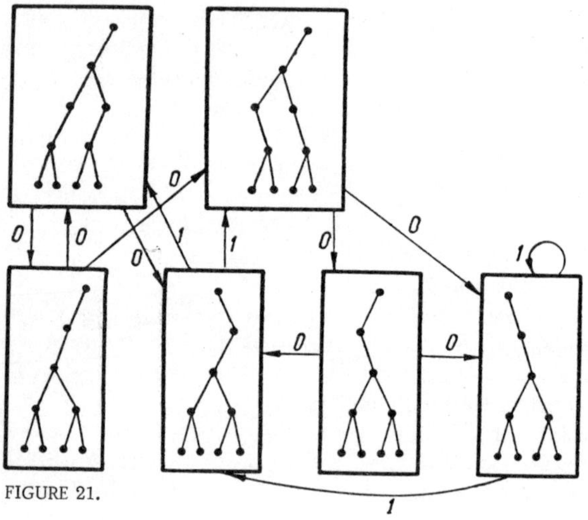

FIGURE 21.

The vertices in the diagram of B_1 may also be replaced by subtrees of type $(2, 2)$, as follows. The subtrees replacing the states t_1, t_3, t_5, t_8, t_9 all define the set of words {00, 01}; those replacing the states $t_2, t_4, t_6, t_7, t_{10}$ define {10, 11}; those replacing t_{11} and t_{12} define {00, 11} and {01, 10}, respectively. Table 23 is the table of the resulting automaton (the states are indexed as in Table 22).

TABLE 23.

	0	1		0	1		0	1
t_1	t_9, 0	t_{10}, 0	t_5	t_1, 0	t_2, 0	t_9	t_5, 0	t_6, 0
t_2	t_{10}, 1	t_9, 1	t_6	t_3, 1	t_4, 1	t_{10}	t_7, 1	t_8, 1
t_3	t_{11}, 0	t_{12}, 0	t_7	t_1, 1	t_2, 1	t_{11}	t_5, 0	t_6, 1
t_4	t_{12}, 1	t_{11}, 1	t_8	t_3, 0	t_4, 0	t_{12}	t_7, 0	t_8, 1

While the construction of ILS-I-L automata is fairly simple, the situation is vastly different for ILS-II-L automata. In the absence of tools like those used to investigate IL-I-N automata, there are no really general methods for synthesis and analysis of IL-II-N automata. The problem may be solved with some degree of success only when it is reducible to an analogous problem for IL-I-N automata. This may be done in the following cases.

Suppose we have an automaton A(SI, N) whose table has the property that each column contains each state at most once (we shall call this a permutation automaton). Then the table of A may be viewed as the formation table of some other automaton A_1, which is ILS-II-N. Table 24 gives an example of such an automaton A, and Table 25 is the table of an automaton A_1 for which Table 24 is the formation table.

TABLE 24.

	0	1
s_1	s_3, 0	s_4, 0
s_2	s_4, 1	s_3, 1
s_3	s_5, 0	s_6, 1
s_4	s_6, 0	s_5, 1
s_5	s_1, 0	s_2, 1
s_6	s_2, 0	s_1, 1

TABLE 25.

	0	1
s_1	s_5, 0	s_6, 1
s_2	s_6, 0	s_5, 1
s_3	s_1, 0	s_2, 1
s_4	s_2, 1	s_1, 0
s_5	s_3, 0	s_4, 1
s_6	s_4, 0	s_3, 1

In the transition table of a permutation automaton, any state-output pair may be moved to a new position in the same column. This yields a table which may again be treated as the formation table of a suitable automaton, whose transition and output tables are readily constructed. Table 26 is obtained from Table 24 in this way. It may be verified that the graph $G_{\text{II}}(A)$ based on Table 26, viewed as a formation table, contains no cycles or vertices (s_i, s_i). The maximum length of a path in $G_{\text{II}}(A)$ is 2. Thus the automaton defined by Table 27, obtained from the formation table (Table 26), is ILS-II-3.

TABLE 26.

	0	1
s_1	s_3, 0	s_4, 0
s_2	s_4, 1	s_3, 1
s_3	s_5, 0	s_1, 1
s_4	s_6, 0	s_2, 1
s_5	s_1, 0	s_5, 1; s_6, 1
s_6	s_2, 0	—

TABLE 27.

	0	1
s_1	s_5, 0	s_3, 1
s_2	s_6, 0	s_4, 1
s_3	s_1, 0	s_2, 1
s_4	s_2, 1	s_1, 0
s_5	s_3, 0	s_5, 1
s_6	s_4, 0	s_5, 1

It is evident from Tables 24 and 28 (the latter is obtained from the former by moving the pair $(s_3, 0)$) that not every displacement of a state — output pair in the table of an ILS-I-N permutation automaton produces the formation table of some ILS-II-N automaton.

Let A(SII, 2) be the automaton defined by Table 29. Its formation table is Table 30. Whichever of the pairs $(s_3, 1)$ or $(s_4, 1)$ we move to the empty position in Table 30, the result is not the table of an IL-I-N automaton. It follows that not every IL-II-N automaton may be obtained as described by displacing one state—output pair in the table of an IL-I-N permutation automaton.

TABLE 28.

	0	1
s_1	—	s_4, 0
s_2	s_4, 1; s_3, 0	s_3, 1
s_3	s_5, 0	s_6, 1
s_4	s_6, 0	s_5, 1
s_5	s_1, 0	s_2, 1
s_6	s_2, 0	s_1, 1

TABLE 29.

	0	1
s_1	s_3, 0	s_1, 2
s_2	s_4, 0	s_2, 1
s_3	s_1, 0	s_3, 1
s_4	s_2, 1	s_3, 1

TABLE 30.

	0	1
s_1	s_3, 0	s_1, 2
s_2	s_4, 1	s_2, 1
s_3	s_1, 0	s_3, 1; s_4, 1
s_4	s_2, 0	—

Using the tools available for ILS-I-N automata and the above-described properties of permutation automata, one can prove certain results for IL-II-N automata whose inverses are SA-M.

Theorem 53. For any $N \geqslant 2$, there exists an automaton B (SII, N) having an inverse with delay N which is SA-N relative to any error set.

Proof. Construct a normal graph $\Gamma(x)$ with Nd input subtrees, which can be divided into N groups so that the following conditions hold: (1) each group of subtrees defines a partition of the set of all words of length N over $\mathfrak{A}$ into subsets of equal cardinalities; (2) for each group there is exactly one group such that from each subtree of the first there are arcs going only to subtrees of the second. A graph $\Gamma(x)$ meeting these requirements is that constructed in Step 1 of the proof of Theorem 46. Suppose that some subtree in $\Gamma(x)$ is not the end of exactly K arcs. Then there must be a subtree which is the end of at least $K+1$ arcs. Suppose this subtree is x_i, and let it belong to a group of subtrees to which there are arcs from the subtrees in another group, say $\mathfrak{R}$. Then the vertex χ_i is identified with $K+1$ first level vertices of subtrees in $\mathfrak{R}$. Since the subtrees of $\mathfrak{R}$ define a partition of the set of words of length N into disjoint subsets, this is impossible. Consequently, each subtree is the end of exactly K arcs. Thus we may assign letters of $\mathfrak{B}$ to the arcs of $\Gamma(x)$ in such a way that the resulting graph $\Gamma(tx)$ defines a permutation automaton B_1. If B_1 is ILS-I-N, then the automaton B whose formation table is the table of B_1 will in turn be ILS-II-N. Any type I inverse with delay N for B_1 (SI, N) is a type II inverse with delay N for B.

It follows from the properties of the subtrees employed in Step 1 of the proof of Theorem 46 that the graph $\Gamma(tx)$ may be so constructed that B_1 is indeed ILS-I-N.

Let A be a type I standard inverse with delay N for B_1 and $(x_i, a_v\alpha)$ one of its states. For any letters a_k, a_l ($a_k \neq a_l$) we have

$$\delta((x_i, a_v\alpha), a_l) = (x_{j_1}, \alpha a_l), \quad \delta((x_i, a_v\alpha), a_k) = (x_{j_2}, \alpha a_k),$$

where x_{j_1} and x_{j_2} belong to the same group of subtrees. For any word α_1 of length N,

$$\delta((x_{j_1}, \alpha a_l), \alpha_1) = (x_{n_1}, \alpha_1), \ \delta((x_{j_2}, \alpha a_k), \alpha_1) = (x_{n_2}, \alpha_1),$$

where x_{n_1} and x_{n_2} are again in the same group. Since the sets of words defined by any two subtrees of the same group are disjoint and the automaton A has states (x_i, α) only for words defined by x_i, it follows that necessarily $x_{n_1} = x_{n_2}$. Thus A is SA-N relative to any error set, and the proof is complete.

Chapter III

NUMERICAL ESTIMATES

§1. LENGTH OF AN EXPERIMENT IDENTIFYING INCOMPATIBLE STATES OF A STANDARD INVERSE

Our first problem is to determine, given an automaton A, its sets of compatible states. Let $\mathfrak{S}_0$ denote the state set of A. We construct a set $\mathfrak{S}_1=\{\mathfrak{S}_{11},\dots,\mathfrak{S}_{1i_1}\}$, where the $\mathfrak{S}_{1j}$ are sets of states of A defined as follows. Each $\mathfrak{S}_{1j}$ is a maximal set such that, for any $s_i\in\mathfrak{S}_{1j}$, $s_k\in\mathfrak{S}_{1j}$ and any letter a_l for which $\lambda(s_i,a_l)$ and $\lambda(s_k,a_l)$ are defined, $\lambda(s_i,a_l)=\lambda(s_k,a_l)$. We then define $\mathfrak{S}_1$ to be the set of all $\mathfrak{S}_{1j}$ satisfying this condition.

Suppose that we have constructed the set $\mathfrak{S}_j=\{\mathfrak{S}_{j1},\dots,\mathfrak{S}_{ji_j}\}$. The set $\mathfrak{S}_{j+1}$ will then consist of all maximal sets $\mathfrak{S}_{j+1,l}$ satisfying the conditions:

(1) Each $\mathfrak{S}_{j+1,l}$ is a subset of one of the sets $\mathfrak{S}_{j\varkappa}$.

(2) For any states s_i, s_k in the same set $\mathfrak{S}_{j+1,l}$ and any letter a_m for which $\delta(s_i,a_m)$ and $\delta(s_k,a_m)$ are defined, the states $\delta(s_i,a_m)$ and $\delta(s_k,a_m)$ belong to the same set $\mathfrak{S}_{j\lambda}$.

It follows from the definition that the set $\mathfrak{S}_1$ satisfies the conditions:

(1) Any two states s_i, s_j satisfying $\lambda(s_i,a_k)=\lambda(s_j,a_k)$ for any a_k such that both $\lambda(s_i,a_k)$ and $\lambda(s_j,a_k)$ are defined occur either together or not at all in each $\mathfrak{S}_{1j}$.

(2) If $s_\varkappa$ and s_λ are states for which there is a letter a_μ such that $\lambda(s_\varkappa,a_\mu)$ and $\lambda(s_\lambda,a_\mu)$ are both defined but $\lambda(s_\varkappa,a_\mu)\neq\lambda(s_\lambda,a_\mu)$, then $s_\varkappa$ and s_λ cannot occur together in any $\mathfrak{S}_{1j}$.

Now suppose that $\mathfrak{S}_k$ $(k\geqslant 1)$ satisfies the following conditions:

(1) Any two states s_i, s_j satisfying $\lambda(s_i,\alpha)=\lambda(s_j,\alpha)$ for any word α of length k or less such that $\lambda(s_i,\alpha)$ and $\lambda(s_j,\alpha)$ are defined occur either together or not at all in each $\mathfrak{S}_{kr}$.

(2) If $s_\varkappa$ and s_λ are states and α a word of length k or less such that $\lambda(s_\varkappa,\alpha)$ and $\lambda(s_\lambda,\alpha)$ are both defined but $\lambda(s_\varkappa,\alpha)\neq\lambda(s_\lambda,\alpha)$, then $s_\varkappa$ and s_λ cannot occur together in any $\mathfrak{S}_{kr}$.

We claim that the set $\mathfrak{S}_{k+1}$ also satisfies these conditions. Let s_i and s_j be states satisfying $\lambda(s_i,\alpha)=\lambda(s_j,\alpha)$ for any word α of length $k+1$ such that $\lambda(s_i,\alpha)$ and $\lambda(s_j,\alpha)$ are defined. Let $\mathfrak{S}_{kr}$ be a set containing one of the states s_i or s_j. By condition 1, $\mathfrak{S}_{kr}$ contains the other state too. Let $\alpha=a_\varkappa\alpha'$. Then

$$\lambda(\delta(s_i,a_\varkappa),\alpha')=\lambda(\delta(s_j,a_\varkappa),\alpha').$$

By condition 1, the states $\delta(s_i,a_\varkappa)$ and $\delta(s_j,a_\varkappa)$ are always in the same set $\mathfrak{S}_{kr}$. This is true for words α beginning with any letter. Thus the states s_i and s_j occur together or not at all in any given set $\mathfrak{S}_{k+1,p}$.

Let s_i and s_j be states such that for some word $a_\varkappa \alpha_1 a_\lambda$ of length $k+1$ for which $\lambda(s_i, a_\varkappa \alpha_1 a_\lambda)$ and $\lambda(s_j, a_\varkappa \alpha_1 a_\lambda)$ are defined we have $\lambda(s_i, a_\varkappa \alpha_1 a_\lambda) \neq \neq \lambda(s_j, a_\varkappa \alpha_1 a_\lambda)$. If $\lambda(s_i, a_\varkappa \alpha_1) \neq \lambda(s_j, a_\varkappa \alpha_1)$, it follows from condition 2 that s_i and s_j can never occur together in any $\mathfrak{S}_{kr}$. By the definition of $\mathfrak{S}_{k+1}$, neither can they occur together in any $\mathfrak{S}_{k+1,p}$. Now let $\lambda(s_i, a_\varkappa \alpha_1) = \lambda(s_j, a_\varkappa \alpha_1)$, so that s_i and s_j are in the same $\mathfrak{S}_{kr}$. We must have

$$\lambda(\delta(s_i, a_\varkappa), \alpha_1 a_\lambda) \neq \lambda(\delta(s_j, a_\varkappa), \alpha_1 a_\lambda)$$

and both values are defined. Since $|\alpha_1 a_\lambda| = k$ it follows from condition 2 that the states $\delta(s_i, a_\varkappa)$ and $\delta(s_j, a_\varkappa)$ are never in the same $\mathfrak{S}_{kr}$. Then, again by the definition of $\mathfrak{S}_{k+1}$, s_i and s_j cannot be in the same $\mathfrak{S}_{k+1,p}$.

We have thus proved the following

Theorem 54. Let s_i and s_j be states such that $\lambda(s_i, \alpha) = \lambda(s_j, \alpha)$ for all words α of length k or less $(k=1,2,\ldots)$ for which $\lambda(s_i, \alpha)$ and $\lambda(s_j, \alpha)$ are defined. Then s_i and s_j occur either together or not at all in any given set $\mathfrak{S}_{kr}$. If s_i and s_j are such that for some word α of length k or less $(k=1,2,\ldots)$ we have $\lambda(s_i, \alpha) \neq \lambda(s_j, \alpha)$ and both values are defined, then s_i and s_j cannot both be elements of the same set $\mathfrak{S}_{kr}$.

The construction of the sets $\mathfrak{S}_j$ need be continued only up to a value of $j = j_0$ for which $\mathfrak{S}_{j_0-1} \neq \mathfrak{S}_{j_0}$ but $\mathfrak{S}_{j_0} = \mathfrak{S}_{j_0+1}$.

An apt designation for the number j_0 is the length of an experiment identifying incompatible states of the automaton; indeed, by Theorem 54 j_0 is the smallest number such that for any two incompatible states s_i, s_j there exists a word α of length j_0 for which $\lambda(s_i, \alpha) \neq \lambda(s_j, \alpha)$ and both $\lambda(s_i, \alpha)$ and $\lambda(s_j, \alpha)$ are defined.

Although j_0 may be determined by actual construction of the sets $\mathfrak{S}_j$, one is nevertheless interested in estimating it in terms of the various numerical parameters of the automaton A. It is known (see /10/) that $j_0 \leqslant n(n-1)/2$, where n is the number of states of A. This estimate is best possible: for any number n one can construct an automaton with n states such that $\mathfrak{S}_{n(n-1)/2-1} \neq \mathfrak{S}_{n(n-1)/2}$ but $\mathfrak{S}_{n(n-1)/2} = \mathfrak{S}_{n(n-1)/2+1}$.

For standard inverse automata, one can use the results of Chap. I (§6) to estimate j_0 in terms of the number of states of the original automaton.

We first show how to identify which states are consistent (or inversely consistent) with delay N.

Let A be an automaton. We shall construct two graphs $G_{\text{H}}(A)$ and $G_{\text{ic}}(A)$; the vertex set of both graphs consists of all unordered pairs of states, plus one distinguished vertex denoted by X.

The arcs of $G_c(A)$ are defined as follows. Consider each vertex (s_i, s_j) together with each letter b_k. The following cases may arise:

(1) There are letters $a_{i_1}, \ldots, a_{i_l}$ such that $\lambda(s_i, a_{i_\lambda}) = \lambda(s_j, a_{i_\lambda}) = b_k$ $(\lambda=1,\ldots,l)$. An arc will then go from (s_i, s_j) to each of the vertices $(\delta(s_i, a_{i_\lambda}), \delta(s_j, a_{i_\lambda}))$. *

(2) There exist distinct letters a_n, a_m such that $\lambda(s_i, a_n) = \lambda(s_j, a_m) = b_h$, and the states $\delta(s_i, a_n)$ and $\delta(s_j, a_m)$ are not disjoint of order N. An arc will then go from (s_i, s_j) to the vertex X.

* Note that since we are concerned with unordered pairs there is no difference between $(s_\varkappa, s_\mu)$ and $(s_\mu, s_\varkappa)$.

(3) For one of the states, say s_i, there is no letter a_m with $\lambda(s_i, a_m)=b_k$. Then no arcs emanate from the vertex (s_i, s_j).

Theorem 55_{I}. *States s_i and s_j are consistent with delay N if and only if there is no path in the graph $G_c(A)$ from (s_i, s_j) to X.*

Proof. Suppose that s_i and s_j are not consistent with delay N, i. e., there exist words $\alpha a_k\alpha'$ and $\alpha a_l\alpha''$, $a_k\neq a_l$, $|\alpha'|=|\alpha''|=N$, such that $\lambda(s_i, \alpha a_k\alpha')=\lambda(s_j, \alpha a_l\alpha'')$. If α is not empty, it follows from rule 1 in the definition of $G_c(A)$ that there is a path from (s_i, s_j) to $(\delta(s_i, \alpha), \delta(s_j, \alpha))$. Since $\lambda(\delta(s_i, \alpha a_k), \alpha')=\lambda(\delta(s_j, \alpha a_l), \alpha'')$, the states $\delta(s_i, \alpha a_k)$ and $\delta(s_j, \alpha a_l)$ are not disjoint of order N. But then, by rule 2, there is an arc from $(\delta(s_i, \alpha), \delta(s_j, \alpha))$ to the vertex X. If α is empty, then by rule 2 there is an arc from (s_i, s_j) to X. In either case we have a path from (s_i, s_j) to X.

Conversely, suppose there is a path in $G_c(A)$ from (s_i, s_j) to X, passing through the vertices $(s_i, s_j)=(s_{i_1}, s_{j_1}), (s_{i_2}, s_{j_2}), \ldots, (s_{i_n}, s_{j_n}), X$ $(n>1)$. Now there may be an arc from $(s_{i_\varkappa}, s_{j_\varkappa})$ $(\varkappa=1, 2, \ldots, n-1)$ to $(s_{i_{\varkappa+1}}, s_{j_{\varkappa+1}})$ only if there are letters $a_{k_\varkappa}$ and $b_{m_\varkappa}$ such that

$$\lambda(s_{i_\varkappa}, a_{k_\varkappa})=\lambda(s_{j_\varkappa}, a_{k_\varkappa})=b_{m_\varkappa}, \quad \delta(s_{i_\varkappa}, a_{k_\varkappa})=s_{i_{\varkappa+1}}, \quad \delta(s_{j_\varkappa}, a_{k_\varkappa})= s_{j_{\varkappa+1}}.$$

This means that for some word α of length $n-1$

$$\lambda(s_i, \alpha)=\lambda(s_j, \alpha), \quad \delta(s_i, \alpha)=s_{i_n}, \quad \delta(s_j, \alpha)=s_{j_n}.$$

There may be an arc from (s_{i_n}, s_{j_n}) to X only if there are two distinct letters a_r, a_p such that $\lambda(s_{i_n}, a_r)=\lambda(s_{j_n}, a_p)$ and the states $\delta(s_{i_n}, a_r)$ and $\delta(s_{j_n}, a_p)$ are not disjoint of order N, i. e., there exist words α' and α'' of length N such that $\lambda(\delta(s_{i_n}, a_r), \alpha')=\lambda(\delta(s_{j_n}, a_p), \alpha'')$. Combining all these equalities, we see that $\lambda(s_i, \alpha a_r\alpha')= \lambda(s_j, \alpha a_p\alpha'')$, where $a_r\neq a_p$, $|\alpha'|=|\alpha''|=N$, so that the states s_i and s_j are not consistent with delay N. If there is an arc from (s_i, s_j) to X, we see, repeating the arguments presented above for (s_{i_n}, s_{j_n}), that $\lambda(s_i, a_r\alpha') = \lambda(s_j, a_p\alpha'')$, where $a_r\neq a_p$, $|\alpha'|=|\alpha''|=N$, so that the states s_i and s_j are again not consistent with delay N. Q. E. D.

To construct the graph $G_{ic}(A)$, we again consider each vertex (s_i, s_j) in conjunction with each letter b_k. The rules are as follows:

(1) There exist letters $a_{i_1}, \ldots, a_{i_l}$ and two sets of states $\{s_{r_1}, \ldots, s_{r_l}\}$ and $\{s_{j_1}, \ldots, s_{j_l}\}$ such that

$$\delta(s_{r_\lambda}, a_{i_\lambda})=s_i\,; \quad \delta(s_{j_\lambda}, a_{i_\lambda})=s_j, \quad \lambda(s_{r_\lambda}, a_{i_\lambda})=\lambda(s_{j_\lambda}, a_{i_\lambda})=b_k.$$

An arc will then go from (s_i, s_j) to each vertex $(s_{r_\lambda}, s_{j_\lambda})$ $(\lambda=1, \ldots, l)$.

(2) There exist distinct letters a_ρ a_p and states $s_\varkappa$, s_μ, which are not inversely disjoint of order N, such that

$$\delta(s_\varkappa, a_\rho)=s_i, \quad \delta(s_\mu, a_p)=s_j, \quad \lambda(s_\varkappa, a_\rho)=\lambda(s_\mu, a_p)=b_k.$$

An arc will then go from (s_i, s_j) to the vertex X.

(3) For one of the states, say s_i, there exist no letter a_p and state s_r such that $\delta(s_r, a_p)=s_i$ and $\lambda(s_r, a_p)=b_k$. Then no arc emanates from the vertex.

Theorem 55_{II}. *States s_i and s_j are inversely consistent with delay N if and only if there is no path in $G_{\text{ic}}(A)$ from (s_i, s_j) to X.*

Proof. Suppose that s_i and s_j are not inversely consistent with delay N, i. e., there exist states $s_\varkappa$, s_μ and words $\alpha' a_r \alpha$, $\alpha'' a_p \alpha$, where $a_r \neq a_p$, $|\alpha'| = |\alpha''| = N$, such that

$$\delta(s_\varkappa, \alpha' a_r \alpha) = s_i,\ \delta(s_\mu, \alpha'' a_p \alpha) = s_j,\ \lambda(s_\varkappa, \alpha' a_r \alpha) = \lambda(s_\mu, \alpha'' a_p \alpha).$$

If α is not the empty word, it follows from rule 1 in the definition of $G_{\text{ic}}(A)$ that there is a path from (s_i, s_j) to the vertex $(\delta(s_\varkappa, \alpha' a_r),\ \delta(s_\mu, \alpha'' a_p))$. The states $\delta(s_\varkappa, \alpha')$ and $\delta(s_\mu, \alpha'')$ are not inversely disjoint of order N, since $\lambda(s_\varkappa, \alpha') = \lambda(s_\mu, \alpha'')$. Since

$$\lambda(\delta(s_\varkappa, \alpha'), a_r) = \lambda(\delta(s_\mu, \alpha''), a_p),$$

$$\delta(\delta(s_\varkappa, \alpha'),\ a_r) = \delta(s_\varkappa, \alpha' a_r),\quad \delta(\delta(s_\mu, \alpha''), a_p) = \delta(s_\mu, \alpha'' a_p),$$

there is an arc from the vertex $(\delta(s_\varkappa, \alpha' a_r),\ \delta(s_\mu, \alpha'' a_p))$ to X, so that there is a path from (s_i, s_j) to the vertex X.

If α is the empty word, there is an arc from (s_i, s_j) to X.

Conversely, suppose there is a path in $G_{\text{ic}}(A)$ from (s_i, s_j) to X, passing through vertices $(s_i, s_j) = (s_{i_1}, s_{j_1}), (s_{i_2}, s_{j_2}), \ldots, (s_{i_n}, s_{j_n})$. Let $n > 1$. There may be an arc from $(s_{i_\varkappa}, s_{j_\varkappa})$ to $(s_{i_{\varkappa+1}}, s_{j_{\varkappa+1}})$ only if there are letters $a_{k_\varkappa}$ and $b_{m_\varkappa}$ such that

$$\delta(s_{i_{\varkappa+1}}, a_{k_\varkappa}) = s_{i_\varkappa},\quad \delta(s_{j_{\varkappa+1}}, a_{k_\varkappa}) = s_{j_\varkappa},$$
$$\lambda(s_{i_{\varkappa+1}}, a_{k_\varkappa}) = \lambda(s_{j_{\varkappa+1}}, a_{k_\varkappa}) = b_{m_\varkappa} \quad (\varkappa = 1, \ldots, n-1).$$

Consequently, there is a word α such that

$$\delta(s_{i_n}, \alpha) = s_i,\ \delta(s_{j_n}, \alpha) = s_j,\ \lambda(s_{i_n}, \alpha) = \lambda(s_{j_n}, \alpha).$$

There may be an arc from (s_{i_n}, s_{j_n}) to X only if there exist states $s_\varkappa$, s_λ and letters a_p, a_r $(a_p \neq a_r)$, b_m such that

$$\delta(s_\varkappa, a_p) = s_{i_n}, \delta(s_\lambda, a_r) = s_{j_n},\ \lambda(s_\varkappa, a_p) = \lambda(s_\lambda, a_r) = b_m,$$

and the states $s_\varkappa$ and s_λ are not inversely disjoint of order N, i. e., there exist states s_ν, s_μ and words α', α'' of length N such that

$$\lambda(s_\nu, \alpha') = \lambda(s_\mu, \alpha''),\quad \delta(s_\nu, \alpha') = s_\varkappa,\ \delta(s_\mu, \alpha'') = s_\lambda.$$

Combining all these equalities, we see that

$$\delta(s_\nu, \alpha' a_p \alpha) = s_i,\quad \delta(s_\mu, \alpha'' a_r \alpha) = s_j,\quad \lambda(s_\nu, \alpha' a_p \alpha) = \lambda(s_\mu, \alpha'' a_r \alpha),$$

where $a_p \neq a_r$, $|\alpha'| = |\alpha''| = N$, so that the states s_i and s_j are not inversely consistent with delay N.

If there is an arc from (s_i, s_j) to X, we obtain the equalities

$$\delta(s_\nu, \alpha' a_p) = s_i,\quad \delta(s_\mu, \alpha'' a_r) = s_j,\quad \lambda(s_\nu, \alpha' a_p) = \lambda(s_\mu, \alpha'' a_r)$$

for certain states s_ν, s_μ, distinct letters a_p, a_r and words α', α'' of length N. This means that s_i and s_j are not inversely consistent with delay N. Q. E. D.

Theorem 56. Let A be an automaton with n states and B a (type I or II) standard inverse with delay N. For any two incompatible states t_i, t_j of the principal part of B, there is a word β of length at most $n(n-1)/2+N$ such that $\mu(t_i, \beta) \neq \mu(t_j, \beta)$ and both $\mu(t_i, \beta)$ and $\mu(t_j, \beta)$ are defined.

Proof. Suppose that the states (s_i, β_i) and (s_j, β_j) are incompatible. Consider a type I inverse. By Theorem 10_{I}, either there exists a word α such that $\alpha \in \mathfrak{M}_{\text{I}}(s_i, \beta_i)$ and $\alpha \in \mathfrak{M}_{\text{I}}(s_j, \beta_j)$ and the states $\delta(s_i, \alpha)$, $\delta(s_j, \alpha)$ are not consistent with delay N, or else there are two words $\alpha_1 \in \mathfrak{M}_{\text{I}}(s_i, \beta_i)$ and $\alpha_2 \in \mathfrak{M}_{\text{I}}(s_j, \beta_j)$ which first differ in their M-th letters such that $\delta(s_i, \alpha_1)$ and $\delta(s_j, \alpha_2)$ are not disjoint of order M.

Consider the first possibility. Since the number of vertices in $G_{\text{H}}(A)$ is $n(n-1)/2+1$, there is a path from the vertex $(\delta(s_i, \alpha), \delta(s_j, \alpha))$ to the vertex X, of length at most $n(n-1)/2$, since by Theorem 55_{I} there exists a path joining these vertices. This means that for suitable words $\alpha_1 a_r \alpha'$ and $\alpha_1 a_p \alpha''$, where $|\alpha_1| \leqslant n(n-1)/2-1$, $a_r \neq a_p$ and $|\alpha'| = |\alpha''| = N$,

$$\lambda(\delta(s_i, \alpha), \alpha_1 a_r \alpha') = \lambda(\delta(s_j, \alpha), \alpha_1 a_p \alpha'') = \beta.$$

The structure of the standard inverse implies that $\mu((s_i, \lambda(s_i, \alpha)), \beta) = \alpha\alpha_1 a_r$ and $\mu((s_j, \lambda(s_j, \alpha)), \beta) = \alpha\alpha_1 a_p$. Since $|\beta| \leqslant n(n-1)/2+N$, the proof is complete in this case.

Now consider the second possibility. For some word β_1,

$$\mu((s_i, \lambda(s_i, \alpha_1)), \beta_1) = \alpha a_r,$$
$$\mu((s_j, \lambda(s_j, \alpha_2)), \beta_1) = \alpha a_p,$$

where $|\alpha| = M-1$ and $a_r \neq a_p$. Since $|\beta_1| \leqslant N$, we are done.

Consider a type II inverse. By Theorem 10_{II}, there are again two possibilities.

Case I. There exist states s_k, s_l and a word α such that

$$\delta(s_k, \alpha) = s_i, \delta(s_l, \alpha) = s_j, \lambda(s_k, \alpha) = \beta_i^{-1}, \lambda(s_l, \alpha) = \beta_j^{-1},$$

and the states s_k, s_l are not inversely consistent with delay N. Then there is a path in the graph $G_{\text{ic}}(A)$ from (s_i, s_j) to X, of length at most $n(n-1)/2$, i. e., there exist states $s_\varkappa$, s_λ and words $\alpha' a_r \alpha_1$, $\alpha'' a_p \alpha_1$, $|\alpha'| = |\alpha''| = N$, $a_r \neq a_p$, $|\alpha_1| \leqslant n(n-1)/2-1$, such that

$$\delta(s_\varkappa, \alpha' a_r \alpha_1) = s_k, \delta(s_\lambda, \alpha'' a_p \alpha_1) = s_l, \quad \lambda(s_\varkappa, \alpha' a_r \alpha_1) = \lambda(s_\lambda, \alpha'' a_p \alpha_1) = \beta$$

and $|\beta| \leqslant n(n-1)/2+N$. We have

$$\mu((s_i, \beta_i), \beta^{-1}) = \alpha^{-1}\alpha_1^{-1} a_r, \quad \mu((s_j, \beta_j), \beta^{-1}) = \alpha^{-1}\alpha_1^{-1} a_p.$$

Case II. There exist states s_k, s_l and words $\alpha' a_r \alpha_1$, $\alpha'' a_p \alpha_1$, such that

$$\delta(s_k, \alpha' a_r \alpha_1) = s_i, \quad \delta(s_l, \alpha'' a_p \alpha_1) = s_j, \quad \lambda(s_k, \alpha' a_r \alpha_1) = \beta_i^{-1},$$
$$\lambda(s_l, \alpha'' a_p \alpha_1) = \beta_j^{-1}, \quad a_r \neq a_p, \quad |\alpha_1| = M-1,$$

and the states s_k and s_l are not inversely disjoint of order M. As in the case of type I inverses, we see that for some word β_1, $|\beta_1| \leqslant N$,

$$\mu((s_i, \beta_i), \beta_1) \neq \mu((s_j, \beta_j), \beta_1).$$

This completes the proof.

Let us now consider a complete standard inverse. In this case, it follows from Theorem 11_{I} that, if states (s_i, β_i) and (s_j, β_j) are nonequivalent, then either $\mathfrak{M}_{\mathrm{I}}(s_i, \beta_i) \neq \mathfrak{M}_{\mathrm{I}}(s_j, \beta_j)$ or there is a word $\alpha \in \mathfrak{M}_{\mathrm{I}}(s_i, \beta_i)$ for which the states $\delta(s_i, \alpha)$ and $\delta(s_j, \alpha)$ are incompatible, i. e., for some word α_1 we have $\lambda(\delta(s_i, \alpha), \alpha_1) \neq \lambda(\delta(s_j, \alpha), \alpha_1)$ and both values of λ are defined. The first possibility may be detected by a suitable word β_1, $|\beta_1| \leqslant N$. In the second case, there are words α_2, α_3, where $\lambda(s_j, \alpha_2) = \beta_j$ and $\alpha\alpha_1 \neq \alpha_2\alpha_3$, such that $\lambda(\delta(s_i, \alpha), \alpha_1) = \lambda(\delta(s_j, \alpha_2), \alpha_3) = \beta$. By the above-cited result of /10/, the fact that the words $\alpha\alpha_1$ and $\alpha_2\alpha_3$ are different may be detected by a word $\beta\beta_1$ of length at most $n(n-1)/2+N$, and the estimate is no better than that provided by Theorem 56.

It follows from Theorem 11_{II} that if states (s_i, β_i) and (s_j, β_j) are nonequivalent, then either $\mathfrak{M}_{\mathrm{II}}(s_i, \beta_i) \neq \mathfrak{M}_{\mathrm{II}}(s_j, \beta_j)$ or there exist words $\alpha \in \mathfrak{M}_{\mathrm{II}}(s_i, \beta_i)$, α_k and β_k and a state s_m, satisfying the conditions

$$\delta(\delta(s_m, \alpha_k), \alpha) = s_i, \quad \lambda(s_m, \alpha_k) = \beta_k, \quad (\lambda(\delta(s_m, \alpha_k), \alpha))^{-1} = \beta_i,$$

such that there is no state s_n with $\delta(\delta(s_n, \alpha_k), \alpha) = s_j$, $\lambda(s_n, \alpha_k) = \beta_k$ and $(\lambda(\delta(s_n, \alpha_k), \alpha))^{-1} = \beta_j$. In the first case, there is a word β_1 ($|\beta_1| \leqslant N$) such that $\mu((s_i, \beta_i), \beta_1) \neq \mu((s_j, \beta_j), \beta_1)$. In the second case, there must be words $\alpha_\nu \in \mathfrak{M}_{\mathrm{II}}(s_j, \beta_j)$ and α_l and a state s_μ such that $(\lambda(\delta(s_\mu, \alpha_l), \alpha_\nu))^{-1} = \beta_j$, $\delta(\delta(s_m, \alpha_l), \alpha_\nu) = s_j$ and $\lambda(s_m, \alpha_l) = \beta_k$. The minimum length of α_l is equal to the minimum length of α_k, and it may be estimated as follows.

We construct a graph $G'_{\mathrm{ic}}(A)$ whose vertex set consists of all unordered pairs of disjoint sets of states of A plus one distinguished vertex X. To define the arcs, we consider each vertex $(\mathfrak{S}_i; \mathfrak{S}_j)$ together with each pair of letters (a_m, b_n). The following cases occur:

(1) There exist sets of states $\mathfrak{S}_\mu$ and $\mathfrak{S}_\nu$ such that for any $s_\varkappa \in \mathfrak{S}_\mu$ and $s_\lambda \in \mathfrak{S}_\nu$

$$\delta(s_\varkappa, a_m) \in \mathfrak{S}_i, \ \delta(s_\lambda, a_m) \in \mathfrak{S}_j, \ \lambda(s_\varkappa, a_m) = \lambda(s_\lambda, a_m) = b_n.$$

An arc will then go from $(\mathfrak{S}_i; \mathfrak{S}_j)$ to the vertex $(\mathfrak{S}_\mu; \mathfrak{S}_\nu)$.

(2) There exists a set $\mathfrak{S}_\mu$ such that for every state $s_\varkappa \in \mathfrak{S}_\mu$ the state $\delta(s_\varkappa, a_m)$ is in $\mathfrak{S}_i$ (or $\mathfrak{S}_j$) and $\lambda(s_\varkappa, a_m) = b_n$, but for any state $s_\lambda \in \mathfrak{S}_\nu$ either $\delta(s_\lambda, a_m)$ is not in $\mathfrak{S}_j$ (or $\mathfrak{S}_i$) or $\lambda(s_\lambda, a_m) \neq b_n$. An arc will then go from $(\mathfrak{S}_i; \mathfrak{S}_j)$ to the vertex X.

It is evident from the structure of the graph $G'_{\mathrm{ic}}(A)$ that there is an arc from some vertex (s_i, s_j) to X if and only if for one of the states s_i, s_j, say s_i, and suitable words α, β, there is a state s_n such that $\delta(s_n, \alpha) = s_i$, $\lambda(s_n, \alpha) = \beta$, and for any state s_m either $\delta(s_m, \alpha) \neq s_j$ or $\lambda(s_m, \alpha) \neq \beta$. Based only on the number of vertices in $G'_{\mathrm{ic}}(A)$, the maximum length of a path from any vertex to X is bounded by

$$Q = C_n^1 \cdot 2^{n-2} + C_n^2 \cdot 2^{n-3} + \ldots + C_n^{n-1} - 2^n + 1,$$

since this is precisely the number of unordered pairs of disjoint subsets of a set containing n elements. The minimum length of the word α_l is estimated by Q, but j_0 must be estimated by $Q+N$, for the first N letters of the output are made up of words from the sets $\mathfrak{M}_{II}(s_i, \beta_i)$ and $\mathfrak{M}_{II}(s_j, \beta_j)$. This estimate is inferior to that provided by Theorem 56.

Theorem 57. Let A be a complete automaton with n states, and B a type I standard inverse of A with delay N. Then for any two nonequivalent states t_i, t_j of the principal part of B there is a word β of length at most $n-1+N$ such that $\mu(t_i, \beta) \neq \mu(t_j, \beta)$.

Proof. Let (s_i, β_i) and (s_j, β_j) be nonequivalent states. If $\mathfrak{M}_I(s_i, \beta_i) \neq \mathfrak{M}_I(s_j, \beta_j)$, the fact that these states are nonequivalent may be detected by a word of length at most N.

Let $\mathfrak{M}_I(s_i, \beta_i) = \mathfrak{M}_I(s_j, \beta_j)$ and suppose that for some words $\alpha \in \mathfrak{M}_I(s_i, \beta_i)$ the states $\delta(s_i, \alpha)$ and $\delta(s_j, \alpha)$ are nonequivalent. Then there is a word α_1 of length at most $n-1$ such that $\lambda(\delta(s_i, \alpha), \alpha_1) \neq \lambda(\delta(s_j, \alpha), \alpha_1)$. Let α_2 be an arbitrary word of length N. Then

$$\mu((s_i, \beta_i), \lambda(\delta(s_j, \alpha), \alpha_1\alpha_2)) \neq \mu((s_j, \beta_j), \lambda(\delta(s_j, \alpha), \alpha_1\alpha_2)),$$

since otherwise we would have

$$\lambda(\delta(s_i, \alpha), \alpha_1) = \lambda(\delta(s_j, \alpha), \alpha_1).$$

This completes the proof.

The attempt to carry this theorem over to type II inverses comes up against the same obstacles as in the case that only the type II standard inverse is complete.

Graphs were used to investigate consistency and inverse consistency of states in an automaton (and for other problems) in /11/.

§2. MAXIMUM N FOR WHICH AN AUTOMATON WITH n STATES MAY BE ILS-I-N

It follows from Theorem 2_I that an automaton with n states cannot be ILS-I-N if $N > n(n-1)/2$. Indeed, the number $N-1$ is the maximum length of a path in the graph $G_I(A)$. Since the vertices of this graph are pairs of distinct states, of which there are at most $n(n-1)/2$, the length of a path in $G_I(A)$ (provided there are no cycles) is at most $n(n-1)/2-1$.

We shall show that this estimate is best possible; in other words, for any $n \geqslant 2$ there is a strongly connected automaton A with n states which is ILS-I-$n(n-1)/2$. The automaton $A(\mathrm{SI}, n(n-1)/2)$ may be complete. The only restriction involved in the construction is that that the alphabets $\mathfrak{A}$ and $\mathfrak{B}$ are not wholly arbitrary: if A is complete, $|\mathfrak{B}| = n(n-1)/2 + [(n+1)/2]$ and if A is incomplete $|\mathfrak{B}| = n(n-1)/2$. In both cases, $|\mathfrak{A}| = n$.

Construction of the automaton $A\,(SI, n(n-1)/2)$.

We first construct an incomplete automaton A.

Step 1. Take all unordered pairs of numbers in the set $\{1, 2, \ldots, n\}$ and number them arbitrarily.

Let the last pair in this enumeration be (i_M, j_M). Define

$$\lambda(s_{i_M}, a_1) = \lambda(s_{i_M}, a_2) = b_1, \quad \delta(s_{i_M}, a_1) = s_{i_1}, \quad \delta(s_{i_M}, a_2) = s_{j_1},$$

where (i_1, j_1) is the first pair. The automaton under construction will have an I-indistinguishable pair of states (s_{i_1}, s_{j_1}), produced at Step 1 of Algorithm 1_{I}.

Step $m+1$ $(m = 1, \ldots, n(n-1)/2-1)$.

Suppose that Step m introduced the definition of

$$\lambda(s_{i_{m-1}}, a_\nu) = \lambda(s_{j_{m-1}}, a_\mu) = b_m, \quad \delta(s_{i_{m-1}}, a_\nu) = s_{i_m}, \quad \delta(s_{j_{m-1}}, a_\mu) = s_{j_m}$$

and that the definition of λ and δ at previous steps was such that the pairs of I-indistinguishable states of A are (s_{i_1}, s_{j_1}), $(s_{i_2}, s_{j_2}), \ldots, (s_{i_m}, s_{j_m})$, where the pairs (i_1, j_1), $(i_2, j_2), \ldots, (i_m, j_m)$ are arranged according to the above enumeration, and condition 2 of Definition 3_{I} is satisfied only by states (s_{i_k}, s_{j_k}) and $(s_{i_{k+1}}, s_{j_{k+1}})$ $(k = 1, 2, \ldots, m-1)$.

Let the $(m+1)$-th pair be (i_{m+1}, j_{m+1}). Define

$$\lambda(s_{i_m}, a_\pi) = \lambda(s_{j_m}, a_\rho) = b_{m+1}, \delta(s_{j_m}, a_\rho) = s_{j_{m+1}}, \delta(s_{i_m}, a_\pi) = s_{i_{m+1}},$$

where a_π and a_ρ are any input letters such that the pairs (s_{i_m}, a_π) and (s_{j_m}, a_ρ) were not included in the domain of definition of λ and δ at previous steps. Based on condition 2 of Definition 3_{I}, Step $m+1$ of Algorithm 1_{I} produces a pair of I-indistinguishable states $(s_{i_{m+1}}, s_{j_{m+1}})$, for which condition 2 of Definition 3_{I} holds only with respect to the last pair in the sequence $(s_{i_1}, s_{j_1}), (s_{i_2}, s_{j_2}), \ldots, (s_{i_m}, s_{j_m})$ since the output letter b_{m+1} has not yet appeared.

It follows from the construction that the automaton A is strongly connected and the graph $G_{\mathrm{I}}(A)$ has $n(n-1)/2$ vertices (s_{i_1}, s_{j_1}), $(s_{i_2}, s_{j_2}), \ldots,$ $(s_{i_{n(n-1)/2}}, s_{j_{n(n-1)/2}})$, with an arc going from each pair to its successor in the sequence and no other arcs between these vertices. There is no arc issuing from the last vertex, since according to Step 1 of the construction the automaton cannot produce the same output letter in states $s_{i_{n(n-1)/2}}$ and $s_{j_{n(n-1)/2}}$. Consequently, there are no cycles in $G_{\mathrm{I}}(A)$, and since the maximum length of a path in this graph is $n(n-1)/2-1$, it follows via Theorem 2_{I} that A is ILS-I-$n(n-1)/2$.

Since each number in the set $\{1, \ldots, n\}$ appears in $n-1$ pairs, the functions λ and δ are defined over $n-1$ distinct pairs (s_m, a_π) for every state s_m except $s_{i_{n(n-1)/2}}$ and $s_{j_{n(n-1)/2}}$. In the case of $s_{j_{n(n-1)/2}}$, we need the values of these functions for $n-2$ distinct pairs $(s_{j_{n(n-1)/2}}, a_\rho)$; for $s_{i_{n(n-1)/2}}$, use two different pairs $(s_{i_{n(n-1)/2}}, a_\nu)$ at Step 1 and $n-2$ pairs at the subsequent steps. Thus the construction goes through with n input letters.

The automaton A we have constructed is incomplete: λ and δ are undefined for exactly n pairs (s_i, a_μ), where the input alphabet has n letters.

If we now add $[(n+1)/2]$ output letters, the automaton we have constructed may be used to construct a complete ILS-I-$n(n-1)/2$ automaton.

There exist two letters a_{i_1}, a_{i_2} such that λ and δ are undefined for the pairs $(s_{j_{n(n-1)/2}}, a_{i_1})$ and $(s_{j_{n(n-1)/2}}, a_{i_2})$. Set

$$\lambda(s_{j_{n(n-1)/2}}, a_{i_1}) = \lambda(s_{j_{n(n-1)/2}}, a_{i_2}) = b_{n(n-1)/2+1},$$
$$\delta(s_{j_{n(n-1)/2}}, a_{i_1}) = s_{i_1}, \quad \delta(s_{j_{n(n-1)/2}}, a_{i_2}) = s_{j_1}.$$

This does not alter the graph $G_{\mathrm{I}}(A)$, since the output letter $b_{n(n-1)/2+1}$ has not yet appeared.

Proceeding with the completion of A, we now take all the pairs (s_i, a_j) for which λ and δ are undefined at the present step of the construction and combine them in pairs. If n is odd, one pair remains uncombined. With each pair of pairs we associate exactly one output letter from the set $\{b_{n(n-1)/2+2}, \ldots, b_{n(n-1)/2+[(n+1)/2]}\}$. When n is odd the uncombined pair (s_i, a_j) is associated with the remaining letter.

Suppose the pair $\{(s_{i_1}, a_{j_1}), (s_{i_2}, a_{j_2})\}$ is associated with the letter b_k. Let (i_3, i_4) be any pair appearing in the original enumeration of pairs later than (i_1, i_2). The states s_{i_1} and s_{i_2} are distinct from both $s_{i_{n(n-1)/2}}$ and $s_{j_{n(n-1)/2}}$, since the functions λ and δ are defined for all pairs $(s_{i_{n(n-1)/2}}, a_\pi)$ and $(s_{j_{n(n-1)/2}}, a_\rho)$. Hence there exists a pair (i_3, i_4) with the required properties. We set

$$\lambda(s_{i_1}, a_{j_1}) = \lambda(s_{i_2}, a_{j_2}) = b_k, \quad \delta(s_{i_1}, a_{j_1}) = s_{i_3}, \quad \delta(s_{i_2}, a_{j_2}) = s_{i_4}.$$

Since $s_{i_1} \neq s_{i_2}$, the only change this makes in the graph $G_{\mathrm{I}}(A)$ is to add a new arc going from (s_{i_1}, s_{i_2}) to (s_{i_3}, s_{i_4}), which does not create any cycle because the original graph contains a path from (s_{i_1}, s_{i_2}) to (s_{i_3}, s_{i_4}). The definition is completed in this way for all pairs of pairs (s_i, a_j).

If n is odd, we also put $\lambda(s_i, a_j) = b_l$, $\delta(s_i, a_j) = s_m$, where (s_i, a_j) is the uncombined pair, b_l the corresponding output letter and s_m an arbitrary state. This modification does not add any new arcs to $G_{\mathrm{I}}(A)$.

Consequently, the complete automaton A thus constructed is ILS-I-$n(n-1)/2$.

By contrast, for a normal automaton A with n states the above estimate cannot be achieved. The problem of finding the maximal N for which a normal automaton A with n states may be ILS-I-N is studied in the next sections.

§3. GENERAL AUXILIARY RESULTS

By analogy with the notation B (SI, M, L, R), we shall write $x_l(M, L, R)$ to mean that the subtree x_l is a panicle of type (K, N, M), $|\chi_l| = R$, the subgraphs attached to all L-th level vertices of x_l are complete trees, and there is at least one $(L-1)$-th level vertex of x_l whose attached subgraph is not a complete tree.

The vertices of the graphs considered below will be subtrees of type (K, N) (this will not be mentioned again); in other words, the cardinality of the alphabets $\mathfrak{A}$ and $\mathfrak{B}$ will always be denoted by K and the delay of the various inverse automata by N. In some cases we shall employ the full notation B(SI, K, N, M, L, R) and $x_l(K, N, M, L, R)$.

Subsequent estimates will be based on the following theorem.

Theorem 58. The minimum number of states in a normal automaton $B(SI, M, L, R)$ is equal to the minimum number of subtrees in an admissible strongly connected graph $\Gamma(x)$ satisfying the conditions:

(1) *All subtrees in $\Gamma(x)$ have weight R.*

(2) *The outgoing degree of each subtree is K.*

(3) *The subgraph attached to each L-th level vertex of a subtree is a complete tree.*

(4) *At least one subtree has an $(L-1)$-th level vertex whose attached subgraph is not a complete tree.*

(5) *All subtrees are panicles of one of the types (K, N, m) $(m=1,\ldots,M)$.*

(6) *At least one subtree is a panicle of type (K, N, M).*

Proof. Let B be an automaton with the minimum number of states such that $B(\mathrm{SI}, M, L, R)$. We construct a graph $\Gamma(x)$ as follows. The subtrees correspond in one-to-one fashion with the states of B. The subtree x_j corresponding to a state t_j will represent the set of words over $\mathfrak{A}$ of length N that B can produce when in state t_j. An arc will lead from x_i to another subtree x_j, corresponding to states t_i and t_j, if and only if there is a letter b_μ such that $\varepsilon(t_i, b_\mu)=t_j$ (if there are several such letters, there is one arc for each). Let A be the principal part of a standard inverse automaton of B with delay N. By Theorem 16, B is an inverse of A with delay N. By Theorem 8, B may be obtained by simplification of the principal part B_1 of a standard inverse constructed with delay N for A.

Since $B_1(\mathrm{SI}, M, L, R)$, the graph $\Gamma(B_1)$ satisfies conditions 1 through 6 (see Theorems 22 and 35). The graph $\Gamma(x)$ is strongly connected and satisfies condition 2, since B is strongly connected and complete. The remaining conditions hold for $\Gamma(x)$ because each subtree in $\Gamma(x)$ is isomorphic to some subtree in $\Gamma(Bx)$ and conversely. Vertices of subtrees of $\Gamma(B_1x)$ are identified in accordance with their identification with states of A; when this is done, all conditions for admissibility are satisfied. Since the subtrees in $\Gamma(B_1x)$ and $\Gamma(x)$ are isomorphic and the arcs in the two graphs are defined for isomorphic subtrees, we may identify vertices of subtrees in $\Gamma(x)$ and label the arcs by letters of $\mathfrak{A}$ in such a way that the resulting graph is admissible. The number of subtrees in $\Gamma(x)$ is the same as the number of states of B.

Now let $\Gamma(x)$ be an admissible graph satisfying conditions 1 through 6.* By Theorems 24 and 28, we may construct a corresponding graph $\Gamma(tx)$ which defines an automaton $B(\mathrm{SI}, M, L, R)$. The automaton B has at most as many states as the graph $\Gamma(x)$ has subtrees.

This implies the conclusion of the theorem.

We let $\Gamma(x, M, L, R)$ (or, in full, $\Gamma(x, K, N, M, L, R)$) denote a graph $\Gamma(x)$ satisfying conditions 1 through 6 of Theorem 58. We shall assume henceforth that all automata and graphs under consideration are normal.

Theorem 59. A graph $\Gamma(x, K, N, M, L, C)$ cannot contain less than K^N/C subtrees.

This follows from the fact that $\Gamma(x)$ must contain at least one set of subtrees with identified roots, defining a partition of the set of all words of length N over $\mathfrak{A}$ into disjoint subsets each containing C words.

* Henceforth a strongly connected admissible graph satisfying conditions 1 and 2 will be called normal.

A graph for which the estimate in Theorem 59 is exact may actually be constructed. Let $C=K^l$. Take K^{N-l} subtrees of type $(K, N-l)$, each defining only one word of length $N-l$ over $\mathfrak{A}$, no two subtrees defining the same word. Arcs emanate from the subtree defining a word $a_m\alpha$ to the subtrees defining the words $\alpha a_1, \alpha a_2, \dots, \alpha a_K$. Labeling the arcs emanating from the subtree defining $a_m\alpha$ by the letter a_m, we obtain an admissible graph. The subgraphs attached to the leaves of the subtrees of this graph are complete trees of type (K, l). In this case, $M=l$, $L=N-l$.

Define the numbers K and C as in Theorem 41. Then all subtrees in the graph are critical. As before, we first consider a graph whose vertices are subtrees such that the subgraphs attached to their $(N-1)$-th level vertices are not complete trees, i. e., $l_1=0$. Set

$$\rho_{k\lambda}=\operatorname{sgn}(k \dot{-} (N-l_\lambda-1)),\ \sigma_{k\lambda}=1-\operatorname{sgn}|k+l_\lambda+1-N|,$$

$$m_k=p_{i_1}^{\rho_{k1}j_1} p_{i_2}^{\rho_{k2}j_2} \cdot \ldots \cdot p_{i_\varkappa}^{\rho_{k\varkappa}j_\varkappa} p_{i_1}^{\sigma_{k1}k_1} p_{i_2}^{\sigma_{k2}k_2} \cdot \ldots \cdot p_{i_\varkappa}^{\sigma_{k\varkappa}k_\varkappa}$$

$$(k=0, 1, \dots, N-1, \lambda=1, \dots, \varkappa).$$

For each λ, we have $\rho_{0\lambda} \leqslant \rho_{1\lambda} \leqslant \dots \leqslant \rho_{N-1,\lambda}$. Therefore $m_0 \leqslant m_1 \leqslant \dots \leqslant m_{N-1}$. K is divisible by $m_\varkappa$, $\varkappa=0, 1, \dots, N-1$, and so we can divide $\mathfrak{A}$ into $K/m_\varkappa$ subsets with equal cardinalities. Form such partitions for all values $\varkappa$, in such a way that the result is an imbedded sequence of partitions. Now consider all nonisomorphic critical input subtrees satisfying the following condition: the arcs emanating from vertices on one level are assigned letters from only one class of a partition, in such a way that the arcs emanating from j-th level vertices $(j=0, 1, \dots, N-1)$ are assigned letters from the classes of the partition corresponding to $\varkappa=j$. For the moment, let us call these special subtrees. It is obvious that any word of length N over $\mathfrak{A}$ is defined by some special subtree, and so there are exactly K^N/C special subtrees.

Let x_i be an arbitrary special subtree. Deleting the arcs emanating from the root χ_i, we obtain m_0 distinct subtrees $x_{i_1}, \dots, x_{i_{m_0}}$ defining the same sets of words of length $N-1$. Attach complete trees of type $(K, 1)$ to the leaves of one of these subtrees, say x_{i_1}, and denote the resulting subtree by x_j. Since the partitions of $\mathfrak{A}$ that we are using form an imbedded sequence, there exist K/m_0 special subtrees $x_{j_1}, \dots, x_{j_L}$ $(L=K/m_0)$ such that $\mathfrak{M}(x_j)=\mathfrak{M}(x_{j_1}) \cup \dots \cup \mathfrak{M}(x_{j_L})$. Let m_0 arcs go from the subtree x_i to each of the subtrees $x_{j_1}, \dots, x_{j_L}$. It follows from the relations obtaining among the sets of words defined by $x_j, x_{j_1}, \dots, x_{j_L}$ that we can identify vertices of $x_j, x_{j_1}, \dots, x_{j_L}$ and label their arcs by letters of $\mathfrak{A}$ in such a way that the result is an admissible graph. If $l_1 \neq 0$, we first construct an admissible graph such that the roots of the subtrees have weight $C_1=C/K^n$, where n is the greatest number such that C is divisible by K^n, and all subtrees of the graph are of type $(K, N-n)$. We then attach complete trees of type (K, n) to the leaves of the subtrees.

Definition 33. An incomplete cleavage of rank n of a subtree is a tree that can be obtained from a cleavage of rank n by discarding certain subtrees and the arcs incident with them (both ingoing and outgoing), subject to the condition that for each of the remaining subtrees either all outgoing arcs or none are discarded. An incomplete cleavage is normal if it is obtained in this way from a normal cleavage.

Definition 34. A subtree $x_\varkappa(K, N, M, L, R)$ is lifted in a graph $\Gamma(x, K, N, M_1, L_1, R)$ $(M_1 \geqslant M, L_1 \geqslant L)$ if a normal incomplete cleavage of rank n is constructed for $x_\varkappa$, subject to the following conditions:

(1) The first level of the cleavage contains a subtree $x_l(K, N, M_2, L_2, R)$ with $L_2 \geqslant L$.

(2) If x_m is a subtree of the cleavage which is not isomorphic to any subtree in $\Gamma(x)$, then for any vertex $\chi_{mn\alpha}$ whose attached subgraph is a complete tree, the first level of the cleavage after x_m contains a subtree with a vertex identified with $\chi_{mn\alpha}$ whose attached subgraph is also a complete tree.

(3) If x_m is a subtree of the cleavage which is isomorphic to some subtree x_μ in $\Gamma(x)$, it is necessarily a leaf of the cleavage, and the paths from the root of the incomplete cleavage to x_m and from the root of the tree $T(x_\varkappa, \Gamma(x), n)$ [see p. 61] to x_μ define the same word.

A subtree may be lifted in a graph in a certain standard manner, based on the concept of imbedded sequences of partitions (see Definition 25). Denote the classes of a partition $\mathfrak{A}_i$ by π_{ij}.

An imbedded sequence of partitions of the set of leaf subtrees* of a graph $T(x_k, \Gamma(x), h)$ is said to be normal if one of the following two conditions holds for each class: (1) If a class of the partition $\mathfrak{A}_j$ is a union of classes of $\mathfrak{A}_{j+1}$, it is the union of exactly K classes. (2) If a class π_{ij} of $\mathfrak{A}_i$ is not a union of classes of $\mathfrak{A}_{i+1}$, it is also a class of each partition $\mathfrak{A}_{i+1}, \mathfrak{A}_{i+2}, \ldots, \mathfrak{A}_h$.

An imbedded sequence of partitions is said to be admissible if it is normal and, for every class π_{ij} which is not a class of $\mathfrak{A}_{i-1}$, all words defined by paths in $T(x_k, \Gamma(x), h)$ from the root to subtrees of π_{ij} have identical prefixes of length i.

Definition 35. Let π_{ij} be a class in a partition of the leaf subtrees of the tree $T(x_k, \Gamma(x), h)$. The subtree of the class π_{ij} is constructed as follows. Consider the subtree of $T(x_k, \Gamma(x), h)$ containing just the subtrees of T which are either members of π_{ij} or initial "points" of paths to members of π_{ij} (call these the component subtrees). Now replace each component subtree by a vertex (i. e., disregard the "inner structure" of each vertex of the new subtree as a subtree). To each leaf of the new subtree, attach the component subtree from which it originated prior to the above abstraction. Then the subtree of π_{ij} is defined to be an input subtree of type $(K, N+h)$ representing the same set of words as the new subtree.

The subtree of a class π_{ij} will be denoted by $\pi_{ij}(x_k, \Gamma(x), h)$ or, if it is clear from the context which tree $T(x_k, \Gamma(x), h)$ is meant, by the same symbol π_{ij} as the class itself.

Given two subtrees $\pi_{ij}(x_k, \Gamma(x), h)$ and $\pi_{\nu\lambda}(x_k, \Gamma(x), h)$, identify their roots and all vertices terminating paths from the root which define identical words.

Let $\mathfrak{A}_0, \mathfrak{A}_1, \ldots, \mathfrak{A}_h$ be an admissible imbedded sequence of partitions of the leaf subtrees of a tree $T(x_k, \Gamma(x), h)$. Construct the subtree π_{ij} of each class π_{ij} which is not a class of the partition $\mathfrak{A}_{i-1}$, and define arcs between

* [I.e., the subtrees with no outgoing arcs; we shall use this combination whenever it is necessary to avoid confusion with the leaves of the subtrees themselves. — Trans.]

these subtrees as follows. Let π_{ij} and $\pi_{i+1,l}$ be any two subtrees. An arc will go from π_{ij} to $\pi_{i+1,l}$ if and only if $\pi_{i+1,l}$ is a proper subset of π_{ij}. Attach complete trees of type $(K, j-1)$ to the leaves of each subtree π_{jk} $(j=2, \ldots, h)$ Delete all arcs in π_{01} emanating from $(N+h-1)$-th level vertices. Delete all arcs in π_{jk} $(j=1, \ldots, h)$ emanating from vertices of levels $0, 1, \ldots, j-1$. Since the construction was based on an admissible sequence of partitions, all the vertices participating in these operations have outgoing degree 1 and so each subtree π_{ij} yields only one new subtree.

Denote the resulting tree by $W(\mathfrak{A}_0, \mathfrak{A}_1, \ldots, \mathfrak{A}_h)$. It is clear that all its subtrees are of type $(K, N+h-1)$. Let x_l denote the subtree obtained by attaching complete trees of type $(K, h-1)$ to the leaves of the subtree x_k; then $W(\mathfrak{A}_0, \mathfrak{A}_1, \ldots, \mathfrak{A}_h)$ is an incomplete cleavage of x_l.

We summarize the discussion up to now in a theorem.

Theorem 60. For any normal admissible imbedded sequence of partitions $\mathfrak{A}_0, \mathfrak{A}_1, \ldots, \mathfrak{A}_h$ of the leaf subtrees of $T(x_k, \Gamma(x), h)$, the graph $W(\mathfrak{A}_0, \mathfrak{A}_1, \ldots, \mathfrak{A}_h)$ is an incomplete cleavage of rank h for the subtree obtained by attaching complete trees of type $(K, h-1)$ to the leaves of x_k.

The following theorem embodies a special method for lifting subtrees in a graph.

*Theorem 61. For any lifting of any subtree x_k in a graph $\Gamma(x)$, there exists a normal admissible imbedded sequence of partitions $\mathfrak{A}_0, \mathfrak{A}_1, \ldots \mathfrak{A}_n$ of the leaf subtrees of $T(x_k, \Gamma(x), n)$ such that the graph $W(\mathfrak{A}_0, \mathfrak{A}_1, \ldots, \mathfrak{A}_n)$ is isomorphic to the incomplete cleavage defining the lifting.**

Proof. Denote the cleavage defining the given lifting by $\Gamma_1(x)$. Attach trees to the leaf subtrees of $\Gamma_1(x)$ which are not on the last level, according to the following rule. Let x_l be a leaf on the i-th level of $\Gamma_1(x)$ $(i<n)$, isomorphic to a subtree x_λ of the tree $T(x_k, \Gamma(x), n)$, and suppose that the paths from the respective roots of the two trees to x_l and x_λ define the same word. Then the tree attached to x_l is $T(x_\lambda, \Gamma(x), n-i)$.

Denote the tree obtained from $\Gamma_1(x)$ by all possible operations of the above type by $\Gamma_2(x)$. Since the subtrees x_λ corresponding to x_l is uniquely determined, the trees $T(x_k, \Gamma(x), n)$ and $\Gamma_2(x)$ satisfy the following condition: each leaf subtree of the one tree is isomorphic to exactly one leaf subtree of the other, and the paths to these subtrees from the respective roots of the trees define the same word. We shall refer to them as corresponding subtrees. We now form a sequence of partitions $\mathfrak{A}'_0, \mathfrak{A}'_1, \ldots, \mathfrak{A}'_n$ as follows. For each subtree x_λ on the i-th level of $\Gamma_2(x)$ which is also in $\Gamma_1(x)$, form a class of the partition $\mathfrak{A}'_i$ containing just the leaf subtrees which are ends of paths from x_λ. If x_λ is a leaf in $\Gamma_1(x)$, the class we have formed is also a class in each of the partitions $\mathfrak{A}'_{i+1}, \mathfrak{A}'_{i+2}, \ldots, \mathfrak{A}'_n$. We now define an imbedded sequence $\mathfrak{A}_0, \mathfrak{A}_1, \ldots, \mathfrak{A}_n$ of partitions of the leaf subtrees of $T(x_k, \Gamma(x), n)$: each class of $\mathfrak{A}_i$ will contain all subtrees whose corresponding subtrees in $\Gamma_2(x)$ are members of one class in the partition $\mathfrak{A}'_i$ $(i=0, 1, \ldots, n)$. It is clear that both sequences $\mathfrak{A}'_0, \mathfrak{A}'_1, \ldots, \mathfrak{A}'_n$ and $\mathfrak{A}_0, \mathfrak{A}_1, \ldots, \mathfrak{A}_n$ are imbedded and normal. That the sequence $\mathfrak{A}'_0, \mathfrak{A}'_1, \ldots, \mathfrak{A}'_n$ is admissible follows from its construction. Since paths from the roots to corresponding leaf subtrees in $\Gamma_2(x)$ and $T(x_k, \Gamma(x), n)$ define the same word,

* Two graphs $\Gamma'(x)$ and $\Gamma''(x)$ whose vertices are input subtrees are said to be isomorphic if there is a one-to-one correspondence between their subtrees such that corresponding subtrees are isomorphic and there is an arc in $\Gamma'(x)$ from x'_i and x'_j if and only if there is an arc in $\Gamma''(x)$ from x''_i to x''_j, where x''_i corresponds to x'_i and x''_j to x'_j, and these arcs are labeled by the same letter.

the sequence $\mathfrak{A}_0, \mathfrak{A}_1, \ldots, \mathfrak{A}_n$ is also admissible. We may therefore construct the graph $W(\mathfrak{A}_0, \mathfrak{A}_1, \ldots, \mathfrak{A}_n)$. By construction, the graph $W(\mathfrak{A}'_0, \mathfrak{A}'_1, \ldots, \mathfrak{A}'_n)$ is isomorphic to $\Gamma_1(x)$. By the definition of the correspondence between leaves of $\Gamma_2(x)$ and $T(x_k, \Gamma(x), n)$, the graphs $W(\mathfrak{A}'_0, \mathfrak{A}'_1, \ldots, \mathfrak{A}'_n)$ and $W(\mathfrak{A}_0, \mathfrak{A}_1, \ldots \mathfrak{A}_n)$ are isomorphic. Thus $W(\mathfrak{A}_0, \mathfrak{A}_1, \ldots, \mathfrak{A}_n)$ and $\Gamma_1(x)$ are also isomorphic. Q. E. D.

For the sequel, we shall need another operation, insertion of a tree in a graph, which resembles attaching of a subtree to a vertex of another subtree.

Definition 36. Let $\Gamma_1(x)$ be a tree with root x_k and leaves $x_{k_1}, \ldots, x_{k_n}$, $\Gamma(x)$ a graph containing subtrees $x_\varkappa, x_{\varkappa_1}, \ldots, x_{\varkappa n}$ isomorphic to x_k, $x_{k_1}, \ldots, x_{kn}$, respectively, such that there is a path from $x_\varkappa$ to $x_{\varkappa_j}$ defining the same word as the path from x_k to x_{k_j} $(j=1, \ldots, n)$. We shall say that the graph $\Gamma_1(x)$ has been inserted in $\Gamma(x)$ if the latter is converted into a new graph $\Gamma_2(x)$ as follows:

Step 1. Discard from $\Gamma(x)$ all arcs issuing from $x_\varkappa$. Take subtrees isomorphic to the non-leaf subtrees on the first level of $\Gamma_1(x)$ (we shall say that the latter correspond to the former). Let arcs go from $x_\varkappa$ to the new subtrees, with the same labels as the arcs going from x_k to the corresponding subtrees in $\Gamma_1(x)$. If the first level of $\Gamma_1(x)$ contains leaf subtrees, restore the arcs (labeled as before) going from x_k to the isomorphic counterparts in $\Gamma(x)$ of these leaf subtrees.

Step $j+1$ $(j=0, 1, \ldots, m)$. Suppose that the new subtrees obtained at Step j are $x_{l_1}, \ldots, x_{l_r}$, corresponding to subtrees $x_{\lambda_1}, \ldots, x_{\lambda_r}$ on the j-th level of $\Gamma_1(x)$. For each non-leaf subtree x_ρ on the $(j+1)$-th level of $\Gamma_1(x)$, take an isomorphic subtree x_ν, corresponding to x_ρ; if the subtree corresponding to x_{l_i} is x_{λ_k} and there is an arc from the latter in $\Gamma_1(x)$ to x_ρ, introduce an arc from x_{l_i} to x_ν. If x_ρ is a leaf subtree on the $(j+1)$-th level, no new subtree is introduced, but an arc is added, labeled as in $\Gamma_1(x)$, going to the subtree of $\Gamma(x)$ isomorphic to x_ρ.

Definition 37. We shall say that an input graph $\Gamma_2(x, K, N_2, M_2, L_2, R_2)$ is obtained from an input graph $\Gamma_1(x, K, N_1, M_1, L_1, R_1)$ by lifting if Γ_2 is obtained from Γ_1 as follows:

(1) Attach complete trees of type $(K, N_2 \dot{-} N_1)$ to all leaves of subtrees in Γ_1. Denote the resulting graph by $\Gamma_3(x, K, N_2, M_3, L_3, R_3)$.

(2) Select some set $x_{i_1}, \ldots, x_{i_n}$ of subtrees which are lifted in Γ_3.

(3) Insert in Γ_3 the trees that define the lifting of the above subtrees; denote the resulting graph by Γ_4.

(4) Eliminate all subtrees in Γ_4 not appearing in any cycle; denote the resulting graph by Γ_5.

(5) Discard the arcs of the last $N_1 \dot{-} N_2$ levels in the subtrees of Γ_5, to form the graph $\Gamma_6 = \Gamma_2$.

Another useful operation is shifting of arcs.

Definition 38. A graph $\Gamma'(x)$ is said to be obtained from $\Gamma(x)$ by shifting arcs if it is the result of the following operations:

(1) Discard certain arcs in $\Gamma(x)$ and replace each of them by a new arc, similarly labeled, emanating from the same subtree to a subtree isomorphic to the endpoint of the original arc.

(2) Eliminate all subtrees not appearing in any cycle.

It is clear that $\Gamma'(x)$ is admissible whenever $\Gamma(x)$ is admissible.

Theorem 62. For any normal graph $\Gamma(x)$ there is a sequence of normal graphs $\Gamma_i(x)$ $(i= 0, 1,\dots,P)$ satisfying the following conditions:

(1) Γ_0 contains only critical subtrees.

(2) $\Gamma_P=\Gamma$.

(3) Γ_{i+1} is obtained from Γ_i by either shifting arcs or lifting; in the latter case, all lifting operations are based on an admissible imbedded sequence of partitions of the leaf subtrees of suitable trees $T(x_{i_k}, \Gamma_i(x), n_i)$.

Proof. Let $\Gamma(x)$ contain L subtrees, with roots of weight C. It follows from Theorems 41, 42, 30 and 40 that for any subtree x_i in $\Gamma(x)$ and any critical subtree of type (K, N) with root of weight C there is a normal cleavage V_i satisfying the following conditions: (a) the cleavage contains a subtree x_j isomorphic to x_i; (b) the arcs emanating from x_j end at subtrees $x_{j_1},\dots,x_{j_r}$ isomorphic to the subtrees which terminate the arcs emanating from x_i in $\Gamma(x)$; (c) the last level of the cleavage contains only critical subtrees. To fix ideas, we stipulate that all the critical subtrees are constructed as in the proof of Theorem 58. Based on these cleavages, we form a strongly connected normal graph $\Gamma_{P-1}(x)$, letting arcs issue from the leaf subtrees of each cleavage* to the roots of the other cleavages. If it is permissible to use, in addition to the above-mentioned cleavages, a sufficient number of cleavages containing only suitably chosen critical subtrees, the graph $\Gamma_{P-1}(x)$ may always be constructed. The root subtrees of these basic cleavages, as we shall call them, will be denoted by x_{P-1,l_j} $(j=1,\dots, L_1\geqslant L)$. We shall assume that the cleavage with root x_{P-1,l_j} contains a subtree x_{P-1,n_j} $(j= 1,\dots, L)$ isomorphic to the subtree x_j of $\Gamma(x)$ and satisfying condition (b). The graph $\Gamma(x)$ may be derived from $\Gamma_{P-1}(x)$ by shifting arcs and renaming subtrees. Indeed, for each arc of $\Gamma(x)$, we shift arcs in $\Gamma_{P-1}(x)$ as follows. Suppose that the arc leads from x_ν to x_μ. Delete an arc in $\Gamma_{P-1}(x)$ going from x_{P-1,n_ν} to a subtree isomorphic to x_μ, and introduce a new arc from x_{P-1,n_ν} to x_{P-1,n_μ}. Discarding all subtrees of the resulting graph not occurring in cycles, we obtain a graph containing a subgraph isomorphic to $\Gamma(x)$. In order to obtain $\Gamma(x)$, it suffices to rename the subtrees in this subgraph.

To construct the graph $\Gamma_0(x)$, we take subtrees x_{0,l_j} $(j=1,\dots, L_1)$ isomorphic to x_{P-1,l_j} and form cleavages for them. These cleavages must contain only critical subtrees and have the same number of leaf subtrees as the cleavages of the corresponding critical subtrees in the construction of $\Gamma_{P-1}(x)$, and moreover the leaf subtrees of cleavages of corresponding subtrees must be isomorphic. Each subtree x_{0,l_j} corresponds to x_{P-1,l_j}, and the leaf subtrees of the cleavages correspond to certain subtrees, selected subject to the condition that they are isomorphic and the paths from the roots to corresponding subtrees define the same word. Now form a strongly connected graph $\Gamma_0(x)$, letting arcs connect the roots and leaf subtrees of the cleavages according to the following rule: there is an arc from $x_{0,i}$ to $x_{0,j}$ if and only if the graph $\Gamma_{P-1}(x)$ contains similarly labeled arcs from the subtree corresponding to $x_{0,i}$ to that corresponding to $x_{0,j}$.

Let L_j be the rank of the basic cleavage for x_{0,l_j}.

Consider the trees $T(x_{0,l_j}, \Gamma_0(x), L_j)$ and $T(x_{P-1,l_j}, \Gamma_{P-1}(x), L_j)$, which are precisely the basic cleavages of x_{0,l_j} and x_{P-1,l_j}. Using the correspondences established for the leaf subtrees of these cleavages, we can construct a

* A cleavage is a tree.

normal admissible imbedded sequence of partitions $\mathfrak{A}_0, \mathfrak{A}_1, \ldots, \mathfrak{A}_{L_j}$ of the leaf subtrees of $T(x_{0,l_j}, \Gamma_0(x), L_j)$, such that the graph $W(\mathfrak{A}_0, \mathfrak{A}_1, \ldots, \mathfrak{A}_{L_j})$ is isomorphic to the tree $T(x_{P-1,l_j}, \Gamma_{P-1}(x), L_j)$ or to a tree obtained from $T(x_{P-1,l_j}, \Gamma_{P-1}(x), L_j)$ by attaching trees of type (K, n) (where n is a suitable number) to the leaves of its subtrees. It is obvious that the graph $W(\mathfrak{A}_0, \mathfrak{A}_1, \ldots, \mathfrak{A}_{L_j})$ may be inserted in $\Gamma_0(x)$. *

One thus proceeds to form graphs W and insert them in the subtree $\Gamma_0(x)$ for all $j=1,\ldots,L$. The result is a graph isomorphic to $\Gamma_{P-1}(x)$. However, the sequences of partitions of leaf subtrees used in the construction may not define lifting operations — they may fail to satisfy condition 2 of Definition 34. In that case, the sequences must be constructed step by step. One first constructs a sequence $\mathfrak{A}', \mathfrak{A}_1, \ldots, \mathfrak{A}'_{L_j}$ such that the desired condition holds for the graph $W(\mathfrak{A}'_0, \mathfrak{A}'_1, \ldots, \mathfrak{A}'_{L_j})$ and the first level of the latter contains subtrees isomorphic respectively to the first level subtrees of the tree $T(x_{P-1,l_j}, \Gamma_{P-1}(x), L_j)$. That condition 2 can indeed be fulfilled follows from the fact that for each subtree one can construct a normal cleavage along the lines of the proof of Theorem 40. The graph $\Gamma_1(x)$ is formed by lifting the graph $\Gamma_0(x)$, inserting the trees $W(\mathfrak{A}'_0, \mathfrak{A}'_1, \ldots, \mathfrak{A}'_{L_j})$ in the latter. The graph $\Gamma_1(x)$ is in turn subjected to a lifting operation, to obtain a graph $\Gamma_2(x)$; in so doing, one uses a sequence of partitions $\mathfrak{A}''_0, \mathfrak{A}''_1, \ldots, \mathfrak{A}''_{L_j}$ chosen in such a way that the graph $W(\mathfrak{A}''_0, \mathfrak{A}''_1, \ldots, \mathfrak{A}''_{L_j})$ contains new subtrees, not in $W(\mathfrak{A}'_0, \mathfrak{A}'_1, \ldots, \mathfrak{A}'_{L_j})$, which are isomorphic to subtrees of the graph $T(x_{P-1,l_j}, \Gamma_{P-1}(x), L_j)$, while retaining the subtrees of $W(\mathfrak{A}'_0, \mathfrak{A}'_1, \ldots, \mathfrak{A}'_{L_j})$. This is possible, because the sequence $\mathfrak{A}'_0, \mathfrak{A}'_1, \ldots, \mathfrak{A}'_{L_j}$ is embedded and lifting of a subtree other than the root of the tree $T(x_{1,l_j}, \Gamma_1(x), L_j)$, say $x_{1,m}$, involves only subdivision of one class of one of the previous partitions. This means that the lifting operation may be carried out by constructing an imbedded sequence of partitions of the leaf subtrees in the tree $T(x_{1,m}, \Gamma_1(x), L'_j)$ $(L'_j<L_j)$. The existence of a suitable lifting for the subtree $x_{1\,m}$ follows from the fact that its isomorphic counterpart in $\Gamma_{P-1}(x)$ has a cleavage.

Repeating the process finitely many times, say $P-1$ times, we finally obtain the graph $\Gamma_{P-1}(x)$.

This completes the proof.

The import of this theorem is that, if one desires to estimate the minimum number of subtrees of a graph $\Gamma(x, K, N, M, L, R)$ for fixed K, N, M, L and R, one may start with a normal graph $\Gamma_1(x)$ containing only critical subtrees, successively forming new graphs by applying lifting and arc-shifting operations; all conclusions may then be based on the numbers of subtrees of the various intermediate graphs.

We shall see later (§6) that subtrees may be lifted by a special technique which splits the operation up into several very simple lifting operations.

§4. SOME SPECIAL GRAPHS AND THEIR PROPERTIES

Let $E(K, n)$ denote the graph defined as follows. The vertices of $E(K, n)$ are all words of length $\mathfrak{A}$ over n. An arc goes from α_1 to α_2 if and only if α_1 and α_2 have the form $\alpha_1=a_{i_1}\alpha_3$, $\alpha_2=\alpha_3 a_{i_2}$; this arc is labeled $a_{i_1}\alpha_3 a_{i_2}$.

The graph $E(2,3)$ is illustrated in Figure 22.

* In the process, one must reduce all subtrees participating in the construction to one type (K, N_1); this may always be achieved by attaching suitable trees to the leaves of subtrees or deleting arcs on the lower levels.

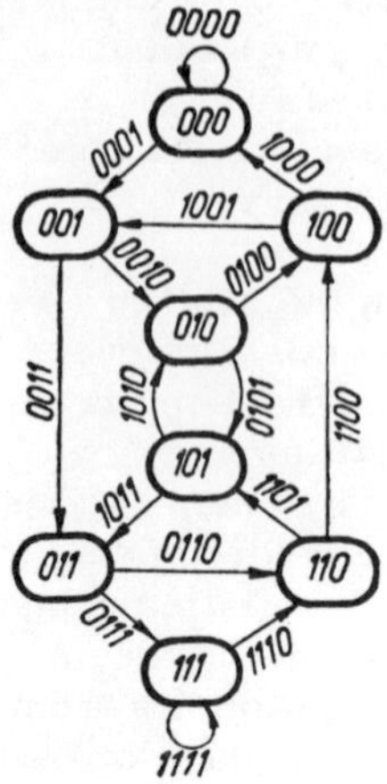

FIGURE 22.

The graph $E(K, n)$ is strongly connected, and the outgoing and ingoing degrees of each of its vertices are equal to K. Therefore, by /13/ (Theorem 2, Chap. 17), $E(K, n)$ has an Eulerian cycle.*

Theorem 63. For any integer l, $1 \leqslant l \leqslant K$, the graph $E(K,n)$ $(n=1,2,\ldots)$ has a cycle passing through each vertex exactly l times, no two occurrences of any vertex being consecutive.

Proof. If $K=l$, the conditions hold for any Eulerian cycle of the graph. If $l=1$, the assertion is obvious. We therefore confine attention to the case $1<l<K$.

Form a multigraph $E_l(K,n-1)$ from the graph $E(K,n-1)$, repeating each arc and its label l times.

Suppose that there is an Eulerian cycle in $E_l(K,n-1)$, satisfying the condition: for any distinct ordered pairs of arcs such that the second arc of each pair follows** the first in the cycle, the corresponding ordered pairs of labels are distinct.

We define a cycle in $E(K,n)$ as follows. A vertex follows another in the cycle if and only if the words corresponding to the vertices label consecutive arcs in the above cycle in $E_l(K,n-1)$. In order to show that this indeed defines a cycle in $E(K,n)$, it will suffice to show that there is an arc between any two vertices which should be consecutive according to this definition. Let v_1 and v_2 be arcs in $E_l(K,n-1)$, the first entering some vertex and the second issuing from it. The words labeling these arcs must have the forms $a_{i_1}\alpha_1$ and $\alpha_1 a_{i_2}$, where $|\alpha_1|=n-1$. In $E(K,n)$, there is an arc between the vertices $a_{i_1}\alpha_1$ and $\alpha_1 a_{i_2}$. It follows from the properties of the cycle in $E_l(K,n-1)$ that the cycle we have constructed in $E(K,n)$ satisfies the conditions of our theorem.

It remains to show that $E_l(K, n-1)$ indeed has a cycle with the above properties.

Let us designate the arcs of $E_l(K,n-1)$ by the letter α with two subscripts: α_{ij}, where $i=0, 1,\ldots, K^n-1$ indexes the different words of length n over $\mathfrak{A}$, and $j=1,\ldots,l$ indexes identically labeled arcs. Divide the set of all arcs into groups, each containing l identically labeled arcs; denote the groups of arcs labeled α by $F(\alpha)$. It is clear that the graph $E_l(K, n-1)$ possesses an Eulerian cycle. Take any Eulerian cycle and assign to each group $F(\alpha_i)$ $(i=0, 1,\ldots, K^n-1)$ a weight $g(\alpha_i)=\Sigma f(\alpha_i, \alpha_j)$, where the sum extends over all words α_j labeling arcs which issue from the endpoint of an arc labeled α_i; $f(\alpha_i, \alpha_j)=0$ if arcs labeled α_i are followed at most once by an arc labeled α_j in the Eulerian cycle, and $f(\alpha_i, \alpha_j)=r$ if such a pair of arcs occurs exactly $r>1$ times. If the cycle has the required properties, then $g(\alpha_i)=0$ for all $i=0, 1,\ldots, K^n-1$. Suppose that not all $g(\alpha_i)$ vanish. Take any vertex which is the endpoint of a group of arcs $F(\alpha_\nu)$ such that $g(\alpha_\nu)\neq 0$. Let $F(\alpha_i)$ be one such group, such that for any other group $F(\alpha_\mu)$ with $g(\alpha_\mu)\neq 0$ the number of groups containing arcs following arcs of $F(\alpha_\mu)$ in the cycle is at

* An Eulerian cycle is a cycle in which each arc of the graph occurs exactly once.

** [Throughout the sequel, "follows," consecutive," etc. are used in the sense of immediate succession. — Trans.]

least the number of groups with the analogous property for $F(\alpha_i)$. There exists a group $F(\alpha_j)$ such that $f(\alpha_i, \alpha_j) \neq 0$. Working with the cardinalities of the groups $F(\alpha_\nu)$, one readily shows that there is a group $F(\alpha_r)$ such that the arcs in $F(\alpha_i)$ and $F(\alpha_r)$ end at the same vertex, and no arc labeled α_r is followed in the cycle by an arc labeled α_j.

Our cycle may be written in one of two forms:

$$\ldots \alpha_{i\nu}\alpha_{j\mu} \ldots \alpha_{i\sigma}\alpha_{j\tau} \ldots \alpha_{r\rho}\alpha_{p\varkappa} \ldots \alpha_{r\pi}\alpha_{q\lambda} \ldots \quad \text{(I)}$$

or

$$\alpha_{i\nu}\alpha_{j\mu} \ldots \alpha_{r\rho}\alpha_{p\varkappa} \ldots \alpha_{i\sigma}\alpha_{j\tau} \ldots \alpha_{r\pi}\alpha_{q\lambda} \ldots \quad \text{(II)}$$

The dots stand for sections of the cycle which remain unchanged throughout the subsequent transformations. The initial section of each written row should be viewed as the continuation of its final section.

If $g(\alpha_r) = 0$, the words α_p and α_q are so chosen that no arcs of $F(\alpha_i)$ are not followed by arcs of $F(\alpha_p)$ and $F(\alpha_q)$. This is possible, since the arcs of $F(\alpha_i)$ are followed in the cycle by arcs of at most $l-2$ groups other than $F(\alpha_j)$, while those of $F(\alpha_r)$ are followed by arcs of l groups (other than $F(\alpha_j)$).

Let $g(\alpha_r) \neq 0$. Then, by the choice of the group $F(\alpha_i)$, at least one of the arcs $\alpha_{p\varkappa}$ or $\alpha_{q\lambda}$ may be so chosen that arcs of $F(\alpha_i)$ are not followed by arcs of at least one of the groups $F(\alpha_p)$ or $F(\alpha_q)$.

Suppose this holds for arcs of the group $F(\alpha_p)$. We form new cycles from (I) and (II), obtaining respectively

$$\ldots \alpha_{i\nu}\alpha_{j\tau} \ldots \alpha_{r\rho}\alpha_{j\mu} \ldots \alpha_{i\sigma}\alpha_{p\varkappa} \ldots \alpha_{r\pi}\alpha_{q\lambda} \ldots \quad \text{(I')}$$

and

$$\ldots \alpha_{i\nu}\alpha_{p\varkappa} \ldots \alpha_{i\sigma}\alpha_{j\mu} \ldots \alpha_{r\rho}\alpha_{j\tau} \ldots \alpha_{r\pi}\alpha_{q\lambda} \ldots \quad \text{(II')}$$

Recall that according to our notational conventions the sequences of arcs represented by dots between two explicitly specified arcs in (I) and (II) remain unchanged in (I') and (II'), provided that the two explicitly given arcs are the same.

If the arcs of $F(\alpha_i)$ are not followed by arcs of $F(\alpha_q)$, we form cycles

$$\ldots \alpha_{i\sigma}\alpha_{q\lambda} \ldots \alpha_{i\nu}\alpha_{j\tau} \ldots \alpha_{r\rho}\alpha_{p\varkappa} \ldots \alpha_{r\pi}\alpha_{j\mu} \ldots \quad \text{(I'')}$$

and

$$\ldots \alpha_{i\nu}\alpha_{j\tau} \qquad \alpha_{r\pi}\alpha_{j\mu} \ldots \alpha_{r\rho}\alpha_{p\varkappa} \ldots \alpha_{i\sigma}\alpha_{q\lambda} \ldots \quad \text{(II'')}$$

If $g(\alpha_r) = 0$, the new cycle may be constructed by either of the above rules.

Now, in the explicitly specified pairs of arcs in (I) and (II), the first arc always ends at the same vertex and the second always issues from the same vertex; hence formula (I') or (II') defines a cycle in which each arc of the graph $E_l(K, n-1)$ occurs once. The values of the functions $g(\alpha_i)$ and $g(\alpha_r)$ may change only when one of these explicitly specified pairs is changed. Since no arc of $F(\alpha_r)$ in cycle (I) or (II) is followed by an arc of $F(\alpha_j)$, the value of the function $g(\alpha_r)$ for cycle (I') or (II') cannot exceed its value for the original cycle. In the first case, an arc of $F(\alpha_i)$ is not followed in cycle (I) or (II) by an arc of $F(\alpha_p)$, and therefore when we go over to cycle (I') or (II') the value of $g(\alpha_i)$ decreases, since the term $f(\alpha_i, \alpha_j)$ becomes smaller. We have thus obtained a cycle such that the value of $g(\alpha_i)$ for one group $F(\alpha_i)$ decreases, while for the other groups it does not increase in comparison with the original cycle.

Similarly, one proves that if $g(\alpha_r)=0$, or $g(\alpha_r)\neq 0$ and the second case obtains then at least one value $g(\alpha_i)$ decreases and the others do not increase when we go over to one of the new cycles.

If the new cycle has $g(\alpha_i)=0$ for all $i=0, 1, \ldots, K^n-1$ with the required properties, and the proof is complete.

If not all $g(\alpha_i)$ vanish, we form a new cycle in accordance with the above rules.

Finitely many repetitions of the above constructions will yield an Eulerian cycle of $E_l(K, n-1)$ such that $g(\alpha_i)=0$ $(i=0, 1, \ldots, K^n-1)$. This completes the proof.

Theorem 64. *For any integer l, $1 \leqslant l \leqslant K$, the graph $E(K, n)$ $(n=1, 2, \ldots)$ contains a cycle passing through each vertex exactly l times, such that, for any word α $(|\alpha|=n-1)$, any two arcs in the cycle labeled $a_{i_1}\alpha$ and $a_{i_2}\alpha$ are followed by differently labeled arcs.*

Proof. Construct a cycle satisfying the assertion of Theorem 63, and consider any two arcs entering the same vertex, α say. The two arcs following them end at different vertices, and therefore have distinct labels, as required.

Theorem 65. *For any integer l, $1 \leqslant l \leqslant K$, the graph $E(K, 0)$ contains a cycle with l arcs, each labeled differently.*

Proof. The assertion is trivial, for $E(K, 0)$ contains exactly one vertex. We may thus select l different letters of the alphabet $\mathfrak{A}$, and define the required cycle to be any sequence of arcs labeled by these letters.

The next theorems concern numberings of occurrences of vertices (or of arcs) in cycles.

Definition 39. An indexing of vertex occurrences (or arc occurrences) on a cycle is specified by assigning to each occurrence of a vertex (or arc) a natural number, subject to the following conditions: (1) each number (index) occurs only once; (2) an occurrence of a vertex (or arc) following an occurrence of a vertex (or arc) indexed n is assigned one of the numbers $n+1$ or 1.

Theorem 66. *Let $2 \leqslant l \leqslant K$, $n \geqslant 1$; divide the vertices of the graph $E(K, n)$ into K^{n-1} groups $\mathfrak{M}_i=\{\alpha a_1, \alpha a_2, \ldots, \alpha a_K\}$ $(i=1, 2, \ldots, K^{n-1})$. Let $\mathfrak{M}$ be a set containing exactly one vertex from each group.*

Then the graph $E(K, n)$ has a cycle in which each vertex of the graph occurs just l times, and the following conditions hold:

(1) *Any two consecutive occurrences in the cycle are of distinct vertices.*

(2) *The occurrences of vertices on the cycle may be indexed in such a way that any vertex $\alpha'\in\mathfrak{M}$ has an occurrence whose index is less than that of any occurrence of any other vertex of the group $\mathfrak{M}_i$ containing α'.*

Proof. By Theorem 63, there is a cycle satisfying condition 1, but not necessarily condition 2. Choosing an arbitrary vertex $\alpha'\in\mathfrak{M}$, we index one of its occurrences by 1, and index the other vertex occurrences inductively as follows. Suppose that some occurrence of a vertex α'' is indexed m and the next occurrence, of a vertex α''', say, is not indexed; the latter is then assigned index $m+1$. This clearly defines an indexing in accordance with Definition 39.

The problem is to ensure satisfaction of condition 2 of our theorem. If it is not satisfied, there is a vertex $\alpha'''\in\mathfrak{M}_\nu$, $\alpha'''\bar{\in}\mathfrak{M}$, having an occurrence in the cycle whose index is less than that of any other vertex of $\mathfrak{M}_\nu$; we may assume that the index of this occurrence of α''' is the smallest possible for which such a situation occurs.

Let $\alpha^{IV}\in\mathfrak{M}$, $\alpha^{IV}\in\mathfrak{M}_\nu$. The cycle may have one of the following forms:

$$\ldots\alpha'\ldots\alpha_1\alpha'''\ldots\alpha_2\alpha'''\ldots\alpha_3\alpha^{IV}\ldots\alpha_4\alpha^{IV}\ldots, \qquad \text{(I)}$$

$$\ldots\alpha'\ldots\alpha_1\alpha'''\ldots\alpha_2\alpha^{IV}\ldots\alpha_4\alpha'''\ldots\alpha_3\alpha^{IV}\ldots, \qquad \text{(II)}$$

$$\ldots\alpha'\ldots\alpha_1\alpha'''\ldots\alpha_2\alpha^{IV}\ldots\alpha_4\alpha^{IV}\ldots\alpha_5\alpha'''\ldots, \qquad \text{(III)}$$

where $\alpha_1\bar{\in}\mathfrak{M}_\nu$, and the occurrence of α' indicated in these formulas has index 1. (In all the above formulas it may happen that $\alpha'\ldots\alpha_1=\alpha'=\alpha_1$, $\alpha'''\ldots\alpha_2=\alpha'''=\alpha_2$, etc.)

Form new cycles as follows:

$$\ldots\alpha'\ldots\alpha_1\alpha^{IV}\ldots\alpha_4\alpha'''\ldots\alpha_2\alpha'''\ldots\alpha_3\alpha^{IV}\ldots, \qquad (\text{I}_1)\ (\text{II}_1)$$

$$\ldots\alpha'\ldots\alpha_1\alpha^{IV}\ldots\alpha_4\alpha'''\ldots\alpha_3\alpha'''\ldots\alpha_2\alpha^{IV}\ldots, \qquad (\text{I}_2)\ (\text{II}_2)$$

$$\ldots\alpha'\ldots\alpha_1\alpha^{IV}\ldots\alpha_4\alpha'''\ldots\alpha_2\alpha^{IV}\ldots\alpha_5\alpha'''\ldots, \qquad (\text{III}_1)$$

$$\ldots\alpha'\ldots\alpha_1\alpha^{IV}\ldots\alpha_5\alpha^{IV}\ldots\alpha_4\alpha'''\ldots\alpha_2\alpha'''\ldots \qquad (\text{III}_2)$$

That these are legitimate cycles follows from the fact that, according to (I), (II), (III) and the arc structure of the graph $E(K,n)$, the vertices participating in these operations must have the form $\alpha_1=a_\nu\alpha$, $\alpha_2=a_\mu\alpha$, $\alpha_3=a_\varkappa\alpha$, $\alpha_4=a_\lambda\alpha$, $\alpha_5=a_\rho\alpha$, $\alpha'''=\alpha a_m$, $\alpha^{IV}=\alpha a_l$. We now index the vertex occurrences in these cycles, assigning the indicated occurrence of α' index 1.

Consider the cycle (I_1). If the original cycle may be written as (I) with no vertex sequences $\ldots\alpha_1\alpha^{IV}\ldots$ or $\ldots\alpha_4\alpha'''\ldots$, the new cycle will satisfy condition 2. Suppose, then, that the cycle contains a sequence $\ldots\alpha_1\alpha^{IV}\ldots$. Then the cycle may be expressed in one of the following forms: (a) formula (I) with $\alpha_1=\alpha_4$, $\alpha_3\neq\alpha_1$; (b) formula (I) with $\alpha_1=\alpha_3$, $\alpha_3\neq\alpha_4$; (c) formula (II) with $\alpha_1=\alpha_2$, $\alpha_2\neq\alpha_3$; (d) formula (II) with $\alpha_1=\alpha_3, \alpha_2\neq\alpha_3$; (e) formula (III) with $\alpha_1=\alpha_2$, $\alpha_2\neq\alpha_4$; (f) formula (III) with $\alpha_1=\alpha_4$, $\alpha_2\neq\alpha_4$.

In case (a), condition 2 will hold for cycle (I_1); in case (b) it will hold for cycle (I_2), provided cycle (I) contains no vertex sequences $\alpha_2\alpha^{IV}$ or

$\alpha_4\alpha'''$; in case (c) cycle (II_1) is the required one, in case (d) cycle (II_2) and in case (e) cycle (III_2), provided cycle (III) contains no sequences $\alpha_5\alpha^{IV}$ or $\alpha_4\alpha'''$; finally, in case (f) cycle (III_1) serves the purpose.

It remains to deal with the exceptions. If we have case (b) and the cycle contains a sequence $\alpha_2\alpha^{IV}$, it may be written in one of the three forms: (i) formula (I) with $\alpha_1=\alpha_3$, $\alpha_2=\alpha_4$; (ii) formula (II) with $\alpha_1=\alpha_2$, $\alpha_3=\alpha_4$; (iii) formula (III) with $\alpha_1=\alpha_2$, $\alpha_4=\alpha_5$. In subcase (i) the condition will hold for cycle (I_2), in subcase (ii) for cycle (II_1), and in subcase (iii) for cycle (III_2).

The treatment of the other exceptions is similar. Thus the original cycle may be reshaped into a new cycle which satisfies the conditions of the theorem, except possibly for condition 2, but now the first index of a vertex occurrence violating the condition is higher than in the original cycle. We may therefore repeat the procedure and, as the number of indices in use is finite, we ultimately obtain a cycle with the desired properties.

The following theorem is a rephrased version of Theorem 66; it may be deduced from the latter in the same way as Theorem 64 was deduced from Theorem 63.

Theorem 67. *Let $2\leqslant l\leqslant K$, $n\geqslant 1$; consider the K^{n-1} groups of vertices in $E(K,n)$ of the form $\mathfrak{M}_i=\{\alpha a_1,\ldots,\alpha a_K\}$ $(i=1,2,\ldots,K^{n-1})$, and let $\mathfrak{M}$ be a set containing exactly one vertex from each group. Then there exists a cycle in $E(K,n)$ in which each vertex occurs exactly l times and the following conditions are satisfied:*

(1) *For any two arcs in the cycle labeled $a_{i_1}\alpha$ and $a_{i_2}\alpha$, the two arcs following them have different labels.*

(2) *The vertex occurrences on the cycle may be indexed in such a way that any vertex $\alpha'\in\mathfrak{M}$ has an occurrence whose index is less than that of any other occurrence of a vertex in the same group $\mathfrak{M}_i$ as α'.*

Lemma 13. *Suppose that the arcs of the graph $E(K,n)$ $(n>1)$ may be divided into classes $\mathfrak{N}_i$ $(i=0,1,\ldots,n)$ and the classes $\mathfrak{N}_i$ into subclasses $\mathfrak{N}_{i_j}$ so that the following conditions are satisfied:*

(1) *The class $\mathfrak{N}_i$ $(i=1,2,\ldots,n)$ contains $K^{i+1}-K^i$ arcs.*

(2) *The class $\mathfrak{N}_0$ contains K arcs.*

(3) *The subclass $\mathfrak{N}_{i_j}$ contains K arcs, which end at the same vertex of $E(K,n)$.*

(4) *If a vertex of $E(K,n)$ is the endpoint of arcs in subclass $\mathfrak{N}_{i_j}$, it is the initial point of $K-1$ arcs of class $\mathfrak{N}_n$ and one arc of class $\mathfrak{N}_{i-1}$ (if $i>0$) or $\mathfrak{N}_0$ (if $i=0$).*

(5) *At least one arc issuing from each vertex is in class $\mathfrak{N}_n$.*

For each vertex, single out one arc of class $\mathfrak{N}_n$ issuing from the vertex. Then there exist an Eulerian cycle of $E(K,n)$ and an indexing of arcs thereon such that each distinguished arc has a smaller index than any other arc issuing from the same vertex.

Proof. The cycle will be constructed inductively.

Step 1. Take any vertex which is the endpoint of arcs of class $\mathfrak{N}_0$, and assign the corresponding distinguished arc index 1.

Step $l+1$ $(l=1,\ldots,K^{n+1}-1)$. Suppose the arc produced by Step l is α, in subclass $\mathfrak{N}_{i_j}$. The following cases may occur.

Case I. There are at most $K-1$ arcs of subclass $\mathfrak{N}_{i_j}$ in the already constructed part of the cycle. Then the next arc of the cycle is taken from class $\mathfrak{N}_n$. If α is the first arc of $\mathfrak{N}_{i_j}$ appearing in the cycle, we take the distinguished arc; otherwise, any other arc will suffice.

Case II. The already constructed part of the cycle contains K arcs of $\mathfrak{N}_{i_j}$. If $i\geqslant 1$, the next arc is taken from subclass $\mathfrak{N}_{i-1}$.

It follows from the assumptions of the lemma that this rule is always applicable if the arcs of the graph $E(K,n)$ have not yet been exhausted. The new arc is assigned index $l+1$.

The arc α selected at Step K^{n+1} is the last arc of the class $\mathfrak{N}_0$, and its endpoint is the initial vertex of the arc with index 1. We have thus obtained an Eulerian cycle. It is clear from the details of the proof that the cycle possesses the desired properties.

Theorem 68. Let $K\geqslant 2$, $n\geqslant 1$, $a_j\in\mathfrak{A}$; considering the K^{n-1} groups of vertices in $E(K,n)$ of the form $\mathfrak{M}_i=\{\alpha a_1,\ldots,\alpha a_K\}$, choose the vertex αa_j from each and combine them into a set $\mathfrak{M}$. There exists a cycle in $E(K,n)$, containing just one occurrence of each vertex, which may be indexed in such a way that the index of any vertex $\alpha\in\mathfrak{M}$ is smaller than that of any other vertex in the same group $\mathfrak{M}_i$ as α.

Proof. If $n=1$, one can take any cycle containing each vertex just once and index the vertices in such a way that the vertex a_j receives index 1.

Let $n\geqslant 2$. Divide the arcs of the graph $E(K,n-1)$ into classes $\mathfrak{N}_i$ $(i=0,1,\ldots,n-1)$ as follows. Take any letter a_l $(a_l\neq a_j)$ and define $\mathfrak{N}_{n-1}$ to be the set of all arcs αa_m, $a_m\neq a_l$. The number of such arcs is K^n-K^{n-1}. We then define $\mathfrak{N}_\rho$ $(\rho=1,2,\ldots,n-2)$ to be the set of all arcs of the form $\alpha a_m \underbrace{a_l\ldots a_l}_{n-\rho-1\text{ times}}$ $(a_m\neq a_l)$; the number of these arcs is $K^{\rho+1}-K^\rho$. Finally, $\mathfrak{N}_0$ will contain all arcs of the form $a_m\underbrace{a_l\ldots a_l}_{n-1\text{ times}}$ (here $a_m=a_l$ is allowed). These classes satisfy conditions 1 and 2 of Lemma 13.

All arcs ending at the same vertex of $E(K,n-1)$ belong to the same class, and so we can divide the classes into subclasses $\mathfrak{N}_{i_j}$ satisfying condition 3 of Lemma 13. The arcs in one subclass have the form $a_i\alpha a_m a_l\ldots a_l$ $(i=1,\ldots,K)$, and end at the vertex $\alpha a_m a_l\ldots a_l$, from which issue the arcs $\alpha a_m a_l\ldots a_l a_i$ $(i=1,\ldots,K)$ Of these last arcs, $K-1$ are in class $\mathfrak{N}_{n-1}$, and one in $\mathfrak{N}_{n-2}$ if $|\alpha|\neq 0$ or in $\mathfrak{N}_0$ if $|\alpha|=0$. We thus have condition 4 of the lemma. That condition 5 holds is obvious. Now let the distinguished arcs be all those of the form αa_j. By Lemma 13, there is an Eulerian cycle in $E(K,n-1)$ which may be indexed in such a way that any arc αa_j has a smaller index than any arc αa_i, $a_i\neq a_j$. To obtain a cycle in $E(K,n)$ as required, we construct a cycle in which the vertices are precisely the arcs in the Eulerian cycle just constructed, and the indices assigned to the vertices are those assigned to the corresponding arcs.

This completes the proof.

§5. FURTHER AUXILIARY RESULTS

The estimates to be established later will be based on the definitions and theorem presented in this section.

Definition 40. An expansion of a graph $\Gamma_1(x)$ is an operation producing a graph $\Gamma_2(x)$ as follows. Select certain subtrees $x_{i_1},\ldots,x_{i_n}$ of $\Gamma_1(x)$ and insert the trees $T(x_{i_1}\Gamma_1(x),j_1),\ldots,T(x_{i_n},\Gamma_1(x),j_n)$ in $\Gamma_1(x)$. In the graph thus obtained, eliminate all subtrees with ingoing degree 0 (i. e., subtrees receiving no arcs from other subtrees).

Definition 41. A subtree x_i is improperly lifted in a graph $\Gamma_1(x)$ if one can construct for x_i a normal incomplete cleavage using some admissible system of imbedded partitions of the leaves of the tree $T(x_i,\Gamma_1(x),n)$.

Definition 42. We shall say that an input graph $\Gamma_2(x,K,N_2,M_2,L_2,R_2)$ is obtained from an input graph $\Gamma_1(x,K,N_1,M_1,L_1,R_1)$ by improper lifting if Γ_2 is the result of applying the following operations to Γ_1:

(1) Attach complete trees of type $(K, N_2 \dot{-} N_1)$ to all leaves of subtrees of Γ_1; denote the resulting graph by $\Gamma_3(x,K,N_3,M_3,L_1,R_3)$.

(2) Select some set of subtrees $x_{i_1},\ldots,x_{i_n}$ in Γ_3 which are lifted (possibly improperly) in Γ_3.

(3) Insert the trees defining the lifting of the selected subtrees in Γ_3, to form the graph Γ_4.

(4) Eliminate from Γ_4 all subtrees with ingoing degree zero, to form the graph Γ_5.

(5) Delete the arcs of the last $N_1 \dot{-} N_2$ levels in the subtrees of Γ_5, to obtain the graph $\Gamma_6=\Gamma_2$.

A system of vertex combinations on a tree $T(x_k,\Gamma(x),n)$ is a system of partitions of the set of vertices on each level.

Definition 43. A lifting (not necessarily proper) of a subtree x_k in a graph $\Gamma(x)$ conforms to a given system of vertex combinations on $T(x_k,\Gamma(x),n)$ if the classes π_{ij} used to construct the lifting satisfy the condition: for any class π_{ij}, the paths from the root of T to the subtrees of the class contain i-th level subtrees of T belonging only to one class in the vertex combination system.

Theorem 69. Let $\Gamma'(x)$ be obtained by a lifting operation from a graph $\Gamma(x)$, in which subtrees $x_{l_1},\ldots,x_{l_n}$ have been lifted by constructing imbedded sequences of partitions of the leaves of the trees $T(x_{l_j},\Gamma(x),n_j)$. Then there exists a sequence of graphs $\Gamma_0(x),\Gamma_1(x),\ldots,\Gamma_L(x)$ satisfying the following conditions:

(1) $\Gamma_0(x)=\Gamma(x)$.

(2) $\Gamma_L(x)=\Gamma'(x)$.

(3) $\Gamma_1(x)$ *is obtained from* $\Gamma_0(x)$ *by an expansion operation.*

(4) $\Gamma_L(x)$ *is obtained from* $\Gamma_{L-1}(x)$ *by shifting arcs.*

(5) $\Gamma_{i+1}(x)$ *is obtained from* $\Gamma_i(x)$ $(i=1,2,\ldots,L-2)$ *by a lifting operation (not necessarily proper) in which certain subtrees $x_{k_1},\ldots,x_{k_n}$ are lifted in $\Gamma_i(x)$ by means of imbedded sequences of partitions of the leaves of the trees $T(x_{k_j},\Gamma_i(x),n_j)$; moreover, the lifting operations for $x_{k_1},\ldots,x_{k_n}$ conform to vertex combination systems on the trees $T(x_{k_j},\Gamma_i(x),n_j)$ for which each class of any partition contains at most two vertices.*

Proof. We confine ourselves to the case that only one subtree x_k is lifted in $\Gamma(x)$, utilizing the tree $T(x_k,\Gamma(x),n)$. We obtain the graph $\Gamma_1(x)$ from $\Gamma(x)$ by an expansion operation involving insertion of $T(x_k,\Gamma(x),n)$ in $\Gamma(x)$. It is clear that the leaves of the trees $T(x_k,\Gamma(x),n)$ and $T_1(x_k,\Gamma_1(x),n)$ may be put in one-to-one correspondence in such a way that corresponding subtrees are isomorphic and paths from the roots of T and T_1 to corresponding vertices define identical words. We shall therefore not distinguish between the leaves of subtrees in T and T_1.

Consider two normal admissible imbedded sequences of partitions of the leaf subtrees of $T(x_k, \Gamma(x), n)$: the partition $\mathfrak{A}_0, \mathfrak{A}_1, \ldots, \mathfrak{A}_n$ used in the lifting of x_k, and a partition $\mathfrak{A}'_0, \mathfrak{A}'_1, \ldots, \mathfrak{A}'_n$ constructed in such a way that a class of the partition $\mathfrak{A}'_i$ $(i=0,1,\ldots,n)$ either contains just those leaves of T which are ends of paths from the same i-th level vertex of T, or is some class of $\mathfrak{A}'_{i-1}$. The second alternative holds if and only if the partition $\mathfrak{A}_{i-1}$ contains a class which is also a class of $\mathfrak{A}'_{i-1}$. Let j be the largest number such that there exist a class $\pi_{j-1,k}$ of $\mathfrak{A}_{j-1}$ and two classes $\pi'_{j-1,l}$ and $\pi'_{j-1,m}$ of $\mathfrak{A}'_{j-1}$ such that $\pi_{j-1,k} \cap \pi'_{j-1,l} \neq \varnothing$, $\pi_{j-1,k} \cap \pi'_{j-1,m} \neq \varnothing$. If the partition sequences $\mathfrak{A}_0, \mathfrak{A}_1, \ldots, \mathfrak{A}_n$ and $\mathfrak{A}'_0, \mathfrak{A}'_1, \ldots, \mathfrak{A}'_n$ are different, these conditions must hold for some j for suitable classes of $\mathfrak{A}'_{j-1}$ and $\mathfrak{A}_{j-1}$. Denote $\pi_{j-1,k} \cap \pi'_{j-1,l} = \pi_1$, $\pi_{j-1,k} \cap \pi'_{j-1,m} = \pi_2$, $\pi_3 = \pi_{j-1,k} \setminus (\pi_1 \cup \pi_2)$. Let π_4, π_5 and π_6 be sets of leaves of T satisfying the conditions $|\pi_4| = |\pi_2|$, $\pi'_{j-1,l} = \pi_1 \cup \pi_4 \cup \pi_5$, $\pi'_{j-1,m} = \pi_2 \cup \pi_6$. We define a partition $\mathfrak{A}''_{j-1}$ thus: $\pi''_{j-1,i} = \pi'_{j-1,i}$ for all i except $i=l$ and $i=m$, $\pi''_{j-1,l} = \pi_1 \cup \pi_2 \cup \pi_5$, $\pi''_{j-1,m} = \pi_4 \cup \pi_6$. Set $\pi''_{\nu,i} = \pi'_{\nu,i}$ for $\nu = j, j+1, \ldots, n$.

Consider the partition $\mathfrak{A}''_j$. There is no class $\pi''_{j\mu}$ of $\mathfrak{A}''_j$ such that $\pi''_{j\mu} \cap \pi_2 \neq \varnothing$ and $\pi''_{j\mu} \cap \pi_6 \neq \varnothing$, since $\mathfrak{A}'_j = \mathfrak{A}_j$ and for no class $\pi_{j\rho}$, coinciding with $\pi''_{j\mu}$, can it be true that $\pi_{j\rho} \subset \pi_{j-1,k} = \pi_1 \cup \pi_2 \cup \pi_3$, even though $\pi_{j\rho} \cap \pi_{j-1,k} \neq \varnothing$. Similarly one proves that there is no class $\pi''_{j\mu}$ of $\mathfrak{A}''_j$ such that $\pi''_{j\mu} \cap \pi_1 \neq \varnothing$ and $\pi''_{j\mu} \cap (\pi_4 \cup \pi_5) \neq \varnothing$. The possibility remains that there is a class $\pi''_{j\mu}$ with $\pi''_{j\mu} \cap \pi_4 \neq \varnothing$ and $\pi''_{j\mu} \cap \pi_5 \neq \varnothing$. But this may be avoided by suitable choice of π_4 and π_5, as we immediately show. It follows from the foregoing that the set π_2 contains pK^{n-j} elements, where p is some natural number. We then let π_4 be the union of p classes of the partition $\mathfrak{A}'_j$, imbedded in $\pi'_{j-1,l}$, which have no elements in common with π_1.

Consequently, the partition $\mathfrak{A}''_j$ is imbedded in $\mathfrak{A}''_{j-1}$. Since $\mathfrak{A}'_i$ is imbedded in $\mathfrak{A}'_{i-1}$, it follows that $\mathfrak{A}''_{i-l}$ is imbedded in $\mathfrak{A}''_{i-1}$ for $i = j+1, \ldots, n$ as well.

Suppose that the classes $\pi'_{j-1,l}$ and $\pi'_{j-1,m}$ of $\mathfrak{A}'_{j-1}$ are subsets of the same class $\pi'_{j-2,r}$ of $\mathfrak{A}'_{j-2}$. Then the classes $\pi''_{j-1,l}$ and $\pi''_{j-1,m}$ of $\mathfrak{A}''_{j-1}$ are also subsets of $\pi'_{j-2,r}$. We then define $\mathfrak{A}''_k = \mathfrak{A}'_k$ for $k = 0, 1, \ldots, j-2$, obtaining an imbedded sequence of partitions. Suppose that for two different classes $\pi'_{j-2,\lambda}$ and $\pi'_{j-2,\mu}$ of $\mathfrak{A}'_{j-2}$ we have $\pi'_{j-1,l} \subset \pi'_{j-2,\lambda}$, $\pi'_{j-1,m} \subset \pi'_{j-2,\mu}$. We set $\pi'_{j-2,\lambda} = \pi_1 \cup \pi_4 \cup \pi_5 \cup \pi_7$, $\pi'_{j-2,\mu} = \pi_2 \cup \pi_6 \cup \pi_8$ and define the partition $\mathfrak{A}''_{j-2}$ as follows: $\pi''_{j-2,\nu} = \pi'_{j-2,\nu}$ for all ν except $\nu = \mu$ and $\nu = \lambda$, $\pi''_{j-2,\lambda} = \pi_1 \cup \pi_2 \cup \pi_5 \cup \pi_7$, $\pi''_{j-2,\mu} = \pi_4 \cup \pi_6 \cup \pi_8$. The sets $\pi''_{j-2,\lambda}$ and $\pi''_{j-2,\mu}$ are so defined that $\pi''_{j-1,l} \subset \pi''_{j-2,\lambda}$, $\pi''_{j-1,m} \subset \pi''_{j-2,\mu}$. Thus $\mathfrak{A}''_{j-1}$ is imbedded in $\mathfrak{A}''_{j-2}$. The partitions $\mathfrak{A}''_{j-3}$, $\mathfrak{A}''_{j-4}$ are defined similarly.

Since the partition $\mathfrak{A}'_0$ consists of only one class, it follows that for some j_0 there is a class $\pi'_{j_0,r}$ such that $\pi'_{j-1,l} \subset \pi'_{j_0,r}$, $\pi'_{j-1,m} \subset \pi'_{j_0,r}$, and the above procedure for changing two classes in each partition $\mathfrak{A}'_0, \mathfrak{A}'_1, \ldots, \mathfrak{A}'_{j-3}$ must terminate.

In order to show that the partition sequence $\mathfrak{A}''_0, \ldots, \mathfrak{A}''_n$ is admissible, we consider the *extended paths** from the root of the tree T_1 to those

* An extended path from the root of T to a leaf subtree is defined as the path composed of the path leading to the subtree itself and the path from the root of the subtree to one of its leaves.

of its leaves belonging to one class of each partition in the sequence. We may confine attention to classes which do not appear in the partitions $\mathfrak{A}'_0, \mathfrak{A}'_1, \ldots, \mathfrak{A}'_n$. By construction, there are such classes only in the partitions $\mathfrak{A}''_{j_0+1}, \ldots, \mathfrak{A}''_{j-1}$, exactly two in each partition.

Consider the classes $\pi_{j-1,k}$, $\pi'_{j-1,l}$, $\pi'_{j-1,m}$, $\pi''_{j-1,l}$ and $\pi''_{j-1,m}$. Since $\mathfrak{A}_0, \ldots, \mathfrak{A}_n$ is an admissible sequence, the sets of extended paths from the vertices of T to the leaves in class $\pi_{j-1,k}$ define a set of words with identical prefixes of length $\varkappa \geqslant j-1$. A similar statement holds for the sets of extended paths leading to the leaves in classes $\pi'_{j-1,l}$ and $\pi'_{j-1,m}$; denote the lengths of the identical prefixes for these classes by λ and μ, respectively. Suppose that the sets of extended paths to vertices of classes $\pi''_{j-1,l}$ and $\pi''_{j-1,m}$ define sets of words with identical prefixes of length λ' and μ', respectively.

Suppose that $\lambda' < \min(\varkappa, \lambda, \mu)$. This may be true only if the sets of words defined by extended paths leading to π_2 and $\pi_1 \cup \pi_5$ have different prefixes of length $\lambda'' \leqslant \min(\varkappa, \lambda, \mu)$. As follows from the structure of $\pi_{j-1,k}$, this may hold only if the sets of words defined by extended paths leading to π_2 and π_5 have different prefixes of length λ''. But this is impossible, for it follows from the structure of the sets $\pi'_{j-1,l}$ and $\pi_{j-1,k}$ that the sets of words defined by extended paths leading to π_1, π_2 and π_5 have identical prefixes of length $\lambda''' = \min(\varkappa, \lambda, \mu)$. Consequently, $\lambda' \geqslant \min(\varkappa, \lambda, \mu)$. One proves similarly that $\mu' \geqslant \min(\varkappa, \lambda, \mu)$, and verifies the following property of the classes $\pi''_{j-2,\lambda}, \ldots, \pi''_{j_0\lambda}$, $\pi''_{j-2,\mu}, \ldots, \pi''_{j_0\mu}$: the words defined by extended paths leading to $\pi''_{i\lambda}$ and $\pi''_{i\mu}$ must have identical prefixes at least as long as the shortest identical prefixes of words defined by extended paths leading to classes of the partitions $\mathfrak{A}_i$ and $\mathfrak{A}'_i$ $(i = j_0, \ldots, j-2)$.

Thus the sequence of partitions $\mathfrak{A}''_0, \mathfrak{A}''_1, \ldots, \mathfrak{A}''_n$ is admissible. By Theorem 60, the graph $W(\mathfrak{A}''_0, \ldots, \mathfrak{A}''_n)$ is an incomplete cleavage of the subtree x_k. Insert the graph $W(\mathfrak{A}''_0, \ldots, \mathfrak{A}''_n)$ in $\Gamma_1(x)$ and denote the resulting graph by $\Gamma_2(x)$. Since no arc-shifting operations are applied, the trees $T(x_k, \Gamma_2(x), n)$ and $T(x_k, \Gamma_1(x), n)$ have the same leaves and so we shall not distinguish between their leaves. The graph Γ_2 is obtained from Γ_1 by a lifting operation (possibly improper).

It is evident from the construction that the lifting of x_k in $\Gamma_1(x)$ based on the partition sequence $\mathfrak{A}''_0, \mathfrak{A}''_1, \ldots, \mathfrak{A}''_n$ conforms to a vertex combination system on $T(x_k, \Gamma_1(x), n)$ such that each combination class of vertices of T contains at most two vertices.

Suppose that the partitions $\mathfrak{A}''_0, \mathfrak{A}''_1, \ldots, \mathfrak{A}''_n$ do not coincide with $\mathfrak{A}_0, \mathfrak{A}_1, \ldots, \mathfrak{A}_n$. We then repeat the procedure, replacing the graph $\Gamma_1(x)$ by $\Gamma_2(x)$ and constructing a sequence of partitions $\mathfrak{A}'''_0, \ldots, \mathfrak{A}'''_n$. If $\pi''_{j-1,l}$ is not a class in $\mathfrak{A}_{j-1}$, the new partition $\mathfrak{A}'''_{j-1}$ is constructed in such a way that the corresponding class $\pi'''_{j-1,l}$ retains all common elements of $\pi_{j-1,k}$ and $\pi''_{j-1,l}$. To do this, it suffices to select a class $\pi''_{j-1,\mu}$ such that $\pi_{j-1,k} \cap \pi''_{j-1,\mu} = \pi_{10} \neq \varnothing$ and to exchange the set π_{10} for some subset π_{11} of $\pi''_{j-1,l}$ such that $\pi_{j-1,k} \cap \pi_{11} = \varnothing$, similar to the exchange of π_2 and π_4 in the construction of $\mathfrak{A}''_{j-1}$.

Now the above procedure for construction of partitions has the following property: for one class $\pi_{\nu\varkappa}$ of each partition $\mathfrak{A}_\nu$, the passage from $\mathfrak{A}_\nu^{(i-1)}$ to $\mathfrak{A}_\nu^{(i)}$ increases the number of elements in one class of $\mathfrak{A}_\nu^{(i)}$ which are also elements of $\pi_{\nu\varkappa}$, and no changes occur in the classes of $\mathfrak{A}_\mu^{(i-1)}$ $(\mu = \nu, \nu+1, \ldots, n)$ which are also classes of $\mathfrak{A}_\mu$. At some stage, therefore, we obtain partitions $\mathfrak{A}_0^{(L-1)}, \ldots, \mathfrak{A}_n^{(L-1)}$ identical with the partitions $\mathfrak{A}_0, \ldots, \mathfrak{A}_n$.

To obtain the graph $\Gamma_L(x)$ from $\Gamma_{L-1}(x)$, it suffices to shift the arcs emanating from the subtrees of $T(x_k, \Gamma_{L-1}(x), n)$ corresponding to the subtrees of $W(\mathfrak{A}_0, \ldots, \mathfrak{A}_n)$ which are connected to subtrees of $\Gamma(x)$ when W is inserted in $\Gamma(x)$ (in the lifting operation producing the graph $\Gamma'(x)$).

It follows from the proof of the theorem that the graphs $\Gamma_1(x), \ldots, \Gamma_L(x)$ have the following property. Let $\Gamma(x)$ and $\Gamma'(x)$ be composed solely of panicles of types (K, N_ν, L_ν) $(\nu=1,2,\ldots)$. Then $\Gamma_1(x), \ldots, \Gamma_L(x)$ contain no panicles of type (K, N, L), $L > L_\nu$. However, we shall not need this property in the sequel. Thanks to Theorems 62 and 69, we shall be able to base all our estimates on consideration of graph transformations, starting from graphs containing only critical subtrees and taking pairs of subtrees into pairs of other subtrees.

§6. PRELIMINARY ESTIMATE OF MINIMUM NUMBER OF STATES IN AN ILS-I-N AUTOMATON

The estimates derived in this section will be based on certain properties of sets of subtrees with identifiable roots. These properties may be described in terms of partitions of sets of subtrees.

Definition 44. A *formation partition* of the set of all subtrees of a graph $\Gamma(x)$ is a partition satisfying the condition: there exist a subtree x_k of $\Gamma(x)$ and a letter a_l such that one class of the partition (the *principal class*) contains all subtrees labeled a_l which are endpoints of arcs emanating from x_k, and the other class contains all other subtrees.

Definition 45. A *combination partition* of the set of all subtrees of a graph $\Gamma(x, K, N, M, L, R)$ is a partition satisfying the condition: one class (the *principal class*) is the union of principal classes of several formation partitions such that the roots of all subtrees in their principal classes are identifiable with the same leaf of some subtree, and the other class contains all other subtrees.

Formation and combination partitions are also called *cleavage partitions*.

Definition 46. The *height* of a cleavage partition is a number ν such that (1) no class of the partition contains a subtree having a ν-th level vertex identifiable with a ν-th level vertex of a subtree in the other class; (2) there exist two subtrees, one in each class, having mutually identifiable $(\nu-1)$-th level vertices.

Two cleavage partitions are *distinct* if their principal classes are not the same.

Theorem 70. If the principal class of any cleavage partition of a graph $\Gamma(x, K, N, M, L, R)$ contains a subtree $x_\mu(K, N, M_1, L, R)$, it contains at least one other subtree $x_\nu(K, N, M_2, L, R)$.

Proof. It is sufficient to prove the theorem for formation partitions. Suppose that the principal class of a formation partition contains a subtree x_μ, a subtree $x_k(K, N, M_3, L_1, R)$ and a letter a_l such that $\Gamma(x)$ contains an arc from x_k to x_μ, labeled a_l. Let $\chi_{\mu, L-1, \alpha}$ be a vertex whose attached subgraph is not a complete tree. This vertex is identifiable with the vertex $\chi_{k, L, a_l \alpha}$.

Since $L \geqslant L_1$, it follows that the vertex $\chi_{k,L,a_l\alpha}$, if it is not a leaf, has an attached complete tree. Since there is no complete tree attached to $\chi_{\mu,L-1,\alpha}$, it follows that $\Gamma(x)$ must contain at least one more subtree x_ν containing a vertex $\chi_{\nu,L-1,\alpha}$, also identifiable with $\chi_{k,L,a_l\alpha}$. Admissibility considerations now dictate the existence of an arc in $\Gamma(x)$ from x_k to x_ν, labeled a_l.

Theorem 71. *Suppose that $\Gamma'(x, K, N, M', L', R)$ is obtained from a graph $\Gamma(x, K, N, M, L, R)$* containing only critical subtrees by lifting and arc shifting. Then, for every $\nu = L, L+1, \ldots, L'-1$, there are at least two cleavage partitions of the subtrees of Γ', of height ν, satisfying the following conditions:*

(1) *The roots of the subtrees in the principal classes of both partitions are identifiable with the same leaf of some subtree.*

(2) *The principal classes of both partitions contain subtrees with mutually identifiable $(\nu-1)$-th level vertices whose outgoing arcs have different sets of labels.*

Proof. To each number $\nu = L, \ldots, L'-1$ we shall assign cleavage partitions of height ν, and then proceed to show that there are at least two such partitions for each number satisfying conditions 1 and 2 of our theorem.

Consider the first two graphs Γ_0 and Γ_1 in the sequence $\Gamma_0, \Gamma_1, \ldots, \Gamma_P$ of Theorem 62. Suppose that the formation of Γ_1 involves insertion in Γ_0 of a tree W with two first level subtrees $x_k(K, N, M_2, L_1, R)$ and $x_l(K, N, M_3, L_1, R)$. As in the proof of Theorem 70, one can show that each of the subtrees x_k and x_l has at least one (L_1-1)-th level vertex identifiable with the same L_1-th level vertex of some subtree in Γ_1. By condition 2 of Definition 34, for every number $j = L, L+1, \ldots, L_1-1$ the tree W contains subtrees $x_{k(j)}$ and $x_{l(j)}$, each of which has a $(j-1)$-th level vertex identifiable with an (L_1-1)-th level vertex of x_k and x_l, respectively. The subtrees $x_{k(j)}$ and $x_{l(j)}$ are formed with the aid of certain classes of a partition $\mathfrak{A}_{L_1-j+1}$ of the leaves of T. It follows from the imbeddability of the partitions that if there is an arc from x_k to $x_{k(L_1-1)}$ labeled a_p, there is no such arc from x_k to $x_{l(L_1-1)}$. Similarly, if there is an arc from $x_{k(j)}$ to $x_{k(j-1)}$, there is no similarly labeled arc from $x_{k(j)}$ to $x_{l(j-1)}$. Consequently, there are $L_1 - L$ formation partitions in Γ_1 such that the principal class of each partition contains the subtree $x_{k(j)}$ but not the subtree $x_{l(j)}$ $(j = L, L+1, \ldots, L_1-1)$. We may thus assign to each number $\nu = j$ a partition whose principal class contains $x_{k(j)}$ but not $x_{l(j)}$.

There are also $L_1 - L$ formation partitions whose principal classes contain $x_{l(j)}$ but not $x_{k(j)}$ $(j = L, L+1, \ldots, L_1-1)$. These partitions are also assigned to the numbers $\nu = j$. The cleavage partitions assigned to ν have height ν.

The partitions we have constructed satisfy conditions 1 and 2, for the roots of the subtrees in the principal classes are identifiable with the same vertex of the root subtree of W.

It may happen that the graph Γ_1 is built up from Γ_0 by lifting several subtrees of Γ_0, or that the above arguments are applicable to two subtrees

* The fact that the subtrees in both graphs are of the same type (K, N) and have roots of the same weight is no restriction; otherwise, by attaching suitable complete trees to the leaves of the subtrees in both graphs we can guarantee that the subtrees of all the graphs $\Gamma_0, \Gamma_1, \ldots, \Gamma_P$ in the proof of Theorem 62 are of the same type (K, N) and have roots with the same weights.

in W. In that case we assign suitable formation partitions to the numbers $\nu = L, \ldots, L_1 - 1$ for each pair of relevant subtrees. Because of this, the symbols $x_{k(j)}$ and $x_{l(j)}$ will be used in what follows for any two subtrees to which the arguments are applicable.

The theorem is thus proved for the subtrees in the graph Γ_1.

In formation of the graph Γ_2, two cases may occur.

Case I. Γ_2 is built up from Γ_1 by an arc-shifting operation. Suppose that some subtree $x_{k(j_0)}$ has been eliminated by shifting its ingoing arcs to an isomorphic subtree $\bar{x}_{k(j_0)}$, retaining the subtrees $x_{k(j)}$ for $j > j_0$. This may happen only if at least two trees W_1 and W_2, containing the subtrees $x_{k(j_0)}$ and $\bar{x}_{k(j_0)}$, respectively, have been inserted in the graph Γ_1. But then we have two formation partitions assigned to $\nu = j_0$, one class of each containing the subtree $\bar{x}_{k(j_0)}$ and the other $\bar{x}_{l(j_0)}$. The set of cleavage partitions for $\nu = j_0$ then contains two members satisfying conditions 1 and 2. Together with $x_{k(j_0)}$, we must also eliminate all subtrees which are ends of arcs from $x_{k(j_0)}$. But the sets assigned to numbers $\nu < j_0$ contain at least two elements, since the graph Γ_2 still contains subtrees of the tree W_2. The proof is similar if both subtrees $x_{k(j_0)}$ and $x_{l(j_0)}$ are eliminated in this way.

By condition 1 of Definition 38, a subtree $x_{k(j_0)}$ may be eliminated without its arcs being transferred to an isomorphic subtree only if all subtrees on certain levels of W, containing subtrees $x_{k(j_0)}, x_{k(j_0+1)}, \ldots, x_k$ and $x_{l(j_0)}, x_{l(j_0+1)}, \ldots, x_l$, are eliminated. If these subtrees are all eliminated, the graph Γ_2 may be derived from a graph Γ_1 which is built up from Γ_0 without inserting the tree W. The graphs Γ_1 and Γ_2 then contain no subtrees with no complete trees attached to their j_0-th level vertices, i. e., $\Gamma_2 = \Gamma_2(x, K, N, M_2, j_0 - 1, R)$. The sets of cleavage partitions of the subtrees of Γ_2 assigned to the numbers $\nu = j_0 - 1, \ldots, L$ contain two partitions satisfying conditions 1 and 2; this follows from the fact that the subtrees $x_{k(j_0-1)}$ and $x_{l(j_0-1)}$ are retained. Thus the theorem remains in force for Γ_2.

Case II. Γ_2 is built up from Γ_1 by a lifting operation.

If $\Gamma_2 = \Gamma_2(x, K, N, M, L_2, R)$, $L_2 > L_1$, the arguments as regards the cleavage partitions assigned to numbers $\nu = L_1, L_1 + 1, \ldots, L_2 - 1$ and their properties follow the same lines as for $\nu = L, L + 1, \ldots, L_1 - 1$ above.

If pairs of subtrees $x_{k(j)}$, $x_{l(j)}$ are retained in Γ_2 for certain values of j, the sets of cleavage partitions assigned to the corresponding ν's will contain two elements.

Suppose that some subtree $x_{k(j)}$ $(L \leqslant j \leqslant L_1 - 1)$ is not retained. Let $\Gamma_{10}, \ldots, \Gamma_{1L}$ be a sequence of graphs satisfying conditions 1 through 5 of Theorem 69. The assertion of our theorem remains valid for Γ_{11}, since for any two subtrees in Γ_1 connected by an arc, the graph Γ_{11} contains two isomorphic subtrees connected by a similarly labeled arc in the same direction.

Consider the graph Γ_{12}. We may assume that Γ_{12} does not contain a subtree $x_{k(j)}$, for otherwise the following reasoning need only be applied to some other graph Γ_{1i_0} $(2 < i_0 \leqslant L - 1)$.

When pairs of subtrees are transformed into pairs of other subtrees, pairs of subtrees on consecutive levels of some tree $T(x_\varkappa, \Gamma_{11}(x), n)$ are combined, provided there are arcs emanating from the subtrees of one pair to the subtrees of the other pair on the next level of T (provided the combination does not end on one level of T). Suppose that these combination operations encompass subtrees $x_{k(j_0)}, x_{k(j_0+1)}, \ldots, x_{k(j_1)}$, which are combined respectively with subtrees $x_{i(j_0)}, x_{i(j_0+1)}, \ldots, x_{i(j_1)}$.

A subtree $x_{k(\rho)}$ may be eliminated only when all classes of formation partitions for Γ_{11} that contain $x_{k(\rho)}$ also contain $x_{i(\rho)}$. Hence the case $x_{i(\rho)}=x_{l(\rho)}$ may occur only when the subtrees x_k and x_l are eliminated; this was considered when constructing the graph Γ_1, so that the theorem remains valid for Γ_{12}.

Suppose that $x_{i(\rho)} \neq x_{l(\rho)}$ and the pairs of subtrees $x_{k(\rho)}, x_{i(\rho)}$ are transformed into pairs $x_{m(\rho)}, x_{n(\rho)}$. As shown above, the set of cleavage partitions of Γ_{11} contains two formation partitions of height $\nu=\rho$. After formation of the subtrees $x_{m(\rho)}$ and $x_{n(\rho)}$, these partitions may become combination partitions of the same height, since the various identifications of the vertices of the subtrees $x_{k(\rho)} \cup x_{i(\rho)}$ and $x_{m(\rho)} \cup x_{n(\rho)}$ with the remaining subtrees of Γ_{12} are not changed. Condition 1 cannot be violated because the roots of $x_{m(\rho)}$ and $x_{n(\rho)}$ are identified with the same leaves of subtrees in Γ_{12} as the roots of $x_{k(\rho)}$ and $x_{i(\rho)}$ in Γ_{11} (if the identification involves a leaf of one of the subtrees $x_{k(\sigma)}$ or $x_{i(\sigma)}$, a new identification relation is introduced in Γ_{12}, involving the corresponding leaf of one of the subtrees $x_{m(\sigma)}$ or $x_{n(\sigma)}$. For the same reasons, neither can condition 2 be violated.

Consider the formation partition of height j_0-1 defined by an arc with label a_l from $x_{k(j_0)}$. Let the principal class of this partition be $\{x_{i_1}, \ldots, x_{i_n}\}$, and suppose that neither of the subtrees $x_{m(j_0)}$ or $x_{n(j_0)}$ defines a formation partition with the same principal class. For any letter a_r, the subtrees with ingoing arcs in Γ_{11} from $x_{k(j_0)}$ and $x_{i(j_0)}$ labeled a_r are also endpoints of arcs in Γ_{12} from $x_{m(j_0)}$ and $x_{n(j_0)}$ with the same label, and vice versa. Consider the principal class $\{x_{\nu_1}, \ldots, x_{\nu_m}\}$ of the partition defined by the letter a_l and the subtree $x_{i(j_0)}$. Since $x_{k(j_0)}$ and $x_{i(j_0)}$ are both in the principal class of some formation partition, their roots are identifiable, as are their vertices $\chi_{k(j_0),1a_l}$ and $\chi_{i(j_0),1a_l}$. Then the roots of all the subtrees $x_{i_1}, \ldots, x_{i_n}, x_{\nu_1}, \ldots, x_{\nu_m}$ are also identifiable, and this set may be viewed as the principal class of some combination partition. Since the subtree $x_{l(j_0)}$ is retained, it follows that the set of subtrees of Γ_{12} has a formation partition defined by $x_{l(j_0)}$ and a_l, whose principal class we denote by $\{x_{\mu_1}, \ldots, x_{\mu_s}\}$. Since $\{x_{i_1}, \ldots x_{i_n}\}$ and $\{x_{\mu_1}, \ldots, x_{\mu_s}\}$ are principal classes of formation partitions satisfying conditions 1 and 2 of our theorem, the same conditions hold for the sets $\{x_{i_1}, \ldots, x_{i_n}, x_{\nu_1}, \ldots, x_{\nu_m}\}$ and $\{x_{\mu_1}, \ldots, x_{\mu_s}\}$. Thus the theorem is valid for the graph Γ_{12}.

Scrutinizing the construction of the graphs $\Gamma_{13}, \Gamma_{14}, \ldots, \Gamma_{1,L-1}$ in analogous fashion, one shows that the theorem is valid for each of them.

In formation of the graph Γ_{1L}, none of the sets of cleavage partitions assigned to $\nu=L, L+1, \ldots, L_2-1$ may contain less than two elements; conditions 1 and 2 must be satisfied, since none of the newly formed subtrees is eliminated and the theorem remains valid for $\Gamma_{1L}=\Gamma_2$.

If the graphs $\Gamma_3, \ldots, \Gamma_n$ are constructed by successive lifting operations, similar arguments show that the theorem remains valid for each of them.

Now suppose that Γ_{n+1} is built up from Γ_n via arc-shifting operations. The case in which subtrees are thereby eliminated only by dint of arcs being transferred to isomorphic subtrees was dealt with above for Γ_1 and Γ_2, and the reasoning here is analogous.

If the operations involve elimination of certain levels of the inserted trees $W_1, \ldots, W_\rho$, the graph Γ_{n+1} may be constructed from Γ_n without using these insertion operations.

Thus the theorem remains valid for the graph Γ_{n+1}.

To complete the proof, it remains only to examine all the other graphs $\Gamma_{n+2}, \ldots, \Gamma_P$ in the same way.

Theorem 72. Suppose that $\Gamma'(x, K, N, M', L', R)$ is obtained from a graph $\Gamma(x, K, N, M, L, R)$ containing only critical subtrees by lifting and arc shifting. Then, for every $\nu = 1, 2, \ldots, L-1$, there are at least two cleavage partitions of the subtrees of Γ', of height ν, satisfying conditions 1 and 2 of Theorem 71.

Proof. The set of all subtrees of Γ which are ends of paths of length l from some subtree x_n may be built up by operations of the following types:

(1) Attach complete trees of type (K, l) to the leaves of x_n; call the resulting subtree x'_n.

(2) Delete all vertices of the first l levels of x'_n, and also all arcs incident with at least one deleted vertex.

(3) Each connected component of the resulting graph splits into critical subtrees (cf. the construction of the graph in Theorem 59). Thus the resulting set of subtrees is the principal part of a cleavage partition of height $L-l$, whence it follows that the theorem holds for the original graph Γ. The rest of the proof is the same as that of Theorem 71.

Definition 47. A *division partition* of the set of all subtrees of a graph $\Gamma(x)$ is a partition satisfying the condition: one class (the *principal class*) contains all subtrees whose roots are identifiable with the same leaf of some subtree, and the other class contains all the remaining subtrees (if such exist). If the graph $\Gamma(x, K, N, M, L, R)$ contains K^N/R subtrees, a division partition comprises only one (principal) class.

Theorem 73. Let $\mathfrak{M}$ be an arbitrary set of subtrees of $\Gamma(x)$, with identifiable roots, containing P elements, and suppose that for each of a sequence of numbers $\nu_1 < \nu_2 < \ldots < \nu_\rho$ this set contains the principal classes of two cleavage partitions of height ν_j $(j = 1, \ldots, \rho)$ satisfying conditions 1 and 2 of Theorem 71. Then $\rho \leqslant P-1$.

Proof. Let $\mathfrak{M}'$ be the partition of the set of subtrees of $\Gamma(x)$ one of whose classes is the set $\mathfrak{M}$, the other consisting of all other subtrees of $\Gamma(x)$. Denote the cleavage partitions of height ν_j whose existence is assumed by $\mathfrak{M}_j$ and $\mathfrak{M}'_j$.

We first prove an auxiliary proposition: The products $\mathfrak{N}_j = \mathfrak{M}' \times \mathfrak{M}_1 \times \ldots \times \mathfrak{M}_j \times \mathfrak{M}'_1 \times \ldots \times \mathfrak{M}'_j$ $(j = 1, \ldots, \rho)$ satisfy the condition: there exist a class π'_j of the partition $\mathfrak{N}_j$, with $\pi'_j \subset \mathfrak{M}$, and two classes π''_{j+1}, π'''_{j+1} of the partition $\mathfrak{N}_{j+1}$, such that $\pi''_{j+1} \cup \pi'''_{j+1} \subseteq \pi'_j$.

This is certainly true for $j = 0$, for the partitions $\mathfrak{M}_1$ and $\mathfrak{M}'_1$ have distinct principal classes and $\mathfrak{N}_0 = \mathfrak{M}'$. Suppose the assertion true for $j = j_0$.

The principal class of one partition of height ν_{j_0+1}, say $\mathfrak{M}_{j_0+1}$, has elements in common with some class π_{j_0} of the partition $\mathfrak{N}_{j_0}$. By conditions 1 and 2, for each of the partitions $\mathfrak{M}_1, \ldots, \mathfrak{M}_{j_0}, \mathfrak{M}'_1, \ldots, \mathfrak{M}'_{j_0}$, the set π'_{j_0} is either a subset of the principal class of the partition or is disjoint from the principal class. Hence π_{j_0} satisfies the following condition: none of the subtrees in π_{j_0} has a

v_{j_0}-th level vertex identifiable with a vertex on the same level of some subtree in another class of $\mathfrak{N}_{j_0}$. Then, by condition 2, the principal class of partition $\mathfrak{M}_{j_0+1}$ cannot be a subset of π_{j_0}. Consequently, at least one class of the partition $\mathfrak{N}_{j_0}$ contains two classes of $\mathfrak{N}_{j_0+1}$, proving our proposition.

It follows from the auxiliary proposition that the only significant factor in the construction of classes of partitions is the cardinality of the sets. Thus estimating the number of classes in $\mathfrak{N}_\rho$ reduces to the following combinatorial problem. Given an interval $[0, P)$, which is divided successively into subintervals with integer endpoints in such a way that each step involves division of at least one subinterval. Estimate the maximum possible number of steps in the process. Now it is clear that the number of steps cannot exceed the number of integers interior to $[0, P)$, and so $\rho \leqslant P-1$.

Theorem 74. Let $\Gamma_1(x, K, N, M_1, L_1, R)$ be a graph containing P subtrees, obtained from a graph $\Gamma_0(x, K, N, M_0, L_0, R)$ containing only critical subtrees. Then $L_1 \leqslant P-[(P-1)R/K^N]-1$.

Proof. By Theorem 70, the principal class of any cleavage partition containing some subtree $x_k(K, N, M_2, L_1, R)$ also contains some other subtree $x_l(K, N, M_3, L_1, R)$.

We first assume that $\Gamma(x)$ contains only two subtrees such that the subgraphs attached to their (L_1-1)-th level vertices are not complete trees. Then the product of all cleavage and division partitions contains a class with two subtrees. Choose a sequence of division partitions of maximum length in which the principal class of each partition is disjoint from the principal classes of more than $K^N/R-1$ pairs of cleavage partitions of different heights satisfying conditions 1 and 2 of Theorem 71.

Suppose that the principal classes of the above division partitions do not exhaust all the subtrees of $\Gamma(x)$. Take any division partition whose principal class is not disjoint from the principal classes of previous partitions, containing, say P' new subtrees. By Theorem 73, this set cannot contain the principal classes of more than $P'-1$ pairs of cleavage partitions with different heights. We continue in this way until all the subtrees of $\Gamma(x)$ have been exhausted.

It should now be clear that the number of possible pairs of cleavage partitions of different heights satisfying conditions 1 and 2 of Theorem 71 may be estimated as follows. Given an interval $[0, P)$ divided into segments with integer endpoints, each of length at most K^N/R. This system of segments is now subdivided into subintervals with integer endpoints, such that at each step at least one segment is subdivided and at the end of the process there remains at least one subinterval of length 2. The maximum number of subdivisions is less by one than the number of interior points of a system of subintervals of length at most K^N/R in $[0, P)$. The number of interior points of such a system is maximal if the subdivision of $[0, P)$ is effected using the minimal number of interior integer points. No such subdivision is possible with less than $[(P-1)R/K^N]$ points. Consequently, under our assumptions, the graph cannot represent more than $P-[(P-1)R/K^N]-2$ pairs of cleavage partitions of different heights.

By Theorems 71 and 72, we can define L_1-1 pairs of cleavage partitions of different heights in Γ_1, and this proves the theorem in this case.

Suppose now that $\Gamma(x)$ contains three subtrees x_k, x_l, x_m such that the subgraphs attached to their (L_1-1)-th level vertices are not complete trees.

If the product of all cleavage and division partitions contains a class composed of two subtrees, the theorem is valid.

If this condition is not satisfied, we consider the principal class of a formation partition containing x_k and x_l. The product of all cleavage and divisions partitions may consist entirely of singletons only if there is also a formation partition whose principal class contains x_k but not x_l. The principal class in question must then contain x_m too.

Consider a division partition whose principal class contains the principal class of a formation partition containing both x_k and x_l. The number of pairs of cleavage partitions of different heights that can be represented in the principal class of this division partition is at most $K^N/R-2$, since the subtrees in the principal class of some formation partition do not have (L_1-1)-th level vertices identifiable with vertices on the same level of a subtree belonging to the other class of the partition. This completes the proof.

Theorem 75. If $B(x, K, N, M, L, C)$ is an automaton with P states, then

$$L \leqslant P-1-[(P-1)C/K^N].$$

Proof. By Theorem 58, an automaton B with P states exists if and only if there is a normal graph $\Gamma(x, K, N, M, L, C)$ containing P subtrees. The desired estimate now follows from Theorem 74.

As we shall show in the next section, this estimate is attained for a certain graph $\Gamma(x, K, N, N, L, K^{N-1})$ for which it is exact.

Theorem 76. A normal automaton $B(I, N)$ over a K-letter input alphabet, with P states, may be ILS-I-L only if $L \leqslant P-2$, when P has prime divisors other than those of K, or if $L \leqslant P-1$ otherwise.

Proof. If P has no prime divisors other than those of K, there exist numbers N and C such that $K^N/C=P$, $[(P-1)C/K^N]=0$, and it follows from Theorem 75 that $L \leqslant P-1$. If P has a prime divisor not dividing K, we can only ensure that $K^N/C<P$. Then $[(P-1)C/K^N] \geqslant 1$ and by Theorem 75 $L \leqslant P-2$.

§7. SHARPNESS OF THE PRELIMINARY ESTIMATE

In this section we shall show that the estimate of Theorem 75 is indeed attained. For this purpose, we shall present an algorithm for construction of normal graphs $\Gamma(x)$, which will also be used later. The algorithm is based on Theorems 62 and 69. It is applied to the transition table of a normal graph $\Gamma(x)$, which is defined as follows.

Let $\Gamma(x)$ be a graph with P subtrees $x_{k_1}, \ldots, x_{k_P}$. The transition table of $\Gamma(x)$ has P rows, designated by the symbols $x_{k_1}, \ldots, x_{k_P}$, and K columns, designated by the letters $a_1, \ldots, a_K$. If $\Gamma(x)$ contains an arc labeled a_l from x_i to x_j, the symbol a_l is entered at the intersection of row x_i and column a_l, x_j. The table is filled in this way for all the arcs of $\Gamma(x)$. The set of symbols at the intersection of any row and column of the transition table will be called a cell.

Algorithm 5.*

Step 1. Select a pair of symbols (x_{i_1}, x_{j_1}) appearing in one or more cells of the transition table of $\Gamma(x)$. Add two new rows $x_{k_{p+1}}$, $x_{k_{p+2}}$ to the table, filling their cells according to the following rules: (1) the cells at the intersection of rows $x_{k_{p+1}}$ and $x_{k_{p+2}}$ and any column a_l will contain all the symbols at the intersection of rows x_{i_1}, x_{j_1} and column a_l, and only these; (2) each row $x_{k_{p+1}}$, $x_{k_{p+2}}$ contains exactly K symbols. Proceed to one of Steps 1, 2, 3 or 4.

Step 2. Select a column a_{l_2} and one symbol in each of rows $x_{k_{p+1}}$, $x_{k_{p+2}}$, say x_{i_2}, x_{j_2}, contained in column a_{l_2}. Add new rows $x_{k_{p+3}}$, $x_{k_{p+4}}$ and fill their cells in accordance with rules 1 and 2 of Step 1. Proceed to one of Steps 2, 3, 4 or 1 (in successive iteration of Step 2 one selects the last pair of new rows).

Step 3. Replace symbol pairs x_{i_n}, x_{j_n} selected at Steps 1 and 2 wholly or partially by the symbol pairs designating the corresponding new rows, observing the following conditions. Symbol pairs selected at Step 1 are replaced only if they are situated in one cell in the old rows. Symbol pairs selected at Step 2 are replaced only if they are situated in one column, each in one of a pair of rows introduced at the previous step (which may be either Step 1 or Step 2). At least one of the pairs selected at each iteration of Steps 1 and 2 is replaced. Proceed to Step 1 or 4.

Step 4. Strike out rows designated by symbols no longer appearing in cells of the transformed table. Proceed to Step 1 or halt.

We shall show that if this algorithm is applied to the transition table of a normal graph $\Gamma(x)$, the result is the transition table of some other normal graph $\Gamma_1(x)$; we shall establish the properties $\Gamma_1(x)$ as depending on the properties of $\Gamma(x)$ and the mode of application of Algorithm 5.

Let us assume that no series of applications of Steps 1 and 2 can contain more than n operations without a repetition of Step 1. We may then assume without loss of generality that $\Gamma(x)=\Gamma(x, K, N\ M, L, R)$, $N-L\geqslant n+1$.

Theorem 77. Suppose that an application of Algorithm 5 to the graph $\Gamma(x)$ satisfies the following conditions:

(1) *Steps 1 and 2 are applied in series of $n_1, \dots, n_\nu$ operations, each beginning with Step 1 and involving thereafter only Step 2.*

(2) *In the last implementation of Step 2 in each series, different rows of the transformed table contain symbols designating subtrees which have mutually identifiable vertices on levels $m_1-1, \dots, m_\nu-1$, respectively, but symbols designating subtrees with mutually identifiable vertices on levels $m_1, \dots, m_\nu$ are located in one row.*

(3) *No symbols produced by application of Steps 1 and 2 are replaced.*

Then the transformed table is the transition table of a normal graph $\Gamma_1(x, K, N, M, \max(n_\nu+m_\nu), R)$.

* The procedure described here does not conform rigorously to the concept of an algorithm as accepted in mathematics, since the operations to be implemented are not specified unambiguously. This may be avoided by introducing additional instructions, for example, as done in /14/. For reasons of simplicity this is not done here, and our description of Algorithm 5 specifies only operations which have significance for subsequent arguments.

Proof. We shall show that successive lifting and arc-shifting operations applied to the graph $\Gamma(x)$ produce a graph $\Gamma_1(x)$ with the required parameters, whose transition table is the transformed transition table of $\Gamma(x)$.

Consider the first series of applications of Steps 1 and 2. Suppose the selected symbol pair is in cells $(x_{k_1}, a_{l_1}), (x_{k_2}, a_{l_2}), \ldots, (x_{k_I}, a_{l_I})$. Construct the trees $T(x_{k_\rho}, \Gamma(x), n_1+1)$ $(\rho=1,\ldots,I)$; we now proceed to form imbedded sequences of partitions for the leaves of these trees. To simplify the description, it will be given in detail only for one of the trees T, say $T(x_{k_1}, \Gamma(x), n_1+1)$, corresponding to the cell (x_{k_1}, a_{l_1}). The partitions to be constructed will be denoted by $\mathfrak{A}_0^\pi, \mathfrak{A}_1^\pi, \ldots, \mathfrak{A}_{n_1+1}^\pi$, where the superscript serves to distinguish between different partition systems.

For each π, the partition $\mathfrak{A}_0^\pi$ will consist of a single class, containing all the leaves of T.

The partition $\mathfrak{A}_1^1$ will contain, first, $K-2$ classes, each consisting of all leaves of $T(x_{k_1}, \Gamma(x), n_1+1)$ which are ends of paths from one first level subtree x_ν of T. To form these classes, select all first level subtrees of T, except for the occurrences of subtrees x_{i_1}, x_{j_1} which are ends of arcs labeled a_{l_1} from the root of T. The other leaves of T are divided into two classes $\pi_{1i_1}^1$ and $\pi_{1j_1}^1$, thus: $\pi_{1i_1}^1$ consists of all subtrees which are ends of paths from the second level subtrees of T whose symbols appear in row $x_{i_{P+1}}$, and $\pi^1_{1j_1}$ is defined similarly for row $x_{i_{P+2}}$. If $n_1=1$, the construction ends here.

If $n_1>1$, construct a system of partitions $\mathfrak{A}_0^1, \mathfrak{A}_1^1, \ldots, \mathfrak{A}_{n_1+1}^1$ such that the partitions $\mathfrak{A}_2^1, \ldots, \mathfrak{A}_{n_1+1}^1$ coincide with $\mathfrak{A}_1^1$.

Suppose that in rows $x_{i_{P+1}}$ and $x_{i_{P+2}}$ the symbols x_{i_2}, x_{j_2} appear in columns $a_{r_1}, \ldots, a_{r_J}$, each of these symbols appearing in each column in exactly one of rows $x_{i_{P+1}}, x_{i_{P+2}}$. Considering the column a_{r_1}, we construct the partition $\mathfrak{A}_2^2$. Its first $K-2$ classes are all the classes of $\mathfrak{A}_1^1$ except $\pi_{1i_1}^1$ and $\pi_{1j_1}^1$. The other classes of $\mathfrak{A}_2^2$ are subsets of $\pi_{1i_1}^1$ and $\pi_{1j_1}^1$, constructed as follows. $2K-2$ classes of $\mathfrak{A}_2^2$ are the sets of all leaves of T which are ends of paths from subtrees x_ν on the second level of T, other than the occurrences of x_{i_2}, x_{j_2} which are ends of paths from the root defining the word $a_{l_1}a_{r_1}$. The other leaves of T are divided into two classes. One includes the subtrees which are ends of paths from all the subtrees x_ν on the third level of T whose symbols appear in rows $x_{i_{P+3}}$ and $x_{i_{P+4}}$, respectively. These last two classes are denoted by $\pi_{2i_2}^2$ and $\pi_{2j_2}^2$. If $n_1=2$, the construction ends.

If $n_1>2$, construct a system of partitions $\mathfrak{A}_0^2, \mathfrak{A}_1^2, \ldots, \mathfrak{A}_{n_1+1}^2$, where the partitions $\mathfrak{A}_3^2, \ldots, \mathfrak{A}_{n_1+1}^2$ coincide with $\mathfrak{A}_2^2$.

Suppose that in rows $x_{i_{P+3}}$ and $x_{i_{P+4}}$ the symbols x_{i_3}, x_{j_3} appear in columns $a_{p_1}, \ldots, a_{p_S}$, each appearing in each column in exactly one row. Considering column a_{p_1}, construct a partition $\mathfrak{A}_3^3$ in the same way as the partition $\mathfrak{A}_2^2$ above. Define $\mathfrak{A}_1^3=\mathfrak{A}_1^2$, $\mathfrak{A}_2^3=\mathfrak{A}_2^2$. If $n_1>3$, the partitions $\mathfrak{A}_4^3, \ldots, \mathfrak{A}_{n_1+1}^3$ coincide with $\mathfrak{A}_3^3$.

This procedure is carried out for all remaining levels of T.

The above construction depends in an obvious manner on a certain word $a_{l_1}a_{r_1}a_{p_1}\ldots$. We now carry out analogous constructions for all possible words and word combinations. With regard to word combinations, we illustrate the procedure briefly for the case of $\mathfrak{A}_1^\pi$. Select the occurrences of the pair (x_{i_1}, x_{j_1}) in several columns of row x_{k_1} (if such exist) and duplicate the construction producing the classes $\pi_{1i_1}{}^1$ and $\pi_{1j_1}{}^1$ above for each occurrence. This procedure is also applied to all levels of $T(x_{k_1}, \Gamma(x), n_1+1)$.

We proceed in this way to construct partitions of leaves for all the other trees $T(x_{k_\sigma}, \Gamma(x), n_1+1)$ such that the cells at the intersection of row x_{k_σ} and certain columns contain symbol pairs (x_{i_1}, x_{j_1}).

All the partitions thus constructed will be referred to as partitions associated with the pair (x_{i_1}, x_{j_1}).

Every return from Step 2 to Step 1 involves construction of new partitions based on the pair of symbols selected at the specific implementation of Step 1 in question.

We shall say that these groups of partitions are associated with the newly selected pair.

The construction of partitions associated with symbol pairs ends when we have constructed partitions associated with the pair selected upon the last return from Step 2 to Step 1.

For each of the partitions constructed, we consider the corresponding tree $W^\pi(\mathfrak{A}_0{}^\pi, \mathfrak{A}_1{}^\pi, \ldots, \mathfrak{A}_{n_\mu+1}{}^\pi)$. It follows from the details of the construction that all our systems of partitions are imbedded and admissible, so that by Theorem 60 the trees W^π are incomplete cleavages of the root subtrees of the appropriate trees T. (Here there is no need to attach complete trees to the leaves of subtrees in $\Gamma(x)$, thanks to our assumption that $N-L \geqslant n_\nu+1$.)

If an implementation of Step 2 is followed by Step 4 and certain rows are thereby eliminated, this means that the graph $\Gamma(x)$ is not strongly connected. We may therefore assume that Step 2 is followed only by an implementation of Step 3.

Suppose that symbol pairs $(x_{i_1}, x_{j_1}), \ldots, (x_{i_n}, x_{j_n})$ are replaced in columns $a_{l_1}, \ldots, a_{l_n}$. We then insert the tree $W(\mathfrak{A}_0{}^\pi, \ldots, \mathfrak{A}_{n_1+1}{}^\pi)$ in $\Gamma(x)$, where the partitions $\mathfrak{A}_0{}^\pi, \mathfrak{A}_1{}^\pi, \ldots, \mathfrak{A}_{n_1+1}{}^\pi$ are such that construction of $\mathfrak{A}_\nu{}^\pi$ was based on selection of the pair $(x_{i\nu}, x_{j\nu})$ in column $a_{l\nu}$. If some of the symbol pairs are replaced in several columns, we insert a tree $W(\mathfrak{A}_0{}^\pi, \ldots, \mathfrak{A}_{n_1+1}{}^\pi)$ such that $\mathfrak{A}_0{}^\pi, \ldots, \mathfrak{A}_{n_1+1}{}^\pi$ are based on several of the associated words.

Similar insertion operations are performed for all series of implementations of Steps 1 and 2.

Consider the first series of implementations of Steps 1 and 2. If the last rows $x_{i_{P+2n_1-1}}$ and $x_{i_{P+2n_1}}$ contain symbols, in different rows, denoting subtrees in $\Gamma(x)$ which have mutually identifiable (m_1-1)-th level vertices, whereas subtrees with mutually identifiable vertices on levels $m_1, m_1+1, \ldots$ appear in the same row, the corresponding tree $W(\mathfrak{A}_0{}^\pi, \ldots, \mathfrak{A}_{n_1+1}{}^\pi)$ will contain two subtrees such that the subgraphs attached to their (m_1+n_1-1)-th level vertices are not all complete trees but all those attached to the (m_1+n_1)-th level vertices of the subtrees of $W(\mathfrak{A}_0{}^\pi, \ldots, \mathfrak{A}_{n_1+1}{}^\pi)$ are complete trees.

It also follows from the construction that the transition table of the resulting graph $\Gamma_1(x)$ is precisely the transformed table of the graph $\Gamma(x)$.

If Step 3 is followed by an implementation of Step 1, the preceding arguments may be repeated.

It follows that the resulting graph is $\Gamma_1(x) = \Gamma_1(x, K, N, M, \max(m_\nu+n_\nu), R)$.

Now consider any implementation of Step 4. Certain symbols x_i, x_j in the transformed table may disappear only by virtue of an application of Step 3.

In that case, the corresponding subtrees are no longer ends of arcs after insertion of the trees W. Thus these subtrees must be discarded in order to obtain an admissible graph.

Repeating these arguments sufficiently many times, we complete the proof of the theorem.

Algorithm 5 does not exhaust all possible constructions of new normal graphs from others, for it does not reflect arc-shifting operations. Our theorem makes it possible to parallel this operation as well.

Algorithm 6.

Step 1. Replace certain symbols in the transition table of $\Gamma(x)$ by others in such a way that the new symbol and the old denote isomorphic subtrees.

Step 2. Strike out rows designated by symbols no longer appearing in the cells after implementation of Step 1.

The following theorem is obvious.

Theorem 78. Repeated application of Algorithms 5 and 6 to the transition table of a normal graph $\Gamma(x)$ *produces the transition table of a normal graph* $\Gamma_1(x)$.

Theorem 78 provides no information about the numerical parameters of the graph $\Gamma_1(x)$, since the transformations effected by Algorithm 6 vary the parameters of the subtrees in intermediate graphs in a highly complicated manner.

Theorem 79. Suppose that $\Gamma_1(x)$ *is obtained from a graph* $\Gamma_0(x)$ *containing only critical subtrees by lifting and arc-shifting operations. Then there exists a sequence of applications of Algorithms 5 and 6 to the transition table of* $\Gamma_0(x)$ *such that the transformed table is the transition table of* $\Gamma_1(x)$.

Proof. The theorem follows directly from Theorems 69, 77 and 78.

As follows from Theorem 79, by applying Algorithms 5 and 6 to the transition table of a normal graph $\Gamma(x)$ containing only critical subtrees we can construct transition tables of other normal graphs. By virtue of Theorem 24, Algorithms 5 and 6 may thus be applied to the construction of ILS-I-N automata. As opposed to the method of Chap. II, §10, here no direct information is forthcoming concerning the types of states of the resulting automata, or, consequently, the numbers N and R for which the automaton $\Gamma(tx)$ and a standard inverse with delay $N_1 \geqslant N$ are respectively ILS-I-N and ILS-I-R.

Algorithms 5 and 6 are nevertheless useful when one is considering the minimum number of states for which a normal automaton may be an ILS-I-N automaton having a standard inverse with delay $N_1 \geqslant N$ which is ILS-I-R.

We now proceed to construct the transition table of certain graphs $\Gamma(x)$ which demonstrate that the estimate in Theorem 75 may be attained.

We first assume that $\Gamma(x)$ contains nK subtrees.

Construct a table with nK rows, designated $x_1, \ldots, x_{nK}$, and K columns, designated $a_1, \ldots, a_K$. In the cells (x_{iK+j}, a_j) $(i=1, \ldots, n-1,\ j=1, \ldots, K)$, insert symbols $x_{(i-1)K+1}, \ldots, x_{iK}$, and in the cells (x_j, a_j) $(j=1, \ldots, K)$ symbols $x_{(n-1)K+1}, \ldots, x_{nK}$. All other cells are empty. It is readily seen that this is the transition table of a normal graph $\Gamma(x)$ containing only complete panicles of type $(K, N, N-1)$. If the subtrees of $\Gamma(x)$ are denoted by the symbols for the rows of the table, it can be shown that the roots of all subtrees $\{x_{(i-1)K+1}, \ldots, x_{iK}\}$ $(i=1, \ldots, n)$ are mutually identifiable, but their first level vertices are not. For Step 1 of Algorithm 5, we select the pair (x_1, x_2) and enter symbols in new rows x_{nK+1} and x_{nK+2} as follows: in cells (x_{nK+1}, a_1) and (x_{nK+2}, a_2) — the symbol x_{nK}, in cells (x_{nK+1}, a_2) and (x_{nK+2}, a_1) — the symbols $x_{(n-1)K+1}, \ldots, x_{nK-1}$. For Step 3, we replace all occurrences of pairs x_1, x_2 by the symbols x_{nK+1} and x_{nK+2}. Then the symbols x_{nK+1} and x_{nK+2} will appear in cells (x_{K+1}, a_1) and (x_{K+2}, a_2). The symbols now no longer appear in the rows of the table and rows x_1, x_2 are stricken out in Step 4. The result is the transition table of a graph $\Gamma_1(x)$ containing nK subtrees which, by Theorem 78, contains a subtree $x(K, N, N, 2, K^{N-1})$.

Now consider the ν-th $(\nu=2, \ldots, n)$ application of Algorithm 5 to the graph $\Gamma_1(x)$. At Step 1 we select the pair $(x_{(\nu-1)K+1}, x_{(\nu-1)K+2})$ and enter in cells $(x_{nK+2\nu-1}, a_1)$ and $(x_{nK+2\nu}, a_2)$ the symbol $x_{nK+2\nu-3}$, in cells $(x_{nK+2\nu-1}, a_2)$ and $(x_{nK+2\nu}, a_1)$ symbols $x_{nK+2\nu-2}, x_{(\nu-2)K+3}, \ldots, x_{(\nu-1)K}$. Replace the symbol pair $(x_{(\nu-1)K+1}, x_{(\nu-1)K+2})$ throughout by $(x_{nK+2\nu-1}, x_{nK+2\nu})$, strike out rows $x_{(\nu-1)K+1}$ and $x_{(\nu-1)K+2}$. At the ν-th implementation of Step 3, symbols $x_{nK+2\nu-1}$ and $x_{nK+2\nu}$ are in both empty cells of the symbol pair selected at the $(\nu+1)$-th implementation of Step 1; hence the n-th implementation of Algorithm 5 gives the transition table of a graph $\Gamma_n(x) = \Gamma_n(x, K, N, N, n+1, K^{N-1})$.

This table possesses the following properties. Each of the two sets of symbols $x_{nK+2\nu-2}$, $x_{(\nu-2)K+3}, \ldots, x_{(\nu-1)K}$ $(\nu=2, 3, \ldots, n)$ and x_{nK+2n}, $x_{(n-1)K+3}, \ldots, x_{nK-1}$ always appears in one cell, and the second set appears in cells (x_3, a_3) and (x_{nK+2}, a_1).

Let us call the above version of the algorithm the "first series," and stipulate that after each n-fold application of Algorithm 5 the next series begins.

First application of Algorithm 5 in second series: At Step 1, select the symbol pair (x_{nK+2}, x_3); enter in cell $(x_{n(K+2)+1}, a_3)$ the symbol $x_{n(K+2)-1}$, and in cell $(x_{n(K+2)+2}, a_3)$ the symbols $x_{n(K+2)}, x_{(n-1)K+4}, \ldots, x_{nK-1}$ together with all other symbols appearing in cell (x_3, a_3). In the other cells of rows $x_{n(K+2)+1}$ and $x_{n(K+2)+2}$, we enter the symbols appearing in the cells of row x_{nK+2}. The latter contains nonempty cells only in two columns, one of the nonempty cells containing one symbol and the other $K-1$ symbols. Consequently, rows $x_{n(K+2)+1}$ and $x_{n(K+2)+2}$ may be filled in such a way that symbols in one cell in row x_{nK+2} appear in one cell in the new rows. As a result we obtain rows containing only two nonempty cells, one of them containing one symbol and the other $K-1$.

ν-th application of Algorithm 5 in second series $(\nu=2, \ldots, n)$: At Step 1, select the pair $(x_{nK+2\nu}, x_{(\nu-1)K+3})$; enter in cell $(x_{n(K+2)+2\nu-1}, a_3)$ the symbol $x_{n(K+2)+2\nu-3}$, in cell $(x_{n(K+2)+2\nu}, a_3)$ the symbols $x_{n(K+2)+2\nu-2}, x_{(\nu-2)K+4}, \ldots, x_{(\nu-1)K}$ together with all other symbols from cell $(x_{(\nu-1)K+3}, a_3)$. The sequel is the same as in the first application of Algorithm 5 in the second series (if $K=3$, then $\nu \leqslant n-1$).

The n-th application of Algorithm 5 in the second series produces a table possessing the following properties. Each of the two sets of symbols $x_{n(K+2)+2\nu-2}, x_{(\nu-2)K+4}, \ldots, x_{(\nu-1)K}$ $(\nu=2, 3, \ldots, n)$ and $x_{n(K+2)+2n}, x_{(n-1)K+4}, \ldots, x_{nK-1}$ is always in one cell, and the second set is also in cells (x_4, a_4) and $(x_{n(K+2)+2}, a_1)$.

First application of Algorithm 5 in m-th series $(m=3, \ldots, K-1)$: At Step 1, select the symbol pair $(x_{n(K+2(m-2))+2}, x_{m+1})$; enter in cell $(x_{n(K+2(m-1))+1}, a_{m+1})$ the symbol $x_{n(K+2(m-1))-1}$, and in cell $(x_{n(K+2(m-1))+2}, a_{m+1})$ the symbols $x_{n(K+2(m-1))}$, $x_{(n-1)K+m+2}, \ldots, x_{nK-1}$ together with all other symbols from cell (x_{m+1}, a_{m+1}). The other cells of the new rows are filled by symbols from row $x_{n(K+2(m-2))+2}$.

ν-th application of Algorithm 5 in m-th series ($\nu=2,\ldots,n$): At Step 1 select the pair $(x_{n(K+2(m-2))+2\nu}, x_{(\nu-1)K+m+1})$; enter in cell $(x_{n(K+2(m-1))+2\nu-1}, a_{m+1})$ the symbol $x_{n(K+2(m-1))+2\nu-3}$, and in cell $(x_{n(K+2(m-1))+2\nu}, a_{m+1})$ symbols $x_{n(K+2(m-1))+2\nu-2}$, $x_{(\nu-2)K+m+2},\ldots,x_{(\nu-1)K}$ together with all other symbols from cell $(x_{(\nu-1)K+m+1}, a_{m+1})$. The other cells of the new rows are filled by symbols from row $x_{n(K+2(m-2))+2\nu}$ in such a way that the $K-1$ symbols in one cell are again in one cell in the new rows.

After completion of the m-th series $(m=3,\ldots,K-2)$, each of the sets $x_{n(K+2(m-1))+2\nu-2}$, $x_{(\nu-2)K+m+2},\ldots,x_{(\nu-1)K}$ $(\nu=2,3,\ldots,n)$ and $x_{n(K+2(m-1))+2n}$, $x_{(n-1)K+m+2},\ldots,x_{nK-1}$ is always in one cell, and the second set is in cells (x_{m+2}, a_{m+2}) and $(x_{n(K+2(m-1))+2}, a_1)$.

Algorithm 5 may actually be used in $K-2$ series, each involving n applications, in such a way that two of the old rows in the table may be eliminated. In the last ($(K-1)$-th) series, $n-1$ applications of the algorithm are possible, each involving elimination of two old rows.

It follows that Algorithm 5 may be applied $(n-1)+(K-2)n=n(K-1)-1$ times without increasing the number of rows of the original table. The sequence of applications is such that each increases by unity the level of the vertices whose attached subgraphs are not complete trees. Consequently, there exists a normal graph $\Gamma(x, K, N, N, n(K-1), K^{N-1})$ containing nK subtrees. It follows that there exists an ILS-I-$n(K-1)$ automaton with nK states.

At the $(n(K-1)-1)$-th application of the algorithm, the pair $(x_{n(K+2(K-3))+2(n-1)}, x_{(n-1)K})$ is selected.

If row $x_{(n-1)K}$ is filled by other symbols, the applications of Algorithm 5 preceding the $(n(K-1)-1)$-th may be transferred to the changed table.

If row $x_{(n-1)K}$ is filled in such a way that cells $(x_{(n-1)K}, a_K)$ and (x_{nK}, a_K) contain the same symbols, we obtain the transition table of a normal graph. After $(n(K-1)-2)$-fold application of Algorithm 5, the result is a table containing two equal rows $x_{(n-1)K}$ and x_{nK}. Hence the corresponding subtrees are isomorphic and one of the symbols may be replaced by the other in accordance with Algorithm 6, the row corresponding to the replaced symbol being stricken out.

Hence it follows that there exists a normal graph $\Gamma(x, K, N, N, n(K-1)-1, K^{N-1})$ containing $nK-1$ subtrees, or an ILS-I-$n(K-1)-1$ automaton with $nK-1$ states.

The pair selected at the last application of Algorithm 5 is in row $x_{n(K+2(K-3))+2n}$. The symbol pair $(x_{n(K+2(K-3))+2n}, x_{nK})$ is in row $x_{n(K+2(K-3))+2n+2}$. We replace the symbols in cell (x_{nK}, a_K) of the original table by $x_{(n-1)K+1},\ldots$ $\ldots, x_{nK}$. The first $n(K-1)-1$ applications of Algorithm 5 carry over without modification to the new table, since row x_{nK} was not selected in any pair.

We now apply Algorithm 5 for the $n(K-1)$-th time to the transformed table, selecting the pair $(x_{n(K+2(K-3))+2n}, x_{nK})$ at Step 1. In rows $x_{nK+2n(K-1)-1}$ and $x_{nK+2n(K-1)}$ we enter the symbols $x_{nK+2n(K-1)-3}$ and $x_{nK+2n(K-1)-2}$, taken from row $x_{n(K+2(K-3))+2n}$ (each symbol in a different row). It is sufficient to enter one symbol in one of the rows and $K-1$ in the other. Thus $K-1$ symbols of the K appearing in cell (x_{nK}, a_K) may be entered in one cell of one of the new rows. We select them in such a way that one cell contains the symbols selected at Step 1. At Step 3 the selected symbols are replaced by new ones, both in the new row and in row x_{nK}. In the resulting table, we have two cells containing symbols $x_{i_1}, x_{i_2}, \ldots, x_{i_{K-3}}, x_l, x_m$, where x_l and are subtrees of the corresponding graph, with $(n(K-1)+1)$-th level vertices whose attached subgraphs are not complete trees. Consequently, the table defines a graph $\Gamma_{n(K-1)}(x, K, N, N, n(K-1)+1, K^{N-1})$ containing $nK+2$ subtrees. The symbols x_l and x_m do not appear in other cells.

In the next application of the algorithm, the pair selected at Step 1 is (x_l, x_{i_1}). The new rows are filled in such a way that one row contains the symbol x_m and the other the symbols $x_{i_1}, \ldots, x_{i_{K-3}}, x_l$. Once the symbols x_{i_1} and x_l have been replaced by new ones, the row x_l is eliminated, since the symbol x_l always appears in the table together with x_{i_1}. We thus obtain the table of a graph $\Gamma_{n(K-1)+1}$ $(x, K, N, N, n(K-1)+2, K^{N-1})$ containing $nK+3$ subtrees. This table has a row x_λ containing symbols $x_{i_2}, \ldots, x_{i_{K-3}}, x_\lambda, x_\nu$ in one cell, where x_λ and x_ν are subtrees in the graph $\Gamma_{n(K-1)+1}$ with $(n(K-1)+2)$-th level vertices whose attached subgraphs are not complete trees. Applying Algorithm 5 again, we select the pair (x_{i_2}, x_λ) and construct the transition table of a graph $\Gamma_{n(K-1)+2}(x, K, N, N, n(K-1)+3, K^{N-1})$ with $nK+4$ subtrees. It is clear that this process may be iterated another $K-4$ times. With each application of Algorithm 5 the number of subtrees increases by one, as does the level at which there are subtrees whose attached subgraphs are not complete trees.

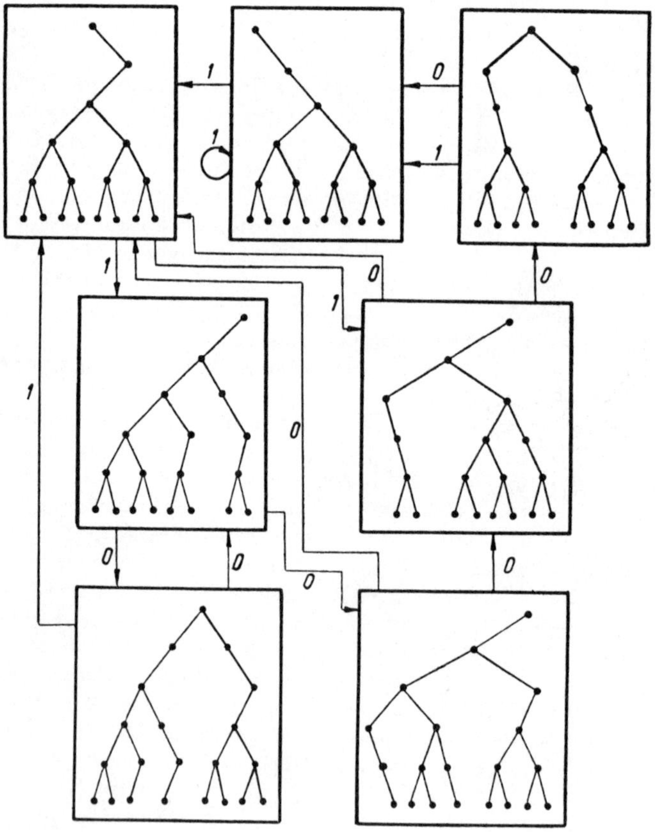

FIGURE 23.

It is readily seen that the estimate of Theorem 75 is attained for the graphs produced by this procedure.

Figure 23 shows that the estimate of Theorem 75 may be attained for other graphs. This indicates that the technique employed to derive our preliminary estimate is inadequate to obtain sharper estimates.

§8. SHARPENING OF THE PRELIMINARY ESTIMATE

A very simple method for sharpening our estimate is applicable to graphs $\Gamma(x, K, N, M, L, R)$ with $M<N$.

Definition 48. A subdivision partition of height M of the set of all subtrees in a graph $\Gamma(x, K, N, M, L, R)$ is a partition satisfying the following condition: one class (the principal class) contains all subtrees whose $(N-M)$-th level vertices are identifiable with the same leaf of some subtree, the other contains all the remaining subtrees.

Theorem 80. Let $\mathfrak{M}$ be an arbitrary set of subtrees in a graph $\Gamma(x, K, N, M, L, R)$ which are elements of the principal class of some subdivision partition of height M. Suppose that $\mathfrak{M}$ contains P elements and, for each of a sequence of numbers $\nu_1<\nu_2<\ldots<\nu_\rho$, contains the principal classes of two cleavage partitions of type ν_j $(j=1,\ldots,\rho)$ satisfying conditions 1 and 2 of Theorem 71. Then $\rho\leqslant P-1$.

The proof is the same as that of Theorem 73.

Theorem 81. Let $\Gamma_1(x, K, N, M_1, L_1, R)$ be a graph containing P subtrees which is obtained from a graph $\Gamma_0(x, K, N, M_0, L_0, R)$ containing only critical subtrees. Then

$$L_1-(N-M_1)\leqslant P-[(P-1)R/K^{M_1}]-1.$$

Proof. The proof differs from that of Theorem 74 only in that Theorem 73 is replaced by Theorem 80 and the interval $[0, P)$ is divided into subintervals of length at most K^{M_1}/R. Note that there is no need to consider cleavage partitions of height $1, 2,\ldots, N-M_1$, since the principal classes of such partitions contain the principal classes of subdivision partitions of height M_1.

Theorem 82. For any automaton $B(x, K, N, M, L, C)$ with P states,

$$L\leqslant P-[(P-1)C/K^M]+N-M-1.$$

This is a direct corollary of Theorems 58 and 81.

Theorem 83. Let $B(I, N)$ be a normal automaton over a K-letter alphabet, with P states, having a standard inverse with delay N which is ILS-I-M. If the representation of the number K to base P is

$$P=a_nK^n+\ldots+a_0 \quad (n\geqslant N,\ a_n\neq 0)$$

and B is ILS-I-L, then

$$L\leqslant P-a_nK^{N-M}-\ldots-a_{n-(N-M)}+N-M.$$

Proof. We have

$$(P-1)C/K^M = a_n K^{n-M}C + \ldots + a_{n-(n-M)}C + (\varphi(K)-1)C/K^M,$$

where $\varphi(K) < K^M$. Hence

$$[(P-1)C/K^M] = a_n K^{n-M}C + \ldots + a_{n-(n-M)}C + [(\varphi(K)-1)C/K^M].$$

If $\varphi(K) > 0$, the number $[(P-1)C/K^M]$ assumes its minimum value for $C=1$, and then

$$[(P-1)C/K^M] \geqslant a_n K^{n-M} + \ldots + a_{n-(n-M)}.$$

If $\varphi(K)=0$, the number $[(P-1)C/K^M]$ is again a minimum for $C=1$, since it follows from the condition $C \leqslant K^M$ that $[-C/K^M] = -1$.

It follows from the inequality

$$a_n K^{n-M} + \ldots + a_{n-(n-M)} \geqslant a_n K^{N-M} + \ldots + a_{n-(N-M)},$$

which is valid for any $n \geqslant N$, that

$$[(P-1)C/K^M] \geqslant a_n K^{N-M} + \ldots + a_{n-(N-M)} - 1,$$

and in view of the estimate of Theorem 82 this implies the required estimate for L.

A sharpened estimate in the general case may probably be achieved by improving the estimate for the number of different division partitions.

Investigation of the graphs $\Gamma(x, 2, N, N, N, 2^{N-2})$ provides good grounds for the conjecture that a graph with $P=4n$ subtrees must have $n+1$ different division partitions.

This implies the estimate $N \leqslant P - P/4 - 1$ for such values of P. If $P \neq 4n$, we have $[(P-1)/4] = [P/4]$. We may therefore conjecture that in this case $N \leqslant P - [P/4] - 1$; this is somewhat superior to the result of Theorem 75, and for $P \geqslant 7$ one can construct a graph for which this estimate is attained.

The graphs $E(K, n)$ may be used to sharpen our estimates. The proof of the following theorem illustrates the principles involved.

Theorem 84. For any automaton $B(x, 2, N, M, L, 2^{M-1})$ *with* P *states,*

$$L \leqslant [P/2] - 2^{N-M-1} + (N-M) \quad (N > M).$$

Proof. We determine the minimum number of subtrees in a normal graph $\Gamma(x, 2, N, M, L, 2^{M-1})$ as a function of N, M, L. Divide the subtrees of $\Gamma(x)$ into groups $G(\alpha)$, where α runs through all words of length $N-M$ over $\mathfrak{A}$: A subtree x_m is an element of $G(\alpha)$ if and only if some path of length $N-M$ from the root of x_m defines the word α. It is clear that for every subtree $x_k(2, N, M_1, L_1, 2^{M-1}) \in G(\alpha)$ there is a subtree $x_r(2, N, M_1, L_1, 2^{M-1}) \in G(\alpha)$ such that $x_k \cup x_r$ is a complete panicle of type (K, N, M) $(M_1 = M, M-1)$.

Let x_ρ and x_π be two subtrees in $\Gamma(x)$ which have mutually identifiable $(L-1)$-th level vertices. Suppose that the respective paths from the roots of x_ρ and x_π to these vertices define the word $a_{i_1} a_{i_2} \ldots a_{i_{L-1}}$. As follows by construction of cleavages for x_ρ and x_π, any segment $a_{i_{j+1}} \dots a_{i_{j+N-M}}$ of this word ($j=1, \dots, L-N+M-1$) corresponds to the fact that the group $G(a_{i_{j+1}} \dots a_{i_{j+N-M}})$ contains two subtrees with complete trees attached to their $(L-j)$-th level vertices and none to their $(L-j-1)$-th level vertices. Take any word α_1 of length $N-M-1$ and consider the groups $G(a_1\alpha_1)$, $G(a_2\alpha_1)$, $G(\alpha_1 a_1)$ and $G(\alpha_1 a_2)$. Suppose that the word $a_{i_1}a_{i_2}\dots a_{i_{L-2}}$ contains l_{α_1} segments $a_1\alpha_1$ and $a_2\alpha_1$. Then the groups $G(\alpha_1 a_1)$ and $G(\alpha_1 a_2)$ contain at least $2(l_{\alpha_1}+1)$ distinct subtrees. Indeed, each segment $a_1\alpha_1$ or $a_2\alpha_1$ is followed in the word $a_{i_1}a_{i_2}\dots a_{i_{L-1}}$ by one of the segments $\alpha_1 a_1$ or $\alpha_1 a_2$. If this holds for only one of the latter, say $\alpha_1 a_1$, the group $G(\alpha_1 a_1)$, as stated above, contains at least $2l_{\alpha_1}$ subtrees and the group $G(\alpha_1 a_2)$ at least two, since it is not empty. If both segments $\alpha_1 a_1$, $\alpha_1 a_2$ follow, then one of them, say $\alpha_1 a_1$, is the more distant from the beginning of the word $a_{i_2}\dots a_{i_{L-1}}$. Let $\alpha_1 a_1$ appear exactly m times. Then the group $G(\alpha_1 a_1)$ contains at least $2m$ subtrees. By the above argument, the group $G(\alpha_1 a_2)$ contains at least $2(l_{\alpha_1}-m)$ subtrees defined by the segments $\alpha_1 a_2$. Suppose that the immediate predecessor of the last occurrence of the segment $\alpha_1 a_1$ in $a_{i_2}\dots a_{i_{L-1}}$ is the letter a_j. Then there exist two subtrees x_ν, x_μ in which there are paths from the roots, of length $N-M$, defining the word $a_j\alpha_1$. There are two arcs issuing from the vertices $\chi_{\nu,N-M,a_j\alpha_1}$ and $\chi_{\mu,N-M,a_j\alpha_1}$, since the subtrees x_ν and x_μ cannot be complete panicles. Thus cleavages of x_ν and x_μ contain two subtrees $x_\varkappa$, x_λ, paths of length $N-M$ from whose roots define the word $\alpha_1 a_2$, $x_\varkappa \in G(\alpha_1 a_2)$, $x_\lambda \in G(\alpha_1 a_2)$. The subtrees $x_\varkappa$ and x_λ cannot coincide with any of the previously mentioned subtrees in $G(\alpha_1 a_2)$, since they have complete trees attached to lower-numbered levels. Thus in this case too the groups $G(\alpha_1 a_1)$ and $G(\alpha_1 a_2)$ contain at least $2(l_{\alpha_1}+1)$ subtrees. Furthermore, the group $G(a_{i_1}\dots a_{i_{N-M}})$ contains subtrees x_ρ and x_π not coinciding with any of those already assigned to the groups. Consequently, the graph $\Gamma(x, 2, N, M, L, 2^{M-1})$ contains at least $2\sum_{\alpha_1} l_{\alpha_1}+2+2^{N-M}$ subtrees. But $\sum_{\alpha_1} l_{\alpha_1}=M-N+L-1$, since this is the number of all segments of length $N-M$ in an $(L-2)$-letter word. Consequently, $\Gamma(x, 2, N, M, L, 2^{M-1})$ contains at least $2(L+M-N+2^{N-M-1})$ subtrees.

Thus, if the graph has P subtrees, the inequality $[P/2] \geqslant L+M-N+2^{N-M-1}$ yields the desired estimate.

In the next section we shall outline the construction of automata for which the estimate of Theorem 84 is attained. This corroborates our assertion that the properties of the graphs $E(K, n)$ indeed enable one to sharpen the estimates.

§9. ASYMPTOTIC SHARPNESS OF THE ESTIMATE

The results of §7 lead to the following theorem.

Theorem 85. For any number K, there exists a sequence of normal automata $B_1, B_2, \dots, B_n, \dots$ over a K-letter alphabet, with $P_1, P_2, \dots, P_n, \dots$ states, which are ILS-I-L_1, ..., ILS-I-L_n, ..., respectively, where $\lim_{n\to\infty} L_n/P_n = 1-1/K$.

Proof. As shown in §7, for any $P_n \geqslant K$ we can construct an automaton $B_n(x, K, N_n, N_n, L_n, K^{N_n-1})$ with P_n states such that $L_n = P_n - 1 - [(P_n - 1)/K]$, i. e., $L_n/P_n = 1 - 1/P_n - [(P_n - 1)/K]/P_n$. If $P_n - 1$ is divisible by K, then

$$[(P_n - 1)/K]/P_n = (P_n - 1)/KP_n = 1/K - 1/KP_n.$$

Otherwise, for some number $1 \leqslant m \leqslant K-1$ we have $[(P_n - 1)/K] = (P_n - m - 1)/K$, so that

$$[(P_n - 1)/K]/P_n = (P_n - m - 1)/KP_n = 1/K - (m+1)/KP_n.$$

Assuming (as we may) that $P_n \to \infty$ as $n \to \infty$, we get the required estimate.

This estimate may be improved slightly, eliminating the term $-1/K$. This is done using the results of §§5 and 7. We shall only sketch the procedure, giving no rigorous proofs.

Choose any cycle in the graph $E(K, n)$ satisfying the conditions of Theorem 64, with $l = K-1$. Consider a graph $\Gamma(x, K, N, M, L, K^M)$, $N - M = n+2$, containing K^{n+2} complete panicles of type (K, N, M), and construct its transition table. With each arc of $E(K, n)$ we associate K subtrees of $\Gamma(x)$ in which a path from the root of length $n+2$ defines the word labeling the arc. Suppose the cycle has the form $\ldots \alpha_1 \alpha_2 \ldots \alpha_{(K-1)K^n} \ldots$. For each arc, choose two of the associated subtrees, satisfying the condition: If the arc α_i is followed in the cycle by α_j and the subtrees chosen for these arcs are x_{i_1}, x_{i_2} and x_{j_1}, x_{j_2}, respectively, the transition table of $\Gamma(x)$ has a nonempty cell in row x_{i_1} containing the symbol pair x_{j_1}, x_{j_2}. We may then use Algorithm 5 to construct the table of an admissible graph $\Gamma_1(x, K, N, M+1, L_1, K^M)$, where $L_1 = N - M + K^n(K-1) - 1$, containing K^{n+2} rows. Another application of Algorithm 5 yields the table of an admissible graph $\Gamma_2(x, K, N, M+2, L_2, K^M)$, where $L_2 = N - M + 2(K^n(K-1) - 1)$, containing $K^{n+2} + 2(K^n(K-1) - 1)$ rows. The procedure may be repeated as many times as necessary to obtain the table of a graph $\Gamma_{N-M}(x, K, N, N, L_{N-M}, K^M)$, where $L_{N-M} = (N-M) + (N-M)(K^n(K-1) - 1)$, containing $K^{n+2} + (N-M+1)(K^n(K-1) - 1)$ rows. If an arc α_n of the original cycle ends at a vertex of the form $a_\nu a_\nu \ldots a_\nu$, then for each m we form a new cycle from the original one by inserting m arcs labeled $a_\nu a_\nu \ldots a_\nu$ between the arcs α_n and α_{n+1}. With this new cycle, we use Algorithm 5 to construct the table of an admissible graph $\Gamma_{1m}(x, K, N, M+1, L_{1m}, K^M)$, * where $L_{1m} = L_1 + m$, containing $K^{n+2} + 2m$ rows. Similarly, we construct the table of a graph $\Gamma_{2m}(x, K, N, M+2, L_{2m}, K^M)$, $L_{2m} = L_2 + 2m$, with $3m$ more rows than in the table of $\Gamma_2(x)$. Continuing the procedure, we finally get the table of a graph $\Gamma_{N-M,m}(x, K, N, N, L_{N-M,m}, K^M)$, where $L_{N-M,m} = L_{N-M} + (N-M)m$, containing $(N-M+1)m$ rows more than the table of $\Gamma_{N-M}(x)$.

If we fix $N-M$ and choose a sequence $\{m_n\}$ such that $m_n \to \infty$ as $n \to \infty$, the above results readily imply that there is a sequence of automata which satisfy the estimate $\lim\limits_{n\to\infty} L_n/P_n = 1 - 1/(N-M+1)$ instead of that of Theorem 85. Finally, choosing a sequence $\{N_n - M_n\}$ such that $N_n - M_n \to \infty$ as $n \to \infty$, we

* It is readily seen that if P is even and $K=2$ the estimate of Theorem 84 is attained in the graph Γ_{1m} $(m=0, 1, \ldots)$. For odd P we need only add one subtree isomorphic to a subtree of Γ_{1m}.

finally see that for a suitable sequence of automata $\lim_{n\to\infty} L_n/P_n = 1$, as intimated above.

A further, though inessential, improvement may be achieved by the use of Theorems 67 and 68.

Chapter IV

GENERALIZED INFORMATION-LOSSLESS AUTOMATA

§1. DETERMINATION OF INPUT WORD FOR WHICH AN AUTOMATON PRODUCES A PRESCRIBED RESPONSE

In a more detailed formulation, the problem specified in the heading of this section may be stated as follows. Given an automaton whose response to a given input word is a certain output word, find an input word for which the automaton, starting from the same initial state, has the same response. We are concerned here only with the case that the input word may be determined for any output word produced by the automaton in any known initial state.

Definition 49_I. An automaton B is called a type I generalized inverse with delay N for an automaton A if every initial state s_i may be associated with a state t_j so that the following condition holds. Let α' be a word of length N and α a word of arbitrary length such that $\lambda(s_i, \alpha\alpha')$ is defined. Then $\mu(t_j, \lambda(s_i, \alpha\alpha')) = \alpha'''\alpha''$ and $\lambda(s_i, \alpha'') = \lambda(s_i, \alpha)$.

By analogy with type II inverse automata, we may also consider the input word as a function of the state into which the automaton passes after emission of the output word.

Definition 49_{II}. An automaton B is called a type II generalized inverse with delay N for an automaton A if, for every reachable state s_i, there is a state t_j such that the following condition holds. Let α' be a word of length N and α a word of arbitrary length such that there is a state s_k with the property $\delta(s_k, \alpha'\alpha) = s_i$. Then $\mu(t_j, (\lambda(s_k, \alpha'\alpha))^{-1}) = \alpha'''\alpha''$ and there is a state s_l such that $\delta(s_l, (\alpha'')^{-1}) = s_i$ and $\lambda(s_l, (\alpha'')^{-1}) = \lambda(\delta(s_k, \alpha'), \alpha)$.

The meaning of Definition 49_I is as follows. For any output word β of length $N_1 > N$ which is a possible response of A in state s_i to any of the words $\alpha_1, \alpha_2, \ldots, \alpha_M$, the response of the automaton B in a state t_j to input β will be N letters (it is immaterial which) followed by the prefix α'_ν of length $N_1 - N$ of one of the words α_ν $(1 \leqslant \nu \leqslant M)$.

The concept of generalized inverse automata is related to the problem of deciding whether a given set of words is enumerated by a finite automaton and to similar questions in recursive function theory.

Let $\mathfrak{N}$ be a recursively enumerable set of natural numbers and $\varphi(n)$ any enumerating function. If $\mathfrak{N}$ is also recursive, there exists a recursive function $\psi(n)$ such that $\varphi(\psi(n)) = n$ for every natural number $n \in \mathfrak{N}$. Indeed, let $\Phi(n) = 1$ if and only if $n \in \mathfrak{N}$, $\Phi(n) = 0$ otherwise. Then there exists an algorithm which, in finitely many steps, finds the minimum number k such that $(k) = n$ and $\Phi(n) = 1$, and the function $\psi(n)$ may be defined thus:

$$\psi(n)=\begin{cases}k, & \text{if } \Phi(n)=1,\\ 0, & \text{otherwise.}\end{cases}$$

The generalized inverse automaton is an analog of the function $\psi(n)$.

The meaning of Definition 49$_{\text{II}}$ is as follows. For any word β of length $N_1>N$ for which there exist pairs $(s_{i_1}, \alpha_1), \ldots, (s_{i_M}, \alpha_M)$ such that $\delta(s_{i_\nu}, \alpha_\nu^{-1}) = s_i, \lambda(s_{i_\nu}, \alpha_\nu^{-1}) = \beta^{-1}$ $(\nu=1,\ldots,M)$, the response of the automaton B in state t_j to input β will be N letters followed by the prefix α'_ν of length N_1-N of one of the words α_ν.

For brevity, we shall say that the state s_i of the automaton A (or simply the state s_i) may yield response β if there is a word α such that $\lambda(s_i,\alpha)=\beta$. Similarly, the state s_i (of the automaton A) is reachable with response β if there exist a state s_k and a word α such that $\delta(s_k,\alpha)=s_i$, $\lambda(s_k,\alpha)=\beta$.

It follows from Definition 49$_{\text{I}}$ that the choice of the word α_ν from the set of words $\alpha_1,\ldots,\alpha_M$ (cf. the explanation of the definition) must guarantee that the state $\delta(s_i,\alpha'_\nu)$ of the automaton A may yield the same response as any of the states $\delta(s_i,\alpha'_\mu)$ (where α'_μ is the prefix of length N_1-N of the word α_μ, $\mu=1,\ldots,M$). A similar condition holds for type II generalized inverses.

Existence proofs and construction methods for generalized inverses will utilize these conditions in an essential manner.

We shall say that a state s_i of an automaton A b_l-succeeds (b_l-precedes) a state s_j if there is a letter a_k such that

$$\lambda(s_j,a_k)=b_l,\ \delta(s_j,a_k)=s_i\quad (\lambda(s_i,a_k)=b_l,\ \delta(s_i,a_k)=s_j).$$

Definition 50. A word β is called a type I-i-l-k (II-i-l-k) characteristic word (for the automaton A) if, whenever the state s_i of A may yield a response $b_l\beta\beta'$ (whenever the state s_i is reachable in A with response $\beta'\beta b_l$), the state s_k may yield response $\beta\beta'$ (the state s_k is reachable in A with response $\beta'\beta$).

Lemma 14. If β is a type I-i-l-k *(*II-i-l-k*) characteristic word, then any word $\beta\beta''$ ($\beta'''\beta$) which is a possible response in state s_k (which is a response with which s_k is reachable) is also characteristic, of the same type.*

Proof. Set $\beta'=\beta''\beta'''$. Let β be a type I-i-l-k characteristic word. Then, if state s_i of A can yield response $b_l\beta\beta''\beta'''$, then state s_k can yield $\beta\beta''\beta'''$. It thus follows from Definition 50 that $\beta\beta''$ is type I-i-l-k characteristic, since β' and therefore also β''' are arbitrary words.

Now let β be a type II-i-l-k characteristic word. Then if s_i is reachable with output $\beta''\beta'''\beta b_l$, the state s_k is reachable with output $\beta''\beta'''\beta$. As before, it follows from Definition 50 that the word $\beta'''\beta$ is as required, proving the lemma.

Definition 51. A set of states $\mathfrak{S}'=\{s_{i_1},\ldots,s_{i_n}\}$ is called a type I-i-j successor (type II-i-j predecessor) with delay M (in the automaton A) if it satisfies the following conditions: (1) Each of the states s_{i_ν} $(\nu=1,\ldots,n)$ b_j-succeeds (b_j-precedes) the state s_i. (2) Any word β of length M such that $b_j\beta$ is a possible response in state s_i (such that s_i is reachable with output βb_j) is a type I-i-j-i_ν (II-i-j-i_ν) characteristic word for at least one i_ν $(1\leqslant\nu\leqslant n)$.

In the sequel, successors and predecessors will be denoted by symbols with triple indices: the first two indicate the type and the third differentiates successors and predecessors of one type.

Using successors and predecessors, we now construct a special graph for each pair of indices (i, j), where i indicates the state and j the output letter.

Algorithm 7.

Step 1. Suppose there are exactly r states $s_{i_1}, \ldots, s_{i_r}$ which b_j-succeed s_i (b_j-precede s_i). The vertices of the graph will then be all r-tuples of sets of states of the automaton A (including the empty set).

Step 2. Consider every triple consisting of an ordered pair of vertices and an output letter, say $V_1 = (\mathfrak{S}_{i_1}; \ldots; \mathfrak{S}_{i_r})$, $V_2 = (\mathfrak{S}_{j_1}; \ldots; \mathfrak{S}_{j_r})$ and b_k.

If all the nonempty sets $\mathfrak{S}_{i_\nu}$ coincide or all the sets $\mathfrak{S}_{j_\nu}$ are empty, the vertices are not connected by any arc.

Otherwise: if $\mathfrak{S}_{j_\mu}$ is a set of states in A of maximum cardinality such that each of the states $s_l \in \mathfrak{S}_{j_\mu}$ b_k-succeeds some state $s_m \in \mathfrak{S}_{i_\mu}$ (each of the states $s_l \in \mathfrak{S}_{j_\mu}$ b_k-precedes some state $s_m \in \mathfrak{S}_{i_\mu}$), $\mu = 1, \ldots, r$, the graph will contain an arc from V_1 to V_2 labeled b_k. If these conditions are not satisfied, there is no arc.

Step 3. Choose one of the vertices $(s_{l_1}; \ldots; s_{l_r})$, where $l_\rho \neq l_\sigma$ for $\rho \neq \sigma$ and each of the states s_{l_ν} $(\nu = 1, \ldots, r)$ b_j-succeeds (b_j-precedes) the state s_i, and eliminate all vertices which receive no arcs from this vertex (which is called the initial vertex).

The graph constructed by Algorithm 7 for an index pair (i, j) will be called the type I-i-j (II-i-j) decision graph.

Lemma 15_{I}. *Suppose that the type* I-i-j *decision graph contains a path from the vertex* $(\mathfrak{S}_{10}; \ldots; \mathfrak{S}_{r0})$ *to the vertex* $(\mathfrak{S}_{1L}; \ldots; \mathfrak{S}_{rL})$, *through vertices* $(\mathfrak{S}_{1\mu}; \ldots; \mathfrak{S}_{r\mu})$ $(\mu = 1, \ldots, L-1)$ *and arcs labeled* $b_{i_1}, \ldots, b_{i_L}$. *Then the word* $\beta = b_{i_1}, \ldots, b_{i_L}$ *is a possible response in at least one of the states* $s_k \in \mathfrak{S}_{\nu 0}$ $(1 \leqslant \nu \leqslant r)$ *provided* $\mathfrak{S}_{\nu L}$ *is nonempty. Each nonempty set* $\mathfrak{S}_{\nu L}$ *has the property that for any state* $s_l \in \mathfrak{S}_{\nu L}$ *there exist a state* $s_m \in \mathfrak{S}_{\nu 0}$ *and a word* α *such that* $\delta(s_m, \alpha) = s_l$ *and* $\lambda(s_m, \alpha) = \beta$.

Proof. If $L = 1$, the conclusion follows from the details of Step 2 in Algorithm 7.

Assuming the conclusion true for $L = L_0$, let us prove that it remains true for $L = L_0 + 1$. Consider a path from a vertex $(\mathfrak{S}_1; \ldots; \mathfrak{S}_r)$ to a vertex $(\mathfrak{S}_{1L_0}; \ldots; \mathfrak{S}_{rL_0})$ through vertices $(\mathfrak{S}_{10}; \ldots; \mathfrak{S}_{r0}), \ldots, (\mathfrak{S}_{1,L_0-1}; \ldots; \mathfrak{S}_{r,L_0-1})$ and arcs labeled $b_{i_0}, b_{i_1}, \ldots, b_{i_{L_0}}$. By hypothesis, for each $\rho = 1, \ldots, r$ and every $s_k \in \mathfrak{S}_{\rho L_0}$ (provided the set $\mathfrak{S}_{\rho L_0}$ is not empty), there exist $s_m \in \mathfrak{S}_{\rho 0}$ and a word α such that $\delta(s_m, \alpha) = s_k$ and $\lambda(s_m, \alpha) = b_{i_1} \ldots b_{i_{L_0}}$. By Step 2 of Algorithm 7, there is an arc from $(\mathfrak{S}_1; \ldots; \mathfrak{S}_r)$ to $(\mathfrak{S}_{10}; \ldots; \mathfrak{S}_{r0})$ labeled b_{i_0} if and only if the state s_m b_{i_0}-succeeds some state $s_n \in \mathfrak{S}_\rho$; in other words, for some letter a_{j_0},

$$\delta(s_n, a_{j_0}) = s_m, \quad \lambda(s_n, a_{j_0}) = b_{i_0}.$$

This means that $\delta(s_n, a_{j_0}\alpha) = s_k$ and $\lambda(s_n, a_{j_0}\alpha) = b_{i_0} \ldots b_{i_{L_0}}$, so that the lemma is also true for $L = L_0 + 1$. The conclusion now follows by induction.

Lemma 15_{II}. *Suppose that the type* II-i-j *decision graph contains a path from the vertex* $(\mathfrak{S}_{10}; \ldots; \mathfrak{S}_{r0})$ *to the vertex* $(\mathfrak{S}_{1L}; \ldots; \mathfrak{S}_{rL})$, *through vertices* $(\mathfrak{S}_{1\mu};\ldots;\mathfrak{S}_{r\mu})$ $(\mu=1,\ldots,L-1)$ *and arcs labeled* $b_{i_1},\ldots,b_{i_L}$. *Then at least one state* $s_k\in\mathfrak{S}_{\rho 0}$ $(\rho=1,\ldots,r)$ *is reachable with response* $\beta=b_{i_L}\ldots b_{i_0}$, *provided the set* $\mathfrak{S}_{\rho L}$ *is not empty. Each nonempty set* $\mathfrak{S}_{\rho L}$ *has the property that for any state* $s_l\in\mathfrak{S}_{\rho L}$ *there exist a state* $s_m\in\mathfrak{S}_{\rho 0}$ *and a word* α *such that* $\delta(s_l,\alpha)=s_m$ *and* $\lambda(s_l,\alpha)=\beta$.

Proof. The proof is analogous to that of Lemma 15_{I}, except that in the induction step one considers the vertex $(\mathfrak{S}_1;\ldots;\mathfrak{S}_r)$ at the end of the path.

It follows from the condition that the set $\mathfrak{S}_{j\mu}$ in Step 2 of Algorithm 7 is of maximum cardinality that no vertex of a type I-i-j or II-i-j graph has two similarly labeled outgoing arcs. Hence the following lemma:

Lemma 16. For every vertex $(\mathfrak{S}_1;\ldots;\mathfrak{S}_r)$ *of a type* I-i-j (II-i-j) *decision graph and every word* β, *there is at most one path beginning at* $(\mathfrak{S}_1;\ldots;\mathfrak{S}_r)$ *and defining the word* β.

Lemma 17. Suppose that the type I-i-j (II-i-j) *decision graph has an initial vertex* $(s_{i_1};\ldots;s_{i_n})$ *and a state* s_{i_ν} $(1\leqslant\nu\leqslant r)$ *which may yield response* β *(a state* s_{i_ν} *which is reachable with response* β*). Then there are no paths from the initial vertex defining the word* β *if and only if there is a path from the initial vertex to a vertex* $(\mathfrak{S}_1;\ldots;\mathfrak{S}_r)$ *defining a prefix* β' *of* β *with* $1\leqslant|\beta'|<|\beta|$, *and all the nonempty sets* $\mathfrak{S}_\rho$ $(\rho=1,\ldots,r)$ *coincide.*

Proof. Suppose that some prefix β' of β leads from the initial vertex to a vertex $(\mathfrak{S}_1;\ldots;\mathfrak{S}_r)$ with the stipulated properties. According to Step 2 of Algorithm 7, there is no arc emanating from the vertex $(\mathfrak{S}_1;\ldots;\mathfrak{S}_r)$. It follows from Lemma 16 that there is no other path from the initial vertex defining the word β'. Thus there are no paths from the initial vertex that define the word β.

Conversely, suppose that there are no paths from the initial vertex that define the word $\beta=b_{i_1}\ldots b_{i_n}$. Since the states s_{i_ν} may yield response b_{i_1} (the state s_{i_ν} is reachable with response b_{i_1}), the graph contains a vertex $(\mathfrak{S}_{11};\ldots;\mathfrak{S}_{r1})$, where $\mathfrak{S}_{\nu 1}$ is not empty, which is the endpoint of an arc labeled b_{i_1} from the initial vertex (see Step 2 of Algorithm 7). If all the nonempty sets $\mathfrak{S}_{\mu 1}$ $(\mu=1,\ldots,r)$ are identical, there are no arcs emanating from the vertex $(\mathfrak{S}_{11};\ldots;\mathfrak{S}_{r1})$. By Lemma 16, there is only one vertex which is the endpoint of an arc labeled b_{i_1}, and the proof is complete in this case.

Now suppose that not all the nonempty sets $\mathfrak{S}_{\rho 1}$ $(\rho=1,\ldots,r)$ are identical. Since the state s_{i_ν} may yield response $b_{i_1}b_{i_2}$ (state s_{i_ν} is reachable with response $b_{i_2}b_{i_1}$), at least one state $s_m\in\mathfrak{S}_{\nu 1}$ can yield response b_{i_2} (is reachable with response b_{i_2}) and the graph contains an arc going from the vertex $(\mathfrak{S}_{11};\ldots;\mathfrak{S}_{r1})$ to some vertex $(\mathfrak{S}_{12};\ldots;\mathfrak{S}_{r2})$, labeled b_{i_2}. If all nonempty sets $\mathfrak{S}_{\mu 2}$ $(\mu=1,\ldots,r)$ are identical, the proof is complete. Otherwise, we continue in similar fashion. If there were no prefix $\beta'=b_{i_1}\ldots b_{i_m}$ $(m<n)$ of β such that the path defining β' leads from the initial vertex to some vertex $(\mathfrak{S}_{1m};\ldots;\mathfrak{S}_{rm})$ such that not all nonempty sets $\mathfrak{S}_{\mu m}$ are identical, it would follow that the graph contains a path from the initial vertex defining β, contrary to assumption. This completes the proof.

Let $\mathfrak{S}_1,\ldots,\mathfrak{S}_N$ be sets of states of an automaton A. We shall say that one of these sets $\mathfrak{S}_i$ is response-maximal with respect to $\mathfrak{S}_1,\ldots,\mathfrak{S}_N$ if, for any set $\mathfrak{S}_j$ $(j=1,\ldots,N)$, any state $s_m\in\mathfrak{S}_j$ and any word β such that s_m may yield response β, there exists a state $s_l\in\mathfrak{S}_i$ which may also yield response β. A set $\mathfrak{S}_i$ is *pre-response-maximal* with respect to $\mathfrak{S}_1, \ldots, \mathfrak{S}_N$ if, for any set $\mathfrak{S}_j$ $(j=1,\ldots,N)$, any state $s_m \in \mathfrak{S}_j$ and any word β such that s_m is reachable with response β, there exists a state $s_l \in \mathfrak{S}_i$ which is also reachable with response β.

It will always be clear from the context which type of maximality is intended, and we shall omit the qualifying words "response" or "pre-response."

Lemma 18. Let $(\mathfrak{S}_1;\ldots;\mathfrak{S}_r)$ *be a vertex in the type* I-i-j (II-i-j) *decision graph. A set* $\mathfrak{S}_i$ $(1 \leqslant i \leqslant r)$ *is maximal with respect to* $\mathfrak{S}_1,\ldots,\mathfrak{S}_r$ *if and only if any path from* $(\mathfrak{S}_1;\ldots;\mathfrak{S}_r)$ *leads to a vertex* $(\mathfrak{S}'_1;\ldots;\mathfrak{S}'_r)$ *such that* $\mathfrak{S}'_i$ *is nonempty.*

Proof. Suppose that a path β from the vertex $(\mathfrak{S}_1;\ldots\,\mathfrak{S}_r)$ leads to a vertex $(\mathfrak{S}'_1;\ldots;\mathfrak{S}'_r)$, where $\mathfrak{S}'_i$ is empty. Not all the sets $\mathfrak{S}'_\mu$ $(\mu=1,\ldots,r)$ can be empty, for otherwise there would be no arc leading to this vertex; let $\mathfrak{S}'_j$ be nonempty. Set $\beta=\beta' b_r$. Let the path defining β' lead from $(\mathfrak{S}_1;\ldots;\mathfrak{S}_r)$ to a vertex $(\mathfrak{S}''_1;\ldots;\mathfrak{S}''_r)$. We may assume that $\mathfrak{S}''_i$ is not empty, for otherwise we need only replace β by one of its prefixes. We shall consider only the type I-i-j decision graph — the reasoning for type II-i-j is analogous. By Lemma 15, there exist states $s_m \in \mathfrak{S}_j$, $s_l \in \mathfrak{S}_i$ and words α, α' such that $\lambda(s_m,\alpha)=\lambda(s_l,\alpha')=\beta'$. Since $\mathfrak{S}'_j$ is not empty, there is a letter a_k such that $\lambda(s_m, \alpha a_k)=\beta' b_r$. Let $s_n \in \mathfrak{S}_i$ be an arbitrary state which may yield response β'. Suppose there exists a word $\alpha''' a_\nu$ such that $\lambda(s_n,\alpha''' a_\nu)=\beta' b_r$. Then $\delta(s_n,\alpha''') \in \mathfrak{S}''_i$. Since $\lambda(\delta(s_n,\alpha'''),a_\nu)=b_r$, it follows that there is an arc from the vertex $(\mathfrak{S}''_1;\ldots;\mathfrak{S}''_r)$, labeled b_r, to a vertex $(\mathfrak{S}'_1;\ldots;\mathfrak{S}'_r)$ such that $\delta(\delta(s_n,\alpha'''),a_\nu) \in \mathfrak{S}'_i$. But this contradicts the assumption that $\mathfrak{S}'_i$ is empty.

Conversely, let $\mathfrak{S}_i$ be maximal with respect to $\mathfrak{S}_1,\ldots,\mathfrak{S}_r$. Take an arbitrary set $\mathfrak{S}_j$ $(j \neq i)$ and a word β such that there is a state $s_l \in \mathfrak{S}_j$ which may yield response β. Then for some state $s_m \in \mathfrak{S}_i$ and word α we have $\lambda(s_m,\alpha)=\beta$ and $\delta(s_m,\alpha) \in \mathfrak{S}'_i$, where $(\mathfrak{S}'_1;\ldots;\mathfrak{S}'_r)$ is the endpoint of a path from $(\mathfrak{S}_1;\ldots;\mathfrak{S}_r)$ defining the word β. This completes the proof.

Lemma 19. Suppose there exists a type I-i-j *successor (type* II-i-j *predecessor) with delay* N. *Then for any* r *sets of states* $\mathfrak{S}_1,\ldots,\mathfrak{S}_r$ *such that the type* I-i-j (II-i-j) *decision graph contains a path of length* N *from the initial vertex to the vertex* $(\mathfrak{S}_1;\ldots;\mathfrak{S}_r)$, *there is at least one set* $\mathfrak{S}_l$ *which is maximal with respect to* $\mathfrak{S}_1,\ldots,\mathfrak{S}_r$.

Proof. Let β be an arbitrary word of length N such that the type I-i-j decision graph contains a path from the initial vertex to $(\mathfrak{S}_1;\ldots;\mathfrak{S}_r)$ defining β.

Suppose there is no maximal set $\mathfrak{S}_l$ $(1 \leqslant l \leqslant r)$ among the sets, $\mathfrak{S}_1,\ldots,\mathfrak{S}_r$. This means that for any set $\mathfrak{S}_\nu$ $(\nu=1,\ldots,r)$ there is a word β_ν which is a possible response of the automaton A in some state $s_{j_\nu} \in \bigcup_{\mu=1}^{r} \mathfrak{S}_\mu \setminus \mathfrak{S}_\nu$, but not in any of the states $s_j \in \mathfrak{S}_\nu$. Let the initial vertex be $(s_{i_1};\ldots;s_{i_r})$. By the construction of the decision graph, every state s_{i_ν} $(\nu=1,\ldots,r)$ in A b_j-succeeds the state s_i. Suppose that state s_{i_ν} can yield the response β. Since $\mathfrak{S}_\nu$ is not maximal with respect to $\mathfrak{S}_1,\ldots,\mathfrak{S}_r$, there exist a set $\mathfrak{S}_{l_\nu}$ and a state $s_{m_\nu} \in \mathfrak{S}_{l_\nu}$ such that s_{m_ν} can yield response β_ν but no state $s_m \in \mathfrak{S}_\nu$ can yield response β_ν. Then state s_i may yield response $b_j \beta \beta_\nu$, but state s_{i_ν} cannot yield response $\beta\beta_\nu$. Consequently, β is not a type I-i-j-i_ν characteristic word for A. This argument goes through for any state s_{i_ν} $(1 \leqslant \nu \leqslant r)$ which can yield the response β. If some state s_{i_ν} cannot yield response β, then again (by Definition 50) β is not type I-i-j-i_ν characteristic. The set of states $\{s_{i_1}, \ldots, s_{i_r}\}$ (or any subset thereof) satisfies condition 1 of Definition 51 but not condition 2, since β is not a type I-i-j-i_ν characteristic word for any $(\nu=1, \ldots, r)$. Thus there exists no type I-i-j successor.

The proof for a type II-i-j predecessor is analogous.

Lemma 20. A set of states $\mathfrak{S}_\nu$ *is maximal with respect to* $\mathfrak{S}_1, \ldots, \mathfrak{S}_r$ *such that the type* I-i-j (II-i-j) *decision graph contains a path from the initial vertex* $(s_{i_1}, \ldots, s_{i_r})$ *to the vertex* $(\mathfrak{S}_1; \ldots; \mathfrak{S}_r)$ *defining a word* β *if and only if* β *is type* I-i-j-i_ν (II-i-j-i_ν) *characteristic for* A.

Proof. Let β be type I-i-j-i_ν characteristic. Then for any possible response $b_j\beta\beta'$ of the automaton A in state s_i, the word $\beta\beta'$ is a possible response in state s_{i_ν}. Suppose there exist a word β'', a set $\mathfrak{S}_j$ $(j\neq\nu)$ and a state s_k, $s_k\in\mathfrak{S}_j$, such that s_k may yield the response β'' but no state $s_l\in\mathfrak{S}_\nu$ may yield the same response. Then $\mathfrak{S}_\nu$ is not maximal with respect to $\mathfrak{S}_1; \ldots; \mathfrak{S}_r$. But then the state s_i may yield response $b_j\beta\beta''$ while the state s_{i_ν} cannot yield response $\beta\beta''$. Thus β is not type I-i-j-i_ν characteristic, contrary to assumption.

Conversely, let $\mathfrak{S}_\nu$ be maximal with respect to $\mathfrak{S}_1, \ldots, \mathfrak{S}_r$, and hence nonempty. Suppose that state s_i may yield a response $b_j\beta\beta'$. Let β' be a possible response of A in state $s_l\in\mathfrak{S}_j$ $(j\neq\nu)$. Then there exists a state $s_m\in\mathfrak{S}_\nu$ which can also yield response β'. Now it follows from Lemma 15 and the construction of the decision graph that there exists a word $a_\rho\alpha$ such that

$$\delta(s_i, a_\rho)=s_{i_\nu},\ \delta(s_{i_\nu}, \alpha)=s_m,\ \lambda(s_{i_\nu}, \alpha)=\beta;$$

thus state s_{i_ν} can yield response $\beta\beta'$.

The type II-i-j decision graph is treated similarly.

Theorem 86. Let M be the maximum length of a proper path in the type I-i-j (II-i-j) *decision graph and suppose there exists a type* I-i-j *successor (type* II-i-j *predecessor)* $\mathfrak{S}_{ijk}$ *with delay* $M'>M$. *Then* $\mathfrak{S}_{ijk}$ *is a type* I-i-j *successor (type* II-i-j *predecessor) with delay* M.

Proof. We first prove an auxiliary proposition:

A word β of length M is type I-i-j-i_μ characteristic for an automaton A, where $s_{i_\mu}\in\mathfrak{S}_{ijk}$, if some word $\beta\beta'$ of length M' is type I-i-j-i_ν characteristic $(s_{i_\nu}\in\mathfrak{S}_{ijk})$ for A.

Indeed, suppose that some path of length M' in the type I-i-j decision graph, from the initial vertex $(s_{i_1}; \ldots; s_{i_r})$ to a vertex $(\mathfrak{S}_1; \ldots; \mathfrak{S}_r)$, defines a word $\beta\beta'$ which is type I-i-j-i_ν characteristic for A $(1\leqslant\nu\leqslant r)$. By Lemma 19, $\mathfrak{S}_\nu$ is a maximal set with respect to $\mathfrak{S}_1, \ldots, \mathfrak{S}_r$. Suppose that a proper path of length $M''\leqslant M$ from the initial vertex, defining the prefix β'' of length M'' in β, also leads to the vertex $(\mathfrak{S}_1; \ldots; \mathfrak{S}_r)$. Then, by Lemma 20, β'' is type I-i-j-i_ν characteristic, and by Lemma 14 so is β.

Suppose now that no path of length $M''\leqslant M$ defining a prefix of β leads from the initial vertex to $(\mathfrak{S}_1; \ldots; \mathfrak{S}_r)$. This may be true only if the decision graph contains a cycle through vertices

$$(\mathfrak{S}_{11}; \ldots; \mathfrak{S}_{1r}),\ (\mathfrak{S}_{21}; \ldots; \mathfrak{S}_{2r}), \ldots, (\mathfrak{S}_{m1}; \ldots; \mathfrak{S}_{mr}),$$

the word $\beta\beta'$ has the form $\beta''(\beta''')^n\beta^{IV}$, and the following conditions hold:

(1) There is a path from the initial vertex to $(\mathfrak{S}_{11};\ldots;\mathfrak{S}_{1r})$ defining β''.

(2) A proper cycle through the above vertices defines the word β''' (where β''' is defined by the path

$$(\mathfrak{S}_{11};\ldots;\mathfrak{S}_{1r}),\quad (\mathfrak{S}_{21};\ldots;\mathfrak{S}_{2r}),\ldots,(\mathfrak{S}_{m1};\ldots;\mathfrak{S}_{mr}),\quad (\mathfrak{S}_{11};\ldots;\mathfrak{S}_{1r})).$$

(3) There is a path from $(\mathfrak{S}_{11};\ldots;\mathfrak{S}_{1r})$ to $(\mathfrak{S}_1;\ldots;\mathfrak{S}_r)$ defining β^{IV}.

We may assume the cycle to have been chosen in such a way that β'' is the shortest possible word satisfying these conditions.

Suppose that none of the sets $\mathfrak{S}_{1\mu}$ such that $s_{i_\mu}\in\mathfrak{S}_{ijk}$ is maximal with respect to $\mathfrak{S}_{11},\ldots,\mathfrak{S}_{1r}$. Since there are paths of arbitrary length from the initial vertex to $(\mathfrak{S}_{11};\ldots;\mathfrak{S}_{1r})$, it follows that the corresponding word β^V has the property that state s_i may yield the response $b_j\beta^V$, and so by Lemma 20 β^V is not type I-i-j-i_μ characteristic for any i_μ such that $s_{i_\mu}\in\mathfrak{S}_{ijk}$. But then the set $\mathfrak{S}_{ijk}$ cannot be a type I-i-j successor with delay $|\beta^V|>M'$, and this is impossible by virtue of Lemma 14.

Consequently, one of the sets, say $\mathfrak{S}_{1\mu}$, such that $s_{i_\mu}\in\mathfrak{S}_{ijk}$ is maximal with respect to $\mathfrak{S}_{11},\ldots,\mathfrak{S}_{1r}$. It then follows from Lemma 20 that some prefix β'' of β, of length $M''\leqslant M$, is type I-i-j-i_μ characteristic. By Lemma 14, the same holds for β.

Suppose that the decision graph contains no path of length M' defining the word $\beta\beta'$, and the state s_i may yield response $b_j\beta\beta'$. By Lemma 17, this is possible only if there is a path defining a prefix β'' of $\beta\beta'$, leading from the initial vertex to a vertex $(\mathfrak{S}_1;\ldots;\mathfrak{S}_r)$ in which all nonempty sets are identical. Since $\beta\beta'$ is a type I-i-j-i_ν characteristic word for some i_ν such that $s_{i_\nu}\in\mathfrak{S}_{ijk}$, it follows that state s_i may yield response $b_j\beta\beta'$ and state s_{i_ν} response $\beta\beta'$. Thus the set $\mathfrak{S}_\nu$ is nonempty and is therefore trivially maximal with respect to $\mathfrak{S}_1;\ldots;\mathfrak{S}_r$. If the length of β'' is greater than M, it has the form $\beta''=\beta^{IV}\beta'''$, and there is a path from the initial vertex defining the word $\beta^{IV}\beta'''$. The rest of the proof is the same as before, and so our auxiliary proposition is proved.

Now let $b_j\beta$, where β is of length M, be a possible response of the automaton in state s_i. Then state s_i may also yield the response $b_j\beta\beta'$, where $\beta\beta'$ is of length M'. Since $\mathfrak{S}_{ijk}$ is a type I-i-j successor, the word $\beta\beta'$ is characteristic of some type I-i-j-l, where $s_l\in\mathfrak{S}_{ijk}$. By the auxiliary proposition, the word β is characteristic of some type I-i-j-m, where $s_m\in\mathfrak{S}_{ijk}$. Hence follows the desired conclusion for a type I-i-j successor.

The proof for a type II-i-j predecessor is analogous.

Theorem 87. Let $\mathfrak{S}_{ij}=\{s_{i_1};\ldots;s_{i_r}\}$ *be the set of all states that* b_j*-follow (*b_j*-precede) a state* s_i*. Then any subset* $\mathfrak{S}_{ijk}\subseteq\mathfrak{S}_{ij}$ *satisfying the following condition is a type I-i-j successor (type II-i-j predecessor) with delay* M'*. Let* β *be an arbitrary word of length* M' *such that state* s_i *may yield response* $b_j\beta$ *(state* s_i *is reachable with response* $\beta^{-1}b_j$*). Then there must be a state* $s_{i_l}\in\mathfrak{S}_{ijk}$ *with the following properties:*

(1) *If there is a path defining* β *in the type* I-i-j (II-i-j) *decision graph, leading from the initial vertex* $(s_{i_1};\ldots;s_{i_r})$ *to a vertex* $(\mathfrak{S}_{\beta 1};\ldots;\mathfrak{S}_{\beta r})$*, then* $\mathfrak{S}_{\beta l}$ *is maximal with respect to* $\mathfrak{S}_{\beta 1};\ldots;\mathfrak{S}_{\beta r}$.

(2) *If some prefix* β' *of* β *is defined by a path from the initial vertex to a vertex* $(\mathfrak{S}_{\beta' 1};\ldots;\mathfrak{S}_{\beta' r})$ *such that all the nonempty sets* $\mathfrak{S}_{\beta'\nu}$ $(\nu=1,\ldots,r)$ *are identical, then the set* $\mathfrak{S}_{\beta' l}$ *is not empty.*

Proof. Let $\mathfrak{S}_{ijk}$ be a set satisfying the conditions of the theorem. It is clear that condition 1 of Definition 51 holds. If the type I-i-j (II-i-j) decision graph contains a path of length M' from the initial vertex to a vertex $(\mathfrak{S}_{\beta 1}; \ldots ; \mathfrak{S}_{\beta r})$, defining the word β, then by condition 1 of the theorem there is a state $s_{i_l} \in \mathfrak{S}_{ijk}$ such that $\mathfrak{S}_{\beta l}$ is maximal with respect to $\mathfrak{S}_{\beta 1}; \ldots ; \mathfrak{S}_{\beta r}$. By Lemma 20, β is type I-i-j-i_l (II-i-j-i_l) characteristic, so that condition 2 of Definition 51 also holds.

Suppose that the type I-i-j (II-i-j) decision graph contains no path from the initial vertex defining a word β of length M, and that state s_i may yield response $b_j\beta$ (state s_i is reachable with response $\beta^{-1}b_j$). As follows from Lemma 17, there is a prefix β' of β which is defined by a path from the initial vertex to some vertex $(\mathfrak{S}_{\beta' 1}; \ldots ; \mathfrak{S}_{\beta' r})$ and all nonempty sets $\mathfrak{S}_{\beta' \nu}$ $(\nu = 1, \ldots , r)$ are identical. By condition 2 of our theorem, there is a state $s_{i_l} \in \mathfrak{S}_{ijk}$ such that $\mathfrak{S}_{\beta' l}$ is maximal with respect to $\mathfrak{S}_{\beta' 1}; \ldots ; \mathfrak{S}_{\beta' r}$. Then by Lemma 20 β' is type I-i-j-i_l (II-i-j-i_l) characteristic and by Lemma 14 the same is true of β.

This completes the proof.

In order to check whether there exists a type I-i-j successor (type II-i-j predecessor) for each pair (i, j), one may use the following algorithm.

Algorithm 8.

Step 1. Use Algorithm 7 to construct the type I-i-j (II-i-j) decision graph and set $M_1 = 0$.

Step 2. Form the set of all vertices $(\mathfrak{S}_1; \ldots ; \mathfrak{S}_r)$ of the decision graph such that there is a path of length M_1 from the initial vertex to $(\mathfrak{S}_1; \ldots ; \mathfrak{S}_r)$

Step 3. If the set produced at Step 2 satisfies the condition: each of its elements $(\mathfrak{S}_1; \ldots ; \mathfrak{S}_r)$ is such that at least one set $\mathfrak{S}_\nu$ is maximal with respect to $\mathfrak{S}_1; \ldots ; \mathfrak{S}_r$, then there exists a type I-i-j successor (type II-i-j predecessor) with delay M_1 and the algorithm halts. Otherwise, proceed to Step 4.

Step 4. If $M_1 < M$, where M is the maximum length of a proper path in the decision graph, increase M_1 by one and proceed to Step 2. Otherwise, the algorithm halts.

We now show that this procedure indeed answers the question whether there exists a type I-i-j successor (type II-i-j predecessor), in finitely many steps, and in case of an affirmative answer determines the minimum delay M''. Suppose there exists a type I-i-j successor $\mathfrak{S}_{ijk}$ with delay M'''. If $M''' > M$, it follows from Theorem 86 that $\mathfrak{S}_{ijk}$ is also a type I-i-j successor with delay M. Consequently, it will suffice to verify the existence of a type I-i-j successor only for delays $M''' \leqslant M$. For each $M''' = 0, 1, \ldots , M$, Algorithm 8 checks for the existence of a successor with delay M''' in finitely many operations. Indeed, by Lemma 20, condition 2 of Definition 51 will hold for precisely those words β of length M''' defined by paths from the initial vertex of the type I-i-j decision graph that lead to a vertex $(\mathfrak{S}_1; \ldots ; \mathfrak{S}_r)$, where one of the sets, say $\mathfrak{S}_\mu$, is maximal with respect to $\mathfrak{S}_1; \ldots ; \mathfrak{S}_r$. By Lemma 18, the set $\mathfrak{S}_\mu$ is maximal with respect to $\mathfrak{S}_1; \ldots ; \mathfrak{S}_r$ if and only if any path from the vertex $(\mathfrak{S}_1; \ldots ; \mathfrak{S}_r)$ leads to a vertex $(\mathfrak{S}_{11}; \ldots ; \mathfrak{S}_{1r})$ such that $\mathfrak{S}_{1\mu}$ is nonempty. If there is a path from $\mathfrak{S}_1; \ldots ; \mathfrak{S}_r$ to $(\mathfrak{S}_{11}; \ldots ; \mathfrak{S}_{1r})$, there is such a path of length at most M. Consequently, in order to check whether $\mathfrak{S}_\mu$ is maximal with respect to $\mathfrak{S}_1; \ldots ; \mathfrak{S}_r$ it is sufficient to check whether every path of length $M_1 \leqslant M$ from $(\mathfrak{S}_1; \ldots ; \mathfrak{S}_r)$ leads to a vertex $(\mathfrak{S}_{11}; \ldots ; \mathfrak{S}_{1r})$ such that $\mathfrak{S}_{1\mu}$ is not empty. This may be done in finitely many operations for each component $\mathfrak{S}_\mu$ $(\mu=1,\ldots,r)$ of the vertex $(\mathfrak{S}_1;\ldots,\mathfrak{S}_r)$. Step 2 of Algorithm 8 produces a finite set of vertices, and so Step 3 is also implemented in finitely many steps.

The minimum delay is the minimum number $M_2 \leqslant M$ for which there is a type I-i-j successor.

Similarly one justifies the assertion that Algorithm 8 will ascertain the existence of a type II-i-j predecessor and find the minimum delay.

Theorem 88. Let all states of an automaton A be initial (reachable). Then A has a type I (type II) generalized inverse B with delay M if and only if, for any state s_k and any letter b_l such that s_k may yield response b_l (s_k is reachable with response b_l), there exists a type I-k-l successor (type II-k-l predecessor) with some delay $M'' \leqslant M$.

Proof. We consider a type I generalized inverse.

Sufficiency. For every pair consisting of a state s_i and a letter b_j such that state s_i may yield response b_j, let $\mathfrak{S}_{ijk}$ be a type I-i-j successor with delay M_{ij}.

By Lemma 14 and Theorem 86, the set $\mathfrak{S}_{ijk}$ is also a type I-i-j successor with delay M.

We shall construct the principal part of an automaton B whose states are all pairs $(s_i, b_j\beta)$, where $b_j\beta$ is a word of length M which is a possible response of the automaton A in state s_i (compare the construction of inverse automata in Chap. I, §3).

For any state $(s_i, b_j\beta)$ and letter b_l such that the state s_i of A may yield response $b_j\beta b_l$, we set

$$\varepsilon((s_i, b_j\beta), b_l) = (s_r, \beta b_l),$$

where $s_r \in \mathfrak{S}_{ijk}$, $\mathfrak{S}_{ijk}$ is the selected type I-i-j successor and s_r a state such that the word βb_l is type I-i-j-r characteristic. By Condition 2 of Definition 51, there exists a state s_r with this property. Then we set

$$\mu((s_i, b_j\beta), b_l) = a_p,$$

where a_p is any letter such that $\delta(s_i, a_p) = s_r$, $\lambda(s_i, a_p) = b_j$.

We now construct the initial part of the automaton B. For every state $(s_i, b_{i_1}\ldots b_{i_M})$ we define the following set of states: (s_i, Λ) (where Λ is the empty word), $(s_i, b_{i_1}\ldots b_{i_\mu})$ $(\mu=1,\ldots,M-1)$. Now set

$$\varepsilon((s_i, \Lambda), b_{i_1}) = (s_i, b_{i_1}),$$
$$\varepsilon((s_i, b_{i_1}\ldots b_{i_\mu}), b_{i_{\mu+1}}) = (s_i, b_{i_1}\ldots b_{i_{\mu+1}}) \quad (\mu=1,\ldots,M-1).$$

The output function for these states is defined arbitrarily.

Let s_j be any state of the automaton A. We claim that the conditions of Definition 49_{I} will hold if we let each state (s_j, Λ) of B correspond to the state s_j of A.

For any state s_i of A and any word β of length M which is a possible response of A in state s_i, B has a state (s_i, β), and according to the construction of B we have $\varepsilon((s_i, \Lambda), \beta) = (s_i, \beta)$. Definition 49 admits any word in the capacity of $\mu((s_i, \Lambda), \beta)$, since β is of length M. For any word $b_l\beta b_n$ of length

$M+1$ which is a possible response of A in state s_i, we have $\lambda(s_i, \mu((s_i, b_l\beta), b_n)=b_l$. Consequently, the automaton we have constructed satisfies Definition 49 for output words of A of length $M+1$. In addition, $\delta(s_i, \mu((s_i, b_l\beta), b_n)=s_r$, where βb_n is a type I-i-l-r characteristic word. Thus state s_r of A may yield response $\beta b_n\beta'$, provided the state s_i may yield response $b_l\beta b_n\beta'$.

Let s_i be an arbitrary state of A and suppose the following conditions hold for any possible response $b_{i_1}\dots b_{i_{M+n}}$ $(n\geqslant 1)$ of the automaton A in state s_i:

(1)

$$\lambda(s_i, \mu((s_i, b_{i_1}\dots b_{i_M}), b_{i_{M+1}}\dots b_{i_{M+n}}))=b_{i_1}\dots b_{i_n},$$

i. e., the state of B corresponding to s_i is so chosen that the conditions of Definition 49 hold for all possible responses of the automaton A in state s_i, of length $M+n$ or less.

(2) The state

$$s_r=\delta(s_i, \mu((s_i, b_{i_1}\dots b_{i_M}), b_{i_{M+1}}\dots b_{i_{M+n}}))$$

may yield the response $b_{i_{n+1}}\dots b_{i_{M+n}}\beta$, provided that state s_i may yield the response $b_{i_1}\dots b_{i_{M+n}}\beta$.

(3) $\varepsilon((s_i, b_{i_1}\dots b_{i_M}), b_{i_{M+1}}\dots b_{i_{M+n}})=(s_r, b_{i_{n+1}}\dots b_{i_{M+n}})$.

Suppose that a state s_i of A may yield response $b_{i_1}\dots b_{i_{M+n}}b_{i_{M+n+1}}$. Then

$$\mu((s_i, \Lambda), b_{i_1}\dots b_{i_{M+n}}b_{i_{M+n+1}})=\alpha a_\nu,$$

where $a_\nu=\mu((s_r, b_{i_{n+1}}\dots b_{i_{M+n}}), b_{i_{M+n+1}})$ and $\lambda(s_r, a_\nu)=b_{i_{n+1}}$. Using conditions 1 and 2, we get

$$\lambda(s_i, \mu((s_i, b_{i_1}\dots b_{i_M}), b_{i_{M+1}}\dots b_{i_{M+n}}b_{i_{M+n+1}}))=b_{i_1}\dots b_{i_n}b_{i_{n+1}},$$

i. e., the state of B corresponding to s_i is so chosen that the conditions of Definition 49 hold for all possible responses of length $M+n+1$ of A in state s_i. We set

$$\delta(s_i, \mu((s_i, b_{i_1}\dots b_{i_M}), b_{i_{M+1}}\dots b_{i_{M+n}}b_{i_{M+n+1}}))=s_\rho.$$

It follows from condition 2 that $\delta(s_r, a_\nu)=s_\rho$. Then

$$\varepsilon((s_i, b_{i_1}\dots b_{i_M}), b_{i_{M+1}}\dots b_{i_{M+n+1}})=(s_\rho, b_{i_{n+2}}\dots b_{i_{M+n+1}}).$$

By the construction of the principal part of B, the state s_ρ is such that $b_{i_{n+2}}\dots b_{i_{M+n+1}}$ is a type I-r-i_{n+1}-ρ characteristic word. Thus state s_ρ may produce any response $b_{i_{n+2}}\dots b_{i_{M+n+1}}\beta'$ of A, provided state s_r may produce response $b_{i_{n+1}}\dots b_{i_{M+n+1}}\beta'$. Using condition 2, we see that s_ρ may yield any response $b_{i_{n+2}}\dots b_{i_{M+n+1}}\beta'$ such that s_i yields response $b_{i_1}\dots b_{i_{M+n+1}}\beta'$.

Thus conditions 1—3 are satisfied for any word β'' of length $M+n+1$ which is a possible response of A in state s_i. The sufficiency proof is now completed by induction.

Necessity. Let s_i be an arbitrary state of the automaton A, corresponding in the sense of Definition 49 to a state t_l of a type I generalized inverse B with delay M and to a letter b_k.

For every word $b_k\beta_\nu$ ($\nu=1,\ldots,R$), where β_ν is of length M and $b_k\beta_\nu$ is a possible response of A in state s_i, we set $\mu(t_l, b_k\beta_\nu)=\alpha_\nu a_{l_\nu}$. Form the set $\mathfrak{S}_{ikm}=\{\delta(s_i, a_{l_1}), \delta(s_i, a_{l_2}), \ldots, \delta(s_i, a_{l_R})\}$. Suppose that the word $b_k\beta_\nu\beta'_\nu\beta''_\nu$ (β_ν, β''_ν are words of length M) is a possible response of A in state s_i. Set $\mu(t_l, b_k\beta_\nu\beta'_\nu\beta''_\nu)=\alpha_\nu a_{l_\nu}\alpha'_\nu$. Then, by Definition 49,

$$\lambda(s_i, a_{l_\nu}\alpha'_\nu)=b_k\beta_\nu\beta'_\nu,\ \lambda(\delta(s_i, a_{l_\nu}),\alpha'_\nu)=\beta_\nu\beta'_\nu.$$

Consequently, the word β_ν is type I-i-k-r characteristic, where $s_r=\delta(s_i, a_{l_\nu})$. This means that for any word $b_k\beta_\nu$ of length $M+1$ which is a possible response of A in state s_i there exists a state $s_p\in\mathfrak{S}_{ikm}$ such that β_ν is type I-i-k-p characteristic, and condition 2 of Definition 50 holds. Since $\lambda(s_i, a_{l_\nu})=$ $=b_k$ ($\nu=1,\ldots,R$), condition 1 also holds and so $\mathfrak{S}_{ikm}$ is a type I-i-k successor in A.

The proof for type II generalized inverses is analogous.

If A is an automaton not all of whose states are reachable, one can discard the unreachable states to obtain a new automaton A_1. It is clear that for any N the automaton A has a type II generalized inverse with delay N if and only if A_1 has a type II generalized inverse with the same delay.

Thus the properties of Algorithm 8 and Theorem 88 imply the following.

Theorem 89. There exists an algorithm which, for any given automaton A, determines in finitely many operations, whether A has a type II generalized inverse with delay N, and if an inverse exists computes the minimum delay N.

§2. DETERMINATION OF INPUT WORD FOR WHICH AN INITIALIZED AUTOMATON HAS A PRESCRIBED RESPONSE

We first establish a sufficient condition for an initialized automaton to have a generalized inverse.

Theorem 90. Let A be an automaton with initial states $s_{i_1},\ldots,s_{i_n}$. *Suppose that there is a set* $\mathfrak{S}'$ *of states of A such that* $s_{i_\nu}\in\mathfrak{S}'$ ($\nu=1,\ldots,n$) *and, for every* $s_k\in\mathfrak{S}'$ *and any letter* b_l *which is a possible response of A in state* s_k, *there exists a type I-k-l successor* $\mathfrak{S}_{klm}$ *with delay N,* $\mathfrak{S}_{klm}\subseteq\mathfrak{S}'$. *Then A has a type I generalized inverse with delay N.*

The proof is the same as that of the sufficiency part of Theorem 88.

To make our investigation of the existence of generalized inverses for initialized automata complete, we shall need the following extensions of our earlier definitions.

We shall say that a state s_i in an automata A β-succeeds an initial state s_j if there exists a word α such that $\lambda(s_j,\alpha)=\beta$, $\delta(s_j,\alpha)=s_i$.

Definition 52. A word β' is called a type (i_0, β, i) characteristic word for A if, whenever an initial state s_{i_0} of the automaton may yield a response $\beta\beta'\beta''$, the state s_i may yield a response $\beta'\beta''$.

We shall assume henceforth that the automaton A has only one initial state, s_{i_0}.

Definition 53. A labeled graph G will be called a graph of type (A, s_{i_0}) if each of its vertices may be put in correspondence with a nonempty set of states of an automaton A such that the following conditions hold:

(1) There is a vertex V_0 of the graph that corresponds to the set $\{s_{i_0}\}$.

(2) There is a path from V_0 to each vertex of G.

(3) Let V be a vertex corresponding to a set of states $\mathfrak{S}'$, and suppose that for each letter $b_j \in \mathfrak{B}$ we define $\mathfrak{S}'_j$ to be the set of states s_ν with the property: there exists a state $s_\mu \in \mathfrak{S}'$ such that s_ν b_j-succeeds the state s_μ. Then for each nonempty set $\mathfrak{S}'_j$ the graph G contains a vertex V_j, corresponding to the set $\mathfrak{S}'_j$, such that there is an arc from V to V_j labeled b_j, and there are no arcs from V other than those satisfying this condition.

When considering graphs of type (A, s_{i_0}) we shall always assume that the correspondence of sets of states and vertices is given once and for all.

A graph of type (A, s_{i_0}) such that the sets corresponding to distinct vertices are different will be denoted by $G(s_{i_0})$. Thus, the vertices of a graph $G(s_{i_0})$ may be identified with the corresponding sets of states.

In the [general] case of a graph of type (A, s_{i_0}) one cannot identify the vertices and the corresponding sets of states completely; nevertheless, throughout the sequel we shall use the terms "vertex" and "set of states corresponding to a vertex" interchangeably.

Definition 54. A set of states $\mathfrak{S}$ is a type (i_0, β) successor with delay N for A if:

(1) each state $s_\mu \in \mathfrak{S}$ β-follows the state s_{i_0};

(2) any word β' of length N such that state s_{i_0} may yield the response β' is (i_0, β, ν) characteristic, where $s_\nu \in \mathfrak{S}$.

Given a pair (i_0, β), one can check for the existence of a type (i_0, β) successor by means of a certain graph, called the type (i_0, β) decision graph. This graph is constructed with the help of an algorithm which is a slight modification of Algorithm 7.

Algorithm 9.

Step 1. Suppose there are exactly r states $s_{i_1}, \ldots, s_{i_r}$ which β-succeed s_{i_0}. Then the vertices of the graph will be all r-tuples of sets of states of the automaton A.

Step 2. Consider every triple consisting of an ordered pair of vertices and an output letter, and join the vertices by an arc in accordance with the following rule. Suppose the vertices in question are $V_1 = (\mathfrak{S}_{i_1}; \ldots; \mathfrak{S}_{i_r})$ and $V_2 = (\mathfrak{S}_{j_1}; \ldots; \mathfrak{S}_{j_r})$ and the letter is b_k.

If all the sets $\mathfrak{S}_{j_\rho}$ $(\rho = 1, \ldots, r)$ are empty or all the nonempty sets $\mathfrak{S}_{j_\rho}$ are identical, there is no arc.

Otherwise, if each of the sets $\mathfrak{S}_{i_\rho}$ is a set of states of maximum cardinality such that each state $s_i \in \mathfrak{S}_{j_\rho}$ b_k-succeeds some state $s_m \in \mathfrak{S}_{i_\rho}$ $(\rho = 1, \ldots, r)$, there is an arc from V_1 to V_2 labeled b_k.

If these conditions are not satisfied, the vertices are not connected by any arc.

Step 3. Select one of the vertices $(s_{i_1}; \ldots; s_{i_r})$, where $i_\rho \neq i_\sigma$ for $\rho \neq \sigma$, each of the states s_{i_ρ} $(\rho = 1, \ldots, r)$ β-succeeds the state s_{i_0}, and delete vertices of the graph which receive no paths from the selected vertex (the latter will be called the initial vertex).

Lemmas 14, 15_{I}, 16, 18 — 20 carry over in an obvious manner to the generalized concepts of characteristic word, successor and decision graph. We shall therefore refer to these lemmas without further ado in order to justify various arguments in the generalized setting.

In what follows we shall not distinguish between decision graphs of types (i_0, β_1) and (i_0, β_2) if the paths in the graph $G(s_{i_0})$ from the vertex $\{s_{i_0}\}$, defining the words β_1, β_2, respectively, lead to the same vertex.

It follows from Algorithm 9 that any two such decision graphs may be obtained from one another by permuting components of their vertices.

Henceforth, therefore, instead of "type (i_0, β) decision graphs" we shall speak of "type $(i_0, \mathfrak{S})$ decision graphs," where $\mathfrak{S}$ is some vertex of the graph $G(s_{i_0})$. Similarly, instead of "type (i_0, β, k) characteristic words" we shall use "type $(i_0, \mathfrak{S}, k)$ characteristic words."

A set of decision graphs of types $(i_0, \mathfrak{S}_1), \ldots, (i_0, \mathfrak{S}_R)$, where $\mathfrak{S}_\nu \neq \mathfrak{S}_\mu$ for $\mu \neq \nu$ and each vertex of $G(s_{i_0})$ other than $\{s_{i_0}\}$ is one of the sets $\mathfrak{S}_\rho$ $(1 \leqslant \rho \leqslant R)$, will be called a complete system of decision graphs for the automaton A.

Apart from graphs of type (A, s_{i_0}), we shall also consider graphs of type (A, s_{i_0}, N), which may be obtained from the former by assigning to the states in the vertices words of length N over the alphabet $\mathfrak{B}$. (One state in a vertex may be assigned several words, and conversely the same word may be assigned to several states in the same vertex.)

In the sequel we shall sometimes deal with the vertices of a graph of type (A, s_{i_0}, N) without regard for the fact that their states are assigned words. It will always be clear from the context whether these words are to be taken into consideration or not.

Definition 55. A graph G of type (A, s_{i_0}, N) will be called an admissible system of successors with delay N (for an automaton A with initial state s_{i_0}) if the following conditions hold:

(1) Let $\mathfrak{S}$ be any vertex of G and β an arbitrary word of length N such that there is a state $s_j \in \mathfrak{S}$ which can yield the response β. Then β is assigned to at least one state $s_\nu \in \mathfrak{S}$.

(2) If a state s_i in a vertex $\mathfrak{S}$ is assigned the word β, then β is a type $(i_0, \mathfrak{S}, i)$ characteristic word.

(3) Suppose there is an arc in G from a vertex $\mathfrak{S}_1$ to a vertex $\mathfrak{S}_2$, labeled b_j, a state $s_i \in \mathfrak{S}_1$ is assigned the word $b_j\beta$ in $\mathfrak{S}_1$ and $b_{i_1}, \ldots, b_{i_k}$ are all letters such that $\beta b_{i_\varkappa}$ is assigned to states in $\mathfrak{S}_2$. Then every word $\beta b_{i_\varkappa}$ is assigned to a state $s_{m_\varkappa}$ in the vertex $\mathfrak{S}_2$ such that $s_{m_\varkappa}$ b_j-succeeds the state s_i $(\varkappa = 1, \ldots, k)$.

Theorem 91. If the automaton A has an admissible system of successors G with delay N, it has a type I generalized automaton with delay N.

Proof. We shall construct the principal part of the proposed generalized inverse B. Its states will be all triples $(\mathfrak{S}, s_i, \beta)$, where $\mathfrak{S}$ is a vertex of G, $s_i \in \mathfrak{S}$, and β is a word assigned to the state s_i in $\mathfrak{S}$.

The next-state and output functions for the principal part of B are defined as follows. Let $(\mathfrak{S}, s_i, b_j\beta)$ be an arbitrary state and b_k an arbitrary letter. If there is no path from $\mathfrak{S}$ defining the word $b_j\beta b_k$, then $\varepsilon((\mathfrak{S}, s_i, b_j\beta), b_k)$ and $\mu((\mathfrak{S}, s_i, b_j\beta), b_k)$ are undefined. Otherwise, $\varepsilon((\mathfrak{S}, s_i, b_j\beta), b_k) = (\mathfrak{S}_1, s_l, \beta b_k)$, where $\mathfrak{S}_1$ is a vertex which is the endpoint of an arc of G labeled b_j, emanating from $\mathfrak{S}$, the state $s_l \in \mathfrak{S}_1$ b_j-succeeds the state s_i, and s_t is assigned the word βb_k in $\mathfrak{S}_1$. If there is an arc from $\mathfrak{S}$ labeled b_j, it follows from the conditions of Definition 55 that this definition of the value of ε is legitimate. We then set $\mu((\mathfrak{S}, s_i, b_j\beta), b_k) = a_p$, where a_p is a letter such that $\delta(s_i, a_p) = s_l$, $\lambda(s_i, a_p) = b_j$.

Let $b_{i_1} \ldots b_{i_N}$ be a word of length N which is a possible response of A in state s_{i_0}. Then the initial part of B will contain states (s_{i_0}, Λ), $(s_{i_0}, b_{i_1} \ldots b_{i_\nu})$ $(\nu = 1, \ldots, N-1)$. For these states, we set

$$\varepsilon((s_{i_0}, b_{i_1} \ldots b_{i_\nu}), b_{i_{\nu+1}}) = (s_{i_0}, b_{i_1} \ldots b_{i_{\nu+1}}) \ (\nu = 0, 1, \ldots, N-2),$$
$$\varepsilon((s_{i_0}, b_{i_1} \ldots b_{i_{N-1}}), b_{i_N}) = (\mathfrak{S}_0, s_{i_0}, b_{i_1} \ldots b_{i_N}),$$

where $\mathfrak{S}_0$ is some vertex corresponding to the set $\{s_{i_0}\}$. The values of μ for these states are arbitrary.

We now show that the automaton B thus defined is a type I generalized inverse with delay N for A, provided the state s_{i_0} of A is associated with the state (s_{i_0}, Λ) of B.

For any word β of length N which is a possible response of A in state s_{i_0}, we have $\varepsilon((s_{i_0}, \Lambda), \beta) = (\mathfrak{S}_0, s_{i_0}, \beta)$.

Let $b_l\beta b_n$ be a word of length $N+1$ which is a possible response of A in state s_{i_0}. By the construction of B, we have

$$\lambda(s_{i_0}, \mu((\mathfrak{S}_0, s_{i_0}, b_l\beta), b_n)) = b_l \quad \text{and} \quad \delta(s_{i_0}, \mu((\mathfrak{S}_0, s_{i_0}, b_l\beta), b_n)) = s_r,$$

where βb_n is a type (i_0, b_l, r) characteristic word. Thus, for any possible response β of A in state s_{i_0}, of length $N+1$, the automaton B satisfies Definition 49 I.

Suppose that any possible response $b_{i_1} \ldots b_{i_{N+n}}$ $(n \geqslant 1)$ of the automaton A in state s_{i_0} satisfies the following conditions:

(A) $\lambda(s_{i_0}, \mu((\mathfrak{S}_0, s_{i_0}, b_{i_1} \ldots b_{i_N}), b_{i_{N+1}} \ldots b_{i_{N+n}})) = b_{i_1} \ldots b_{i_n}$.

(B) The state

$$s_r = \delta(s_{i_0}, \mu((\mathfrak{S}_0, s_{i_0}, b_{i_1} \ldots b_{i_N}), b_{i_{N+1}} \ldots b_{i_{N+n}}))$$

may yield the response $b_{i_{n+1}} b_{i_{N+n}} \beta$, provided that the state s_{i_0} may yield the response $b_{i_1} \ldots b_{i_{N+n}} \beta$.

(C) $$\varepsilon((\mathfrak{S}_0, s_{i_0}, b_{i_1} \ldots b_{i_N}), b_{i_{N+1}} \ldots b_{i_{N+n}}) = (\mathfrak{S}, s_r, b_{i_{n+1}} \ldots b_{i_{N+n}}),$$

where $\mathfrak{S}$ is a vertex in G which is the endpoint of a path from $\mathfrak{S}_0$ defining the word $b_{i_1} \ldots b_{i_n}$.

Suppose that state s_{i_0} may yield a response $b_{i_1} \ldots b_{i_{N+n}} b_{i_{N+n+1}}$. Then

$$\mu((s_{i_0}, \Lambda), b_{i_1} \ldots b_{i_{N+n}} b_{i_{N+n+1}}) = \alpha a_\nu,$$

where $a_\nu = \mu((\mathfrak{S}, s_r, b_{i_{n+1}} \ldots b_{i_{N+n}}), b_{i_{N+n+1}})$. By construction of the automaton B, we have $\lambda(s_r, a_\nu) = b_{i_{n+1}}$. Using conditions A and B, we obtain

$$\lambda(s_{i_0}, \mu((\mathfrak{S}_0, s_{i_0}, b_{i_1}\dots b_{i_N}), b_{i_{N+1}}\dots b_{i_{N+n+1}})) = b_{i_1}\dots b_{i_{n+1}}.$$

This means that the state of B corresponding to state s_{i_0} of A is so chosen that the conditions of Definition 49_{I} hold for all words of length $N+n+1$ which are possible responses of A in state s_{i_0}. Set

$$\delta(s_{i_0}, \mu((\mathfrak{S}_0, s_{i_0}, b_{i_1}\dots b_{i_N}), b_{i_{N+1}}\dots b_{i_{N+n+1}})) = s_\rho.$$

It follows from condition B that $\delta(s_r, a_\nu) = s_\rho$. By the construction of B,

$$\varepsilon((\mathfrak{S}_0, s_{i_0}, b_{i_1}\dots b_{i_N}), b_{i_{N+1}}\dots b_{i_{N+n+1}}) = (\mathfrak{S}_1, s_\rho, b_{i_{n+2}}\dots b_{i_{N+n+1}}),$$

where $\mathfrak{S}_1$ is a vertex of G which is the endpoint of a path from $\mathfrak{S}_0$ defining the word $b_{i_1}\dots b_{i_{n+1}}$. But then the word $b_{i_{n+2}}\dots b_{i_{N+n+1}}$ is characteristic of type $(i_0, b_{i_1}\dots b_{i_{n+1}}, \rho)$. Thus state s_ρ of the automaton A may yield any response $b_{i_{n+2}}\dots b_{i_{N+n+1}}\beta$, provided the state s_{i_0} may yield the response $b_{i_1}\dots b_{i_{N+n+1}}\beta$.

Thus conditions A, B and C are satisfied for any word β'' of length $N+n+1$ which is a possible response of A in state s_{i_0}.

The conclusion now follows by induction.

Theorem 92. Let A be an automaton having a type I generalized inverse with delay N. Then the automaton A with initial state s_{i_0} has an admissible system of successors G with delay N, containing the same number of vertices as the graph $G(s_{i_0})$.

Proof. We assign words of length N to the states in the vertices of $G(s_{i_0})$ as follows. Let β be any fixed word and $\beta_1, \dots, \beta_R$ all words of length N such that state s_{i_0} may yield the response $\beta\beta_\rho$, $(\rho = 1, \dots, R)$. Set $\mu(t_0, \beta\beta_\rho) = \alpha'_\rho\alpha_\rho$, where t_0 is the state of the generalized inverse corresponding to s_{i_0} and α'_ρ is a word of length N. Then $\lambda(s_{i_0}, \alpha_\rho) = \beta$ and $\delta(s_{i_0}, \alpha_\rho) = s_{i_\rho} \in \mathfrak{S}_1$, where $\mathfrak{S}_1$ is a vertex in $G(s_{i_0})$ which is the end of a path from the vertex $\{s_{i_0}\}$ defining the word β_ρ. The state s_{i_ρ} in the vertex $\mathfrak{S}_1$ is now assigned the word β_ρ. It is clear that condition 1 of Definition 55 holds for the vertex $\mathfrak{S}_1$. For any word β' of arbitrary length and a word β'' of length N such that state s_{i_0} may yield a response $\beta\beta_\rho\beta'\beta''$, we have

$$\lambda(\delta(s_{i_0}, \alpha_\rho), \mu(\varepsilon(t_0, \beta\beta_\rho), \beta'\beta'')) = \beta_\rho\beta'.$$

Hence β_ρ is a type $(i_0, \mathfrak{S}_1, i_\rho)$ characteristic word and condition 2 of Definition 55 is also satisfied. Proceeding in this way, we assign suitable words β to the states in all vertices of the graph $G(s_{i_0})$.

If condition 3 of Definition 55 is satisfied, we have thus constructed an admissible system of successors.

If condition 3 is not satisfied, there exist a vertex $\mathfrak{S}_1$ of $G(s_{i_0})$ and a state $s_j \in \mathfrak{S}_1$ assigned the word $b_k\beta'$ in $\mathfrak{S}_1$, but if $\mathfrak{S}_2$ is the endpoint of an arc in $G(s_{i_0})$ emanating from $\mathfrak{S}_1$ and labeled b_k, there is a word $\beta' b_m$ assigned to states $s_\nu \in \mathfrak{S}_2$ but not to any state s_l which b_k-succeeds the state s_j.

Suppose that the word $b_k\beta'$ was assigned to s_j on the basis of the value of $\mu(t_0, \beta b_k\beta')$, where β is some known word. Then $\mu(t_0, \beta b_k\beta' b_m)$ is defined and its value dictates that some state $s_l \in \mathfrak{S}_2$ which b_k-succeeds s_j is assigned the word $\beta' b_m$ in $\mathfrak{S}_2$. Condition 2 of Definition 55 remains valid throughout.

If condition 3 is still not fulfilled, we continue to assign additional words to the states in vertices of $G(s_{i_0})$. The set of vertices of $G(s_{i_0})$ is finite, as are the number of states in each vertex and the total number of words of length N, and so sufficiently many repetitions of this process necessarily yield a graph satisfying all the requirements of Definition 55. This completes the proof.

Theorem 93. There is an algorithm which, for any given automaton A with initial state s_{i_0} and any given number N, determines in finitely many operations whether A has a type I generalized inverse with delay N.

Proof. It follows from Theorems 91 and 92 that the existence of a type I generalized inverse is equivalent to the existence of an admissible system of successors with delay N. Thus the problem reduces to checking for the existence of such a system.

By Theorem 92, we may confine ourselves to admissible systems of successors which contain the same number of vertices as the graph $G(s_{i_0})$.

Hence it will suffice to assign the states in the vertices of $G(s_{i_0})$ words of length N over the alphabet $\mathfrak{B}$, in all possible ways, and to check in each case whether the result is an admissible system of successors. If the result is positive in some case, this is proof that A has a type I generalized automaton with delay N. Otherwise no such inverse exists.

To check each assignment for condition 1 of Definition 55 requires finitely many operations, since this is what is needed to determine, for all the (finitely many) vertices of $G(s_{i_0})$, the set of words of length N which are possible responses of the automaton A in each state of each vertex. In fact, for each vertex of $G(s_{i_0})$ we need only find all words defined by paths of length N issuing from the vertex in question.

Condition 3 of Definition 55 clearly requires finitely many operations — the method of checking is obvious.

To check for condition 2 of the definition, we construct a complete system of decision graphs for A. As follows from Algorithm 9 and the fact that the number of vertices in $G(s_{i_0})$ is finite, this may be done in finitely many operations. By Lemmas 18 and 20, for each triple $(\mathfrak{S}, s_i, \beta)$, where $\mathfrak{S}$ is a vertex of $G(s_{i_0})$, $s_i \in \mathfrak{S}$ and the word β is assigned to the state s_i in $\mathfrak{S}$, one can establish in finitely many steps whether β is type (i_0, β, i) characteristic. Since the number of such triples is finite for every assignment, we see that verification of condition 2 also requires finitely many operations.

Finally, the number of different assignments of words of length N over $\mathfrak{B}$ to the states in vertices of $G(s_{i_0})$ is finite, and this completes the proof.

Definition 56. $\Gamma(s_{i_0}, N)$ will denote a graph obtained from $G(s_{i_0})$ by assigning to each vertex $\mathfrak{S}$ of $G(s_{i_0})$ a certain number (possibly zero) of triples $(\mathfrak{S}_1, s_i, \mathfrak{S}_2)$, where $\mathfrak{S}_1 \subseteq \mathfrak{S}$, $\mathfrak{S}_2$ is a vertex of $G(s_{i_0})$ and $s_i \in \mathfrak{S}_2$, so that the following conditions hold:

(1) If a vertex $\mathfrak{S}$ is assigned a triple $(\mathfrak{S}_1, s_i, \mathfrak{S}_2)$, then:

(a) there is a path of length N from $\mathfrak{S}_2$ to $\mathfrak{S}$;

(b) if this path defines a word β, then $\mathfrak{S}_1$ is the set of all states of A which β-succeed the state s_i.

(2) Suppose there is a path of length N from the vertex $\mathfrak{S}_2$ to $\mathfrak{S}$, defining a word β, and $s_i \in \mathfrak{S}_2$. Then the triple assigned to $\mathfrak{S}$ is $(\mathfrak{S}_1, s_i, \mathfrak{S}_2)$, where $\mathfrak{S}_1$ is the set of all states of A that β-succeed s_i.

There may be two vertices $\mathfrak{S}$ and $\mathfrak{S}_2$ in $G(s_{i_0})$ for which there are two different paths of length N from $\mathfrak{S}_2$ to $\mathfrak{S}$, defining the words β_1 and β_2, respectively, and for some state $s_i \in \mathfrak{S}_2$ the sets $\mathfrak{S}_{11}$ and $\mathfrak{S}_{12}$ coincide, where $\mathfrak{S}_{1j}$ $(j=1, 2)$ is the set of all states of A that β_j-succeed s_i. In that case the vertex $\mathfrak{S}$ is assigned only one triple $(\mathfrak{S}_{11}, s_i, \mathfrak{S}_2)$.

Lemma 21. Let $\Gamma(s_{i_0}, N_1) = \Gamma(s_{i_0}, N_2)$ for some N_1 and N_2 $(N_1 \neq N_2)$. Then $\Gamma(s_{i_0}, N_1+1) = \Gamma(s_{i_0}, N_2+1)$.*

Proof. We shall show that $\Gamma(s_{i_0}, N+1)$ may be obtained from $\Gamma(s_{i_0}, N)$ using only triples assigned to the corresponding vertices of $G(s_{i_0})$.

Suppose that in construction of the graph $\Gamma(s_{i_0}, N)$ a vertex $\mathfrak{S}$ of $G(s_{i_0})$ is assigned a triple $(\mathfrak{S}', s_i, \mathfrak{S}'')$ and there are arcs from $\mathfrak{S}$ to vertices $\mathfrak{S}_1, \ldots, \mathfrak{S}_n$, labeled respectively $b_{i_1}, \ldots, b_{i_n}$. Then each of the vertices $\mathfrak{S}_j$ $(j=1, \ldots, n)$ of $G(s_{i_0})$ is assigned a triple $(\mathfrak{S}'_j, s_i, \mathfrak{S}'')$, where $\mathfrak{S}'_j$ is the set of all states s_ν of A for which there exists a state $s_\mu \in \mathfrak{S}'$ such that s_ν b_{i_j}-succeeds s_μ. Triples are assigned in this way to the vertices of the graph for each vertex of $\Gamma(s_{i_0}, N)$ and for each triple assigned to the latter. Since condition 1 of Definition 56 holds for the graph $\Gamma(s_{i_0}, N)$, it also holds for the graph $\Gamma(s_{i_0}, N+1)$ thus constructed. Indeed, if a vertex $\mathfrak{S}$ in $\Gamma(s_{i_0}, N)$ is assigned a triple $(\mathfrak{S}_1, s_i, \mathfrak{S}_2)$, there is a path of length N from $\mathfrak{S}_2$ to $\mathfrak{S}$, defining some word β, and $\mathfrak{S}_1$ is the set of all states of A that β-succeed the state s_i. Then there is a path from $\mathfrak{S}_2$ to $\mathfrak{S}_j$ defining the word βb_{i_j}, and $\mathfrak{S}'_j$ is the set of all states of A that βb_{i_j}-succeed s_i.

Suppose that there is a path of length $N+1$ from $\mathfrak{S}''$ to $\mathfrak{S}_j$ in the graph $G(s_{i_0})$, defining a word βb_{i_j}, and let $\mathfrak{S}'_j$ be the set of all states of A that βb_{i_j}-succeed the state s_i. Then there is a path from $\mathfrak{S}''$, of length N, defining the word β and leading to some vertex $\mathfrak{S}$ of $G(s_{i_0})$, and it follows from condition 2 of Definition 56 that when $\Gamma(s_{i_0}, N)$ is constructed the vertex $\mathfrak{S}$ is assigned the triple $(\mathfrak{S}', s_i, \mathfrak{S}'')$, where $\mathfrak{S}'$ is the set of all states of A that β-succeed s_i. But then, on the basis of the triple $(\mathfrak{S}', s_i, \mathfrak{S}'')$ and the vertex $\mathfrak{S}$, the vertex $\mathfrak{S}_j$ is assigned the triple $(\mathfrak{S}'_j, s_i, \mathfrak{S}'')$ and condition 2 is fulfilled for the graph $\Gamma(s_{i_0}, N+1)$.

This completes the proof of the lemma.

Given a graph $\Gamma(s_{i_0}, N)$, we form a new graph $\Gamma(s_{i_0}, N, B)$ discarding some of the triples assigned to the vertices of $\Gamma(s_{i_0}, N)$.

Definition 57. The graph $\Gamma(s_{i_0}, N, B)$ is said to be admissible if it satisfies the following conditions:

(1) If some vertex $\mathfrak{S}$ of $\Gamma(s_{i_0}, N)$ is assigned a triple $(\mathfrak{S}, s_{i_0}, \{s_{i_0}\})$, this triple is retained in $\Gamma(s_{i_0}, N, B)$.

(2) If a vertex $\mathfrak{S}$ of $\Gamma(s_{i_0}, N, B)$ is assigned a triple $(\mathfrak{S}', s_i, \mathfrak{S}_2)$, the set $\mathfrak{S}'$ is maximal with respect to $\mathfrak{S}'$, $\mathfrak{S}$.

(3) If vertices $\mathfrak{S}_1$ and $\mathfrak{S}_2$ of $\Gamma(s_{i_0}, N, B)$ have the property that there is an arc from $\mathfrak{S}_1$ to $\mathfrak{S}_2$ labeled b_j and some vertex $\mathfrak{S}$ of the graph $\Gamma(s_{i_0}, N, B)$ is assigned the triple $(\mathfrak{S}', s_i, \mathfrak{S}_1)$, then any vertex $\mathfrak{S}_3$ which is the endpoint of an arc in $\Gamma(s_{i_0}, N, B)$ from $\mathfrak{S}$ is assigned a triple $(\mathfrak{S}'', s_k, \mathfrak{S}_2)$, where s_k b_j-succeeds s_i.

Lemma 22. Let A be an automaton having a type I generalized inverse with delay N. Then there exists an admissible graph $\Gamma(s_{i_0}, N, B)$.

* By this we mean that for every vertex of $G(s_{i_0})$ the sets of triples assigned to it in construction of the graphs $\Gamma(s_{i_0}, N_1)$ and $\Gamma(s_{i_0}, N_2)$ are the same.

Proof. By Theorem 92, the assumptions of the lemma imply that there is an admissible system of successors G with delay N for A and the initial state s_{i_0}. We shall show that an admissible graph $\Gamma(s_{i_0}, N, B)$ may be built up from G.

Let $\mathfrak{S}$ be an arbitrary vertex of $G, s_i \in \mathfrak{S}$ a state assigned the word β in $\mathfrak{S}$. To each vertex $\mathfrak{S}_1$ of $G(s_{i_0})$ at the end of a path from $\mathfrak{S}$ defining the word β, assign the triple $(\mathfrak{S}', s_i, \mathfrak{S})$, where $\mathfrak{S}'$ is the set of all states of A that β-succeed s_i.

Assign triples in this way for all vertices $\mathfrak{S}$ of G, states $s_i \in \mathfrak{S}$, and words assigned to the state s_i in $\mathfrak{S}$.

Condition 1 of Definition 57 is obviously fulfilled, since triples $(\mathfrak{S}, s_{i_0}, \{s_{i_0}\})$ are assigned in $\Gamma(s_0, N)$ only to sets of states β-succeeding s_{i_0}.

Let s_i be a state to which β is assigned in $\mathfrak{S}$. Then β is a type $(i_0, \mathfrak{S}, i)$ characteristic word. Suppose that $\mathfrak{S}'$ is not maximal with respect to $\mathfrak{S}', \mathfrak{S}_1$. Then there exist a state $s_\nu \in \mathfrak{S}_1$ and a word β' such that s_ν may yield response $\mathfrak{S}'$ but none of the states $s_\mu \in \mathfrak{S}'$ can yield this response. There exists a state $s_l \in \mathfrak{S}$ such that s_ν β-succeeds the state s_l. But then the state s_l can yield the response $\beta\beta'$, while s_i cannot yield this response. Hence the word β is not type $(i_0, \mathfrak{S}, i)$ characteristic. This contradiction shows that condition 2 of Definition 57 must hold.

Suppose that there is an arc from $\mathfrak{S}_1$ to $\mathfrak{S}_2$ in G, labeled b_j, and let the word assigned to a state $s_i \in \mathfrak{S}_1$ in the vertex $\mathfrak{S}_1$ be $b_j\beta$. By condition 3 of Definition 55, for any letter b_k such that there is a path from $\mathfrak{S}_1$ defining the word $b_j\beta b_k$, the word βb_k is assigned to in $\mathfrak{S}_2$ to some state s_m which b_j-succeeds the state s_i. Then there are vertices $\mathfrak{S}_3$ and $\mathfrak{S}_4$ in $G(s_{i_0})$, with an arc going from $\mathfrak{S}_3$ to $\mathfrak{S}_4$ labeled b_k, which are assigned triples $(\mathfrak{S}', s_i, \mathfrak{S}_1)$ and $(\mathfrak{S}'', s_m, \mathfrak{S}_2)$, and moreover $\mathfrak{S}_3$ is uniquely determined by $b_j\beta$ and $\mathfrak{S}_1$. The same argument applies to vertices $\mathfrak{S}$ of the graph $\Gamma(s_{i_0}, N, B)$ to which triples $(\mathfrak{S}, s_{i_0}, \{s_{i_0}\})$ are assigned. It follows that our assignment of triples satisfies condition 3 of Definition 57.

Thus the assignment of triples to the vertices of $G(s_{i_0})$ satisfies all the conditions of Definition 57 and the lemma is proved.

Lemma 23. Let A be an automaton for which there exists an admissible graph $\Gamma(s_{i_0}, N, B)$. Then the automaton A with initial state s_{i_0} has an admissible system of successors.

Proof. Using the graph $\Gamma(s_{i_0}, N, B)$, we shall construct an admissible system of successors G for the automaton A with initial state s_{i_0}.

Let $\mathfrak{S}$ be a vertex of $\Gamma(s_{i_0}, N, B)$ which is assigned a triple $(\mathfrak{S}', s_i, \mathfrak{S}_1)$. Assign to the state s_i in the vertex $\mathfrak{S}_1$ of $G(s_{i_0})$ all words $\beta_1, \ldots, \beta_n$ of length N such that there is a path from $\mathfrak{S}_1$ to $\mathfrak{S}$ defining the word β_j $(j = 1, \ldots, n)$ and $\mathfrak{S}'$ is the set of all states that β_j-succeed s_i in the automaton A. Carrying out this assignment of words for every vertex of $\Gamma(s_{i_0}, N, B)$ and every triple assigned to this vertex, we obtain a graph G.

Let $\mathfrak{S}$ be any vertex of G and β any word of length N which is a possible response of A in some state $s_\nu \in \mathfrak{S}$. Then there is a path from $\mathfrak{S}$ to some vertex $\mathfrak{S}_1$ of G, defining the word β. Suppose there is a path from the vertex $\{s_{i_0}\}$ of $G(s_{i_0})$ to $\mathfrak{S}$, defining a word β_1. Set $\beta_1\beta = b_{i_1} \cdots b_{i_M}$. Since the graph $\Gamma(s_{i_0}, N, B)$ is admissible, every vertex $\mathfrak{S}_{N+j}$ $(j = 0, 1, \ldots, M - N)$ which is the endpoint of a path from $\{s_{i_0}\}$ defining the word $b_{i_1} \ldots b_{i_{N+j}}$ is assigned a triple

$(\mathfrak{S}'_j, s_{\nu_j}, \mathfrak{S}_j)$, where $s_{\nu_j} \in \mathfrak{S}_j$ and $\mathfrak{S}'_j$ is the set of all states of A which $b_{i_{j+1}} \ldots b_{i_{N+j}}$-succeed s_{ν_j}. Then the word β is assigned to the state $s_{\nu_{M-N}} \in \mathfrak{S}_{M-N}$ in the vertex $\mathfrak{S}_{M-N}$. Since $\mathfrak{S}=\mathfrak{S}_{M-N}$, condition 1 in Definition 55 holds for the graph G.

Suppose there exist a vertex $\mathfrak{S}$ of $G(s_{i_0})$, a state $s_i \in \mathfrak{S}$ which is assigned the word β in $\mathfrak{S}$, a word β' and a state $s_k \in \mathfrak{S}$, such that s_k may yield response $\beta\beta'$ but s_i cannot yield this response. Suppose that β is assigned to state s_i in the vertex $\mathfrak{S}$ by consideration of a vertex $\mathfrak{S}_1$ and a triple $(\mathfrak{S}', s_i, \mathfrak{S})$. Then there exists a state $s_l \in \mathfrak{S}_1$ which may yield the response β', but no state $s_\nu \in \mathfrak{S}'$ may yield this response. Hence the set $\mathfrak{S}'$ is not maximal with respect to $\mathfrak{S}', \mathfrak{S}_1$, contradicting the assumption that $\Gamma(s_{i_0}, N, B)$ is an admissible graph. Thus β is a type $(i_0, \mathfrak{S}, i)$ characteristic word and condition 2 of Definition 55 is satisfied.

Finally, suppose that in the graph $G(s_{i_0})$ a state s_i in a vertex $\mathfrak{S}$ is labeled by a certain word $b_j\beta$ by consideration of a vertex $\mathfrak{S}_1$ and the corresponding triple $(\mathfrak{S}', s_i, \mathfrak{S})$. By condition 3 of Definition 57, for any letter b_k such that there is an arc in $\Gamma(s_{i_0}, N, B)$ from $\mathfrak{S}_1$ to some vertex $\mathfrak{S}_2$, labeled b_k, the vertex $\mathfrak{S}_2$ is assigned a triple $(\mathfrak{S}'', s_\varkappa, \mathfrak{S}''')$, where the state $s_\varkappa$ b_j-succeeds the state s_i, and there is an arc in $\Gamma(s_{i_0}, N, B)$ from $\mathfrak{S}$ to $\mathfrak{S}'''$ labeled b_j. But then the state $s_\varkappa$ in the vertex $\mathfrak{S}'''$ of the graph G is assigned the word βb_k. Thus condition 3 of Definition 55 is also satisfied.

We have thus constructed an admissible system of successors G with delay N for the automaton A and the state s_{i_0}.

Lemma 24. Suppose there exists an admissible graph $\Gamma(s_{i_0}, N_1, B)$. If the graphs $\Gamma(s_{i_0}, N_1)$ and $\Gamma(s_{i_0}, N_2)$ coincide for some $N_2 \neq N_1$, then $\Gamma(s_{i_0}, N_1, B)$ is also an admissible graph $\Gamma(s_{i_0}, N_2, B)$.

Proof. It is clear that if we view $\Gamma(s_{i_0}, N_1, B)$ as originating from the graph $\Gamma(s_{i_0}, N_2)$, then condition 1 of Definition 57 is fulfilled.

Condition 2 of the definition is independent of N_1, and so $\Gamma(s_{i_0}, N_1, B)$ still satisfies this condition when viewed as a graph $\Gamma(s_{i_0}, N_2, B)$.

Finally, condition 3 of Definition 57 continues to hold since it too is independent of the number N_1.

Theorem 94. There exists an algorithm which, for any given automaton A with initial states $s_{i_1}, \ldots, s_{i_n}$, determines in finitely many operations whether A has a type I generalized inverse with delay N and, when an inverse exists, determines the minimum delay N.

Proof. Suppose that A has only one initial state s_{i_1}. By Theorem 93, for each number N there is an algorithm which determines, in finitely many operations, whether A has a generalized inverse with delay N. Let N_1 be the smallest number for which the graph $\Gamma(s_{i_1}, N_1)$ coincides with some graph $\Gamma(s_{i_1}, N_2)$, $N_2 < N_1$. Since there are only finitely many different graphs $\Gamma(s_{i_1}, n)$ $(n=0, 1, \ldots)$ the number N_1 may be determined in finitely many steps, by simply following the inductive construction of the graphs $\Gamma(s_{i_1}, n)$ $(n=1, 2, \ldots)$ from $\Gamma(s_{i_1}, 0)$ as outlined in the proof of Lemma 21. It follows from Lemma 21 that every graph $\Gamma(s_{i_1}, N_3)$, $N_3 \geqslant N_1$, coincides with some graph $\Gamma(s_{i_1}, N_4)$, $N_4 < N_1$. Now if some graph $\Gamma(s_{i_1}, N_3)$, $N_3 \geqslant N_1$, can be used to form an admissible graph $\Gamma(s_{i_1}, N_3, B)$, it follows from Lemma 24 that from some graph $\Gamma(s_{i_1}, N_4)$, $N_4 < N_1$, we can also form an admissible graph $\Gamma(s_{i_1}, N_4, B)$. By Lemma 23 and 91, if A has a generalized inverse with delay N_3, it also has a generalized inverse with delay N_4.

To solve the general existence problem, then, it will suffice to check for the existence of type I generalized automata with delays $N=0, 1, \ldots, N_1-1$.

If the automaton has more than one initial state, the algorithm just outlined is applied to the automaton for each of the initial states.

Theorem 95. Let A be an automaton with initial states $s_{i_1}, \ldots, s_{i_n}$, *having a type I generalized automaton with delay N. Then there exists an automaton B with input alphabet* $\mathfrak{B}$ *and output alphabet* $\bar{\mathfrak{A}}=\mathfrak{A}\cup \bar{a}$, *where* $\bar{a}\overline{\in}\mathfrak{A}$, *with the following properties. Each state* s_{i_ν} $(\nu=1,\ldots,n)$ *may be associated with a state* t_{j_ν} *of B satisfying the following conditions:*

(1) *Let* s_{i_ν} *be a state and* $\beta\beta'$ *a word (where* β' *is of length N) which is a possible response of A in state* s_{i_ν}. *Then* $\mu(t_{j_\nu}, \beta\beta')=\alpha'\alpha$, *where* α' *is of length N and* α *a word such that* $\lambda(s_{i_\nu}, \alpha)=\beta$.

(2) *Let* s_{i_ν} *be a state and* $\beta\beta' b_r$ *a word (where* β' *is of length N) such that state* s_{i_ν} *may yield the response* $\beta\beta'$ *but not* $\beta\beta' b_r$. *Then* $\mu(t_{j_\nu}, \beta\beta' b_r)=\alpha\bar{a}$, *where* α *is a word over* $\mathfrak{A}$.

Proof. It will suffice to consider the case that A has only one initial state s_{i_1}, for otherwise we need only repeat the argument for each initial state.

Using the construction in the proof of Theorem 92, we construct an admissible system of successors G with delay N for A and s_{i_1}, and then utilize the method of Theorem 91 to form a type I generalized inverse B' with delay N. For all pairs $((\mathfrak{S}, s_i, \beta), b_j)$ such that $\mu((\mathfrak{S}, s_i, \beta), b_j)$ is not defined in B', we set $\mu((\mathfrak{S}, s_i, \beta), b_j)=\bar{a}$. The value of $\varepsilon((\mathfrak{S}, s_i, \beta), b_j)$ is defined arbitrarily. Denote the automaton thus constructed by B. It follows from the proof of Theorem 91 that for any state $(\mathfrak{S}, s_i, \beta)$ and any letter b_j the value of $\mu((\mathfrak{S}, s_i, \beta), b_j)$ is undefined in B' if and only if there is no path in $G(s_{i_0})$ from the vertex $\{s_{i_0}\}$ that defines the word βb_j.

There is a path from $\mathfrak{S}$ defining the word β. Therefore, for any word β' defined by a path in $G(s_{i_0})$ from the vertex $\{s_{i_0}\}$ to $\mathfrak{S}$, we have $\mu(t_{j_1}, \beta'\beta)=\alpha'\alpha$, where α' is of length N, and $\varepsilon(t_{j_1}, \beta'\beta)=(\mathfrak{S}, s_i, \beta)$, where $\lambda(s_{i_0}, \alpha)=\beta'$, $\delta(s_{i_0}, \alpha)=s_i$. Since $s_i\in\mathfrak{S}$ and there is no path from $\mathfrak{S}$ defining the word βb_j, it follows that the state s_i of A cannot yield the response βb_j. But then $\mu((\mathfrak{S}, s_i, \beta), b_j)=\bar{a}$, or $\mu(t_{j_1}, \beta'\beta b_j)=\alpha'\alpha\bar{a}$, proving the theorem.

Example. Consider the automaton A defined by Table 31, with one initial state s_1.

TABLE 31.

	a_1	a_2		a_1	a_2
s_1	s_2, b_1	s_3, b_1	s_7	s_{10}, b_2	s_{10}, b_2
s_2	s_4, b_1	s_5, b_1	s_8	s_1, b_1	s_1, b_1
s_3	s_6, b_1	s_7, b_1	s_9	s_1, b_2	s_1, b_2
s_4	s_4, b_1	s_8, b_2	s_{10}	s_1, b_1	s_1, b_2
s_5	s_5, b_1	s_9, b_2	s_{11}	s_{11}, b_1	s_{10}, b_2
s_6	s_{11}, b_1	s_{11}, b_1			

We wish to check whether this automaton has a type I generalized inverse and, in case it has, to construct an inverse with minimum delay.

Since $\lambda(s_6, a_1) = \lambda(s_6, a_2)$ and $\delta(s_6, a_1) = \delta(s_6, a_2)$, the automaton is not information-lossless of finite order. It therefore has no inverse in the sense of Definition 5. We shall first try to use Theorem 90 and construct decision graphs. This need be done only for types I-i-j such that the state s_i has more than one b_j-succeeding state, since otherwise there is a uniquely determined I-i-j successor, with minimum delay 0. Figure 24 illustrates all these decision graphs. They are of the following types: a — I-1-1; b — I-2-1; c — I-3-1.

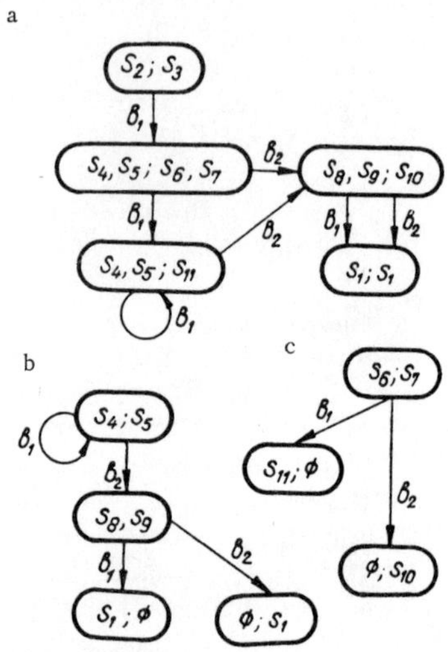

FIGURE 24.

It is evident from Figure 24, a that any of the sets appearing in a vertex of the type I-1-1 decision graph is maximal in the corresponding pair, since the graph contains no paths leading to a vertex in which one of the sets of the pair is empty (see Lemma 18). Thus the type I-1-1 successors with delay 0 are $\{s_2\}$, $\{s_3\}$, $\{s_2, s_3\}$.

One sees from Figure 24, b that the maximum length of a proper path in the type I-2-1 graph is 2. There is a path of length 2 from the initial vertex $(s_4; s_5)$ to the vertex $(s_4; s_5)$, defining the word $b_1 b_1$. It is also clear from the figure that neither of the sets $\mathfrak{S}_1$, $\mathfrak{S}_2$, where $\mathfrak{S}_1 = \{s_4\}$, $\mathfrak{S}_2 = \{s_5\}$, is maximal (see Lemma 18). Thus there is no type I-2-1 successor (see Theorem 86).

According to Figure 24, c, in the type I-3-1 decision graph any path from the initial vertex of length 1 leads to a vertex in which all nonempty sets are identical. Thus neither of the sets $\mathfrak{S}_1 = \{s_6\}$, $\mathfrak{S}_2 = \{s_7\}$ is maximal with respect to $\mathfrak{S}_1$, $\mathfrak{S}_2$ (Lemma 18), and there cannot be a type I-3-1 successor with delay 0.

Consequently, the only type I-3-1 successor is the set $\{s_6, s_7\}$, with minimum delay 1.

As the set $\mathfrak{S}'$ we may take the set $\{s_1, s_3, s_6, s_7, s_{10}, s_{11}\}$, and construct the following system of successors, satisfying the conditions of Theorem 90:

$$\text{I-1-1} - \{s_3\};\ \text{I-3-1} - \{s_6, s_7\};\ \text{I-6-1} - \{s_{11}\};\ \text{I-7-2} - \{s_{10}\};$$
$$\text{I-10-1} - \{s_1\};\ \text{I-10-2} - \{s_1\};\ \text{I-11-1} - \{s_{11}\};\ \text{I-11-2} - \{s_{10}\}.$$

The construction of the principal part of B as in the proof of Theorem 88 yields Table 32.

TABLE 32.

	b_1	b_2		b_1	b_2
(s_1, b_1)	$(s_3, b_1), a_2$	—	(s_{10}, b_1)	$(s_1, b_1), a_1$	—
(s_3, b_1)	$(s_6, b_1), a_1$	$(s_7, b_2), a_2$	(s_{10}, b_2)	$(s_1, b_1), a_2$	—
(s_6, b_1)	$(s_{11}, b_1), a_1$	$(s_{11}, b_2), a_1$	(s_{11}, b_1)	$(s_{11}, b_1), a_1$	$(s_{11}, b_2), a_1$
(s_7, b_2)	$(s_{10}, b_1), a_2$	$(s_{10}, b_2), a_2$	(s_{11}, b_2)	$(s_{10}, b_1), a_2$	$(s_{10}, b_2), a_2$

Note that the responses in states (s_6, b_1) and (s_7, b_1) may be chosen at will. The responses actually selected will enable us ultimately to achieve maximum simplification. Since $\varepsilon((s_{10}, b_1), b_1) = (s_1, b_1)$, we may take (s_{10}, b_1) as the initial state and there is no need to construct the initial part of the automaton B.

Simplification of the automaton defined by Table 32 yields Table 33.

The state s_1 of A corresponds to state t_5 of the generalized inverse defined by Table 33.

It follows from the example that not every noninitialized automaton has a generalized inverse with a certain delay. This follows via Theorem 88 from the fact that there is no type I-2-1 successor.

TABLE 33.

	b_1	b_2
t_1	t_2, a_2	—
t_2	t_3, a_1	t_4, a_2
t_3	t_3, a_1	t_4, a_1
t_4	t_5, a_2	t_6, a_2
t_5	t_1, a_1	—
t_6	t_1, a_2	—

Another conclusion to be drawn from the example is that not every initialized automaton has a generalized inverse with some delay — consider the automaton defined by Table 31 with initial state s_2.

It is impossible to construct a generalized inverse with delay 0 for the example by using Theorem 91, for this would involve defining $\mu((s_1, \Lambda), b_1) = a_1$ or $\mu((s_1, \Lambda), b_1) = a_2$ and would necessarily imply the existence of a successor with delay 0 of one of types I-2-1 or I-3-1.

This section and its predecessor are based on ideas set forth in /15/.

§3. INVERSE AUTOMATA WITH CONSTRAINED INPUT OR OUTPUT WORDS

Definition 58. An automaton A is said to be information-lossless of finite order N relative to a set of words $\mathfrak{L}(\mathfrak{A})$ (ILF-N-$\mathfrak{L}(\mathfrak{A})$) if the following condition holds for $k=N$ but not for $k=N+1$. There exist a state s_i, words $a_l\alpha_1$, $a_j\alpha_2$ $(a_l\neq a_j)$ of length k, a word α and an initial state s_{i_0} such that (1) $\alpha a_l\alpha_1\in\mathfrak{L}(\mathfrak{A})$, $\alpha a_j\alpha_2\in\mathfrak{L}(\mathfrak{A})$; (2) $\delta(s_{i_0},\alpha)=s_i$; (3) $\lambda(s_i,a_l\alpha_1)=$ $=\lambda(s_i,a_j\alpha_2)$ (this includes the case that $s_i=s_{i_0}$ and α is the empty word).

Definition 58 implies the following property of an ILF-N-$\mathfrak{L}(\mathfrak{A})$ automaton A. For any state s_i, knowledge of the output word β of length $N+1$ produced by A in this state is sufficient to determine the first letter of a word $a_j\alpha'$ such that $\lambda(s_i,a_j\alpha')=\beta$, provided that $\alpha a_j\alpha'\in\mathfrak{L}(\mathfrak{A})$ for some word α and $\delta(s_{i_0},\alpha)=s_i$ for some initial state s_{i_0}.

This justifies the following definition.

Definition 59. An automaton B is called an inverse with delay N for A relative to a set of words $\mathfrak{L}(\mathfrak{A})$ if, for each initial state s_{i_0} of A, there is a state t_{j_0} of B satisfying the following condition. For any word α_1 of length N $(N\geqslant 0)$ and any word α such that $\alpha\alpha_1\in\mathfrak{L}(\mathfrak{A})$ and $\lambda(s_{i_0},\alpha\alpha_1)$ is defined,

$$\mu(t_{j_0},\lambda(s_{i_0},\alpha\alpha_1))=\alpha_2\alpha.$$

The next definition is similar.

Definition 60. An automaton B is called a generalized inverse with delay N $(N\geqslant 0)$ for A relative to a set of words $\mathfrak{L}(\mathfrak{B})$ if any initial state s_{i_0} of A may be associated with a state t_{j_0} of B satisfying the following condition. Let α_1 be a word of length N and α any word such that $\lambda(s_{i_0},\alpha\alpha_1)\in\mathfrak{L}(\mathfrak{B})$. Then

$$\mu(t_{j_0},\lambda(s_{i_0},\alpha\alpha_1))=\alpha_3\alpha_2 \quad\text{and}\quad \lambda(s_{i_0},\alpha_2)=\lambda(s_{i_0},\alpha).$$

In what follows, the set $\mathfrak{L}(\mathfrak{A})$ (or $\mathfrak{L}(\mathfrak{B})$) will always be a regular event $\mathfrak{R}(\mathfrak{A})$ (or $\mathfrak{R}(\mathfrak{B})$) such that if $\alpha\in\mathfrak{R}(\mathfrak{A})$ $(\beta\in\mathfrak{R}(\mathfrak{B}))$ and $\alpha=\alpha'\alpha''$ $(\beta=\beta'\beta'')$, then also $\alpha'\in\mathfrak{R}(\mathfrak{A})$ $(\beta'\in\mathfrak{R}(\mathfrak{B}))$. When regular sets are generated by sources, this condition will hold if V_2 is the set of all vertices of the source [see Introduction, p. 6].

We shall say that a set $\mathfrak{N}_1$ of vertices in the source defining a regular event α-succeeds (β-succeeds) a set $\mathfrak{N}$ of vertices if $\mathfrak{N}_1$ is the set of all vertices v_i which are ends of paths from some vertex $v_j\in\mathfrak{N}$ that define the word α (β).

The source defining a regular event $\mathfrak{R}(\mathfrak{A})$ will henceforth be denoted by $R(\mathfrak{A})$. Since the same regular event may be defined by several sources, the notation for the source will be provided with primes, subscripts, etc.

A state s_i and a nonempty set $\mathfrak{N}$ of vertices in the source $R(\mathfrak{A})$ $(R(\mathfrak{B}))$ are said to be combinable if one of the following conditions holds: (1) s_i is an initial state and $\mathfrak{N}$ is the set of all initial vertices of the source; (2) there exist an initial state s_{i_0} and a word α such that $\delta(s_{i_0},\alpha)=s_i$ and the set $\mathfrak{N}$ α-succeeds ($\lambda(s_{i_0},\alpha)$-succeeds) the set of all initial vertices of the source.

To determine whether an automaton A is ILF-N-$\mathfrak{R}(\mathfrak{A})$, we construct a special automaton A_1. Similarly, in order to check whether A has a generalized inverse relative to an event $\mathfrak{R}(\mathfrak{B})$ and to determine the minimum delay, we shall construct an automaton A_2. The automata A_1 and A_2 enable us to reduce these problems to those considered in Chap. I, §2 and §§1, 2 of the present chapter.

The states of the automaton A_1 (A_2) are all pairs consiting of a combinable state of A and set of vertices of the source $R(\mathfrak{A})$ ($R(\mathfrak{B})$) The output and next-state functions are defined as follows:

(1) $\lambda_k((s_i, \mathfrak{N}), a_r) = \lambda(s_i, a_r)$, $\delta_k((s_i, \mathfrak{N}), a_r) = (\delta(s_i, a_r), \mathfrak{N}_1)$ for $k=1$ ($k=2$), provided that $\delta(s_i, a_r)$ is defined and $\mathfrak{N}_1$ is a nonempty set of vertices of the source $R(\mathfrak{A})$ ($R(\mathfrak{B})$) which a_r-succeeds ($\lambda(s_i, a_r)$-succeeds) the set $\mathfrak{N}$.

(2) Otherwise, $\lambda_k((s_i, \mathfrak{N}), a_r)$ and $\delta_k((s_i, \mathfrak{N}), a_r)$ are undefined.

The initial state s_{i_0} corresponds to an initial state $(s_{i_0}, \mathfrak{N}_0)$, where $\mathfrak{N}_0$ is the set of all initial vertices of the source.

Theorem 96. For any initial state s_{i_0} and word α, the value $\lambda_1((s_{i_0}, \mathfrak{N}_0), \alpha)$ or $\lambda_2((s_{i_0}, \mathfrak{N}_0), \alpha)$ is defined if and only if $\lambda(s_{i_0}, \alpha)$ is defined and $\alpha \in \mathfrak{R}(\mathfrak{A})$ or $\lambda(s_{i_0}, \alpha) \in \mathfrak{R}(\mathfrak{B})$. If $\lambda_k((s_{i_0}, \mathfrak{N}_0), \alpha)$ is defined, then $\lambda_k((s_{i_0}, \mathfrak{N}_0), \alpha) = \lambda(s_{i_0}, \alpha)$ ($k = 1, 2$).

Proof. Let $\alpha = a_{i_1}$ or $\lambda(s_{i_0}, \alpha) = b_{j_1}$. If $\lambda(s_{i_0}, \alpha)$ is defined and $a_{i_1} \in \mathfrak{R}(\mathfrak{A})$ or $b_{j_1} \in \mathfrak{R}(\mathfrak{B})$, then the set $\mathfrak{N}_0$ is a_{i_1}-succeeded or b_{j_1}-succeeded by some nonempty set $\mathfrak{N}_1$ of vertices of $R(\mathfrak{A})$ or $R(\mathfrak{B})$. By condition 1 in the definition of A_1 and A_2, we have

$$\delta_k((s_{i_0}, \mathfrak{N}_0), \alpha) = (\delta(s_{i_0}, \alpha), \mathfrak{N}_1),$$

where $k=1$ or $k=2$. If $\lambda(s_{i_0}, \alpha)$ is not defined, then by condition 2 of the definition neither is $\lambda_k((s_{i_0}, \mathfrak{N}_0), \alpha)$ ($k=1,2$). If $a_{i_1} \overline{\in} \mathfrak{R}(\mathfrak{A})$ or $b_{j_1} \overline{\in} \mathfrak{R}(\mathfrak{B})$, the set $\mathfrak{N}_0$ is a_{i_1}-succeeded or b_{j_1}-succeeded by the empty set, and by condition 2 $\lambda_k((s_{i_0}, \mathfrak{N}_0), \alpha)$ is undefined.

Let αa_{i_2} be an arbitrary word for which $\lambda_k((s_{i_0}, \mathfrak{N}_0), \alpha)$ ($k=1,2$) is defined and $\delta_k((s_{i_0}, \mathfrak{N}_0), \alpha) = (\delta(s_{i_0}, \alpha), \mathfrak{N}_2)$, where $\mathfrak{N}_2$ is the set of vertices of $R(\mathfrak{A})$ or $R(\mathfrak{B})$ that α-succeeds or $\lambda(s_{i_0}, \alpha)$-succeeds the set $\mathfrak{N}_0$. If $\alpha a_{i_2} \in \mathfrak{R}(\mathfrak{A})$ or $\lambda(s_{i_0}, \alpha a_{i_2}) \in \mathfrak{R}(\mathfrak{B})$ then the set $\mathfrak{N}_2$ is a_{i_2}-succeeded or $\lambda(\delta(s_{i_0}, \alpha), a_{i_2})$-succeeded by a nonempty set $\mathfrak{N}_3$ and $\lambda_k((\delta(s_{i_0}, \alpha), \mathfrak{N}_2), a_{i_2})$ ($k=1,2$) is defined, provided $\lambda(\delta(s_{i_0}, \alpha), a_{i_2})$ is defined, in which case

$$\delta_k((\delta(s_{i_0}, \alpha), \mathfrak{N}_2), a_{i_2}) = (\delta(s_{i_0}, \alpha a_{i_2}), \mathfrak{N}_3).$$

Hence $\lambda_k((s_{i_0}, \mathfrak{N}_0), \alpha a_{i_2})$ ($k=1,2$) is defined.

Let $\alpha a_{i_2} \overline{\in} \mathfrak{R}(\mathfrak{A})$ or $\lambda(s_{i_0}, \alpha a_{i_2}) \overline{\in} \mathfrak{R}(\mathfrak{B})$. Then the set $\mathfrak{N}_2$ is a_{i_2}-succeeded or $\lambda(\delta(s_{i_0}, \alpha), a_{i_2})$-succeeded by the empty set and by condition 2 in the definition of A_1 and A_2 the value $\lambda_k((\delta(s_{i_0}, \alpha), \mathfrak{N}_2), a_{i_2})$ is not defined. Thus neither is $\lambda_k((s_{i_0}, \mathfrak{N}_0), \alpha a_{i_2})$.

It now follows by induction that the desired conclusion is valid for all nonempty words over $\mathfrak{A}$.

Theorem 97. The automaton A is ILF-N-$\mathfrak{R}(\mathfrak{A})$ if and only if A_1 is ILS-I-N.

Proof. Suppose there is a state $s_{1r} = (s_i, \mathfrak{N})$ such that for suitable words $a_l\alpha_1$ and $a_j\alpha_2$ ($l \neq j$) of length k,

$$\lambda_1(s_{1r}, a_l\alpha_1) = \lambda_1(s_{1r}, a_j\alpha_2) = \beta.$$

Then, by Theorem 96 and the fact that the state s_i and set $\mathfrak{N}$ are combinable, we have $\lambda(s_i, a_l\alpha_1)=\lambda(s_i, a_j\alpha_2)=\beta$ and there exist an initial state s_{i_0} and a word α such that $\delta(s_{i_0}, \alpha)=s_i$, $\alpha a_l\alpha_1\in\mathfrak{R}(\mathfrak{A})$ and $\alpha a_j\alpha_2\in\mathfrak{R}(\mathfrak{A})$.

Suppose there exist a state s_i, words $a_l\alpha_1$, $a_j\alpha_2$ of length k, a word α and an initial state s_{i_0} such that

$$\alpha a_l\alpha_1\in\mathfrak{R}(\mathfrak{A}),\ \alpha a_j\alpha_2\in\mathfrak{R}(\mathfrak{A}),\ \delta(s_{i_0}, \alpha)=s_i.$$

Let $\mathfrak{N}$ be the set of vertices of $R(\mathfrak{A})$ that α-succeed the set $\mathfrak{N}_0$. Then

$$\lambda_1((\delta(s_{i_0}, \alpha), \mathfrak{N}), a_l\alpha_1)=\lambda_1((\delta(s_{i_0}, \alpha), \mathfrak{N}), a_j\alpha_2).$$

To complete the proof, we need only set $k=N$ and $k=N+1$.

By the results of Chap. I and Theorem 97, we have the following

Theorem 98. There is an algorithm which, given any automaton A and any regular event $\mathfrak{R}(\mathfrak{A})$, determines in finitely many operations whether A is ILF-N-$\mathfrak{R}(\mathfrak{A})$ for some N, and if so determines the value of N.

Theorem 99. An automaton A has a generalized inverse with delay N relative to a set of words $\mathfrak{R}(\mathfrak{B})$ if and only if the automaton A_2 has a type I generalized inverse with delay N.

Proof. Suppose that A_2 has a generalized inverse B with delay N, i. e., for any initial state $s_{2i_0}=(s_{i_0}, \mathfrak{N}_0)$, where s_{i_0} is the initial state of A and $\mathfrak{N}_0$ the set of initial vertices of the source $R(\mathfrak{B})$, one can single out a state t_{j_0} such that for any word $\alpha\alpha'$ (α' of length N) for which $\lambda_2(s_{2i_0}, \alpha\alpha')$ is defined,

$$\mu(t_{j_0};\ \lambda_2(s_{2i_0}, \alpha\alpha'))=\alpha'''\alpha'' \text{ and } \lambda_2(s_{2i_0}, \alpha'')=\lambda_2(s_{2i_0}, \alpha).$$

Then, by the construction of A_2 and Theorem 96, $\lambda(s_{i_0}, \alpha)$ and $\lambda(s_{i_0}, \alpha'')$ are defined and $\lambda(s_{i_0}, \alpha)=\lambda(s_{i_0}, \alpha'')$. By Theorem 96, the equality holds for any word $\alpha\alpha'$ such that $\lambda(s_{i_0}, \alpha\alpha')\in\mathfrak{R}(\mathfrak{B})$. Thus B is a generalized inverse with delay N for A relative to $\mathfrak{R}(\mathfrak{B})$.

Conversely, suppose that A has a generalized inverse B with delay N relative to $\mathfrak{R}(\mathfrak{B})$, i. e., for any initial state s_{i_0} there is a state t_{j_0} such that for any words α' of length N and α of arbitrary length for which $\lambda(s_{i_0}, \alpha\alpha')$ is defined and $\lambda(s_{i_0}, \alpha\alpha')\in\mathfrak{R}(\mathfrak{B})$,

$$\mu(t_{j_0}, \lambda(s_{i_0}, \alpha\alpha'))=\alpha'''\alpha'' \text{ and } \lambda(s_{i_0}, \alpha'')=\lambda(s_{i_0}, \alpha).$$

By Theorem 96, $\lambda_2((s_{i_0}, \mathfrak{N}_0), \alpha^{\mathrm{IV}})$ is defined if and only if $\lambda(s_{i_0}, \alpha^{\mathrm{IV}})$ is defined and $\lambda(s_{i_0}, \alpha^{\mathrm{IV}})\in\mathfrak{R}(\mathfrak{B})$, in which case $\lambda_2((s_{i_0}, \mathfrak{N}_0), \alpha^{\mathrm{IV}})=\lambda(s_{i_0}, \alpha^{\mathrm{IV}})$. Hence it follows that $\lambda_2((s_{i_0}, \mathfrak{N}_0), \alpha'')$ is defined and

$$\lambda_2((s_{i_0}, \mathfrak{N}_0), \alpha'')=\lambda_2((s_{i_0}, \mathfrak{N}_0), \alpha).$$

Consequently, B is a type I generalized inverse with delay N for A_2. Moreover, the initial state $(s_{i_0}, \mathfrak{N}_0)$ of A_2 corresponds to the initial state t_{j_0} of B associated with the initial state s_{i_0} of A.

This completes the proof.

By the results of §2 in this chapter and Theorem 99, we have

Theorem 100. There exists an algorithm which, for any given automaton A and any regular event $\mathfrak{R}(\mathfrak{B})$, determines in finitely many operations whether A has a generalized inverse with delay N relative to $\mathfrak{R}(\mathfrak{B})$, and in case an inverse exists determines the minimum value of N.

Theorems 97 and 99 imply the following construction of inverse automata for a given automaton relative to an event $\mathfrak{R}(\mathfrak{A})$ or $\mathfrak{R}(\mathfrak{B})$.

Take any source defining the event $\mathfrak{R}(\mathfrak{A})$ or $\mathfrak{R}(\mathfrak{B})$, construct the automaton A_1 or A_2 and form an inverse or generalized inverse of the latter. This may be done as described in Chap. I, §3 (construction of a standard inverse) or in §§1, 2 of this chapter. In the latter case, we again speak of the standard generalized inverse.

Since the source generating a given regular event is not uniquely determined, the construction of the automata A_1 and A_2 and their standard inverses is not unique. It is therefore important to study the relationship between different versions of the automata A_1 and A_2 and between different (generalized) inverses, based on different sources defining the same regular event.

We shall say that a set $\mathfrak{N}$ of vertices in a source $R(\mathfrak{A})$ $(R(\mathfrak{B}))$ generates a word α (β) if there are vertices $v_i \in \mathfrak{N}$ and v_j in the source such that there is a path from v_i to v_j defining the word $\alpha(\beta)$.

Definition 61. Two sets $\mathfrak{N}_1$ and $\mathfrak{N}_2$ of vertices of two sources R_1 and R_2 are said to be equivalent if they generate the same words.

There is an algorithm telling, for any two sets of vertices in sources R_1 and R_2, whether or not they are equivalent. This algorithm is based on a graph $G(R_1, R_2)$ constructed as follows.

The vertices of $G(R_1, R_2)$ are all ordered pairs of nonempty sets of vertices of the sources, where the first (second) member of each pair is a set of vertices of R_1 (R_2), plus one distinguished vertex X.

Let (V_{1i}, V_{2j}) and (V_{1k}, V_{2l}) be vertices of $G(R_1, R_2)$ other than X, and suppose the source R_1 defines a set of words over an alphabet $\mathfrak{A}'$, R_2 over an alphabet $\mathfrak{A}''$. We consider the pair of vertices $\{(V_{1i}, V_{2j}), (V_{1k}, V_{2l})\}$ in conjunction with each letter $a_i \in \mathfrak{A}' \cup \mathfrak{A}''$.

If the set V_{1k} a_i-succeeds the set V_{1i} and V_{2l} a_i-succeeds V_{2j}, the graph will contain an arc from (V_{1i}, V_{2j}) to (V_{1k}, V_{2l}), labeled a_i.

If there is an arc from some vertex $v_\varkappa \in V_{1i}$ or $v_\rho \in V_{2j}$ labeled a_i but there is no arc from $v_\mu \in V_{2j}$ or $v_\lambda \in V_{1i}$ labeled a_i, the graph will contain an (unlabeled) arc from (V_{1i}, V_{2j}) to X.

The graph contains arcs only as prescribed by the above conditions.

Theorem 101. Sets $\mathfrak{N}_1$ and $\mathfrak{N}_2$ are equivalent if and only if there is no path in the graph $G(R_1, R_2)$ from the vertex $(\mathfrak{N}_1; \mathfrak{N}_2)$ to X.

Proof. Let α be a word generated by $\mathfrak{N}_1$ but not by $\mathfrak{N}_2$. Let $\alpha = \alpha' a_{i_1} \alpha''$, where α' is generated by both sets (one or both of α', α'' may be empty) and α' is the longest possible word satisfying this condition. Then there is a path from the vertex $(\mathfrak{N}_1; \mathfrak{N}_2)$ to some vertex $(\mathfrak{N}_3; \mathfrak{N}_4)$, defining the word α', and moreover there is only one path from $(\mathfrak{N}_1; \mathfrak{N}_2)$ that defines α'.

If there is an arc from some vertex $v_j \in \mathfrak{N}_4$ in the source R_2, labeled a_{i_1}, then the set of vertices $\mathfrak{N}_2$ generates the word $\alpha' a_{i_1}$, but this is impossible by the choice of α'. Since $\mathfrak{N}_1$ generates the word α, there is a vertex $v_k \in \mathfrak{N}_3$ from which an arc of R_1 issues, labeled a_{i_1}. Then, by the construction of $G(R_1, R_2)$, there is an arc from $(\mathfrak{N}_3; \mathfrak{N}_4)$ to X or a path from $(\mathfrak{N}_1; \mathfrak{N}_2)$ to X.

Conversely, suppose there is a path from the vertex $(\mathfrak{N}_1; \mathfrak{N}_2)$ to X. If there is no path from $(\mathfrak{N}_1; \mathfrak{N}_2)$ to X, let $(\mathfrak{N}_3; \mathfrak{N}_4)$ be some vertex on the above-mentioned path from which there is an arc leading to X. Suppose that the path from $(\mathfrak{N}_1; \mathfrak{N}_2)$ to $(\mathfrak{N}_3; \mathfrak{N}_4)$ defines a word α. It follows from the construction of $G(R_1, R_2)$ that both sets $\mathfrak{N}_1$ and $\mathfrak{N}_2$ generate α. There may be an arc from $(\mathfrak{N}_3; \mathfrak{N}_4)$ to X only if there exist a letter a_k and a vertex $v_i \in \mathfrak{N}_3$ or $v_i \in \mathfrak{N}_4$ such that there is an arc in the appropriate source emanating from v_i and labeled a_k, but no such arc emanates from any vertex in the other set $\mathfrak{N}_4$ or $\mathfrak{N}_3$. This means that one of the sets $\mathfrak{N}_1$ or $\mathfrak{N}_2$ generates the word αa_k and the other does not, so that these sets are not equivalent.*

Lemma 25. Let $\mathfrak{N}_1$ and $\mathfrak{N}_2$ be sets of vertices in sources R_1 and R_2, respectively, $\mathfrak{N}_3$ and $\mathfrak{N}_4$ the sets of all vertices which a_r-succeed (b_r-succeed) the sets $\mathfrak{N}_1$ and $\mathfrak{N}_2$. If $\mathfrak{N}_1$ and $\mathfrak{N}_2$ are equivalent, then so are $\mathfrak{N}_3$ and $\mathfrak{N}_4$.

Proof. Since the graph $G(R_1, R_2)$ contains an arc from $(\mathfrak{N}_1; \mathfrak{N}_2)$ to $(\mathfrak{N}_3; \mathfrak{N}_4)$ and there is no path from $(\mathfrak{N}_1; \mathfrak{N}_2)$ to X, neither is there such a path from $(\mathfrak{N}_3; \mathfrak{N}_4)$. By Theorem 101, the sets $\mathfrak{N}_3$ and $\mathfrak{N}_4$ are equivalent.

We now divide the state sets of the automaton A_1 (A_2) into classes $\mathfrak{U}_{11}, \ldots, \mathfrak{U}_{1N_1}$ ($\mathfrak{U}_{21}, \ldots, \mathfrak{U}_{2N_2}$), stipulating that all states $(s_i, \mathfrak{N}_j)$ $(j=1, \ldots, n)$ for equivalent sets $\mathfrak{N}_j$ constitute a class.

Lemma 26. For any word α and any two states $(s_i, \mathfrak{N}_1)$ and $(s_i, \mathfrak{N}_2)$ in the same class $\mathfrak{U}_{kj}$ $(k=1,2)$, the values $\lambda_k((s_i, \mathfrak{N}_1), \alpha)$ and $\lambda_k((s_i, \mathfrak{N}_2), \alpha)$ are either both defined or both undefined, and in the former case $\lambda_k((s_i, \mathfrak{N}_1), \alpha) = \lambda_k((s_i, \mathfrak{N}_2), \alpha)$.

Proof. If both values are defined, the desired equality follows from the construction of the automata A_1 and A_2.

If $\lambda(s_i, \alpha)$ is undefined for some word α, it follows from Theorem 96 that neither $\lambda_k((s_i, \mathfrak{N}_1), \alpha)$ nor $\lambda_k((s_i, \mathfrak{N}_2), \alpha)$ $(k=1,2)$ is defined.

Let $\lambda(s_i, \alpha)$ be defined and set $\alpha = \alpha' a_j \alpha''$, where α' is a word of maximum length such that the set $\mathfrak{N}_1$ is α'-succeeded ($\lambda(s_i, \alpha')$-succeeded) by a nonempty set $\mathfrak{N}_3$ of vertices but $\alpha' a_j$-succeeded ($\lambda(s_i, \alpha' a_j)$-succeeded) by the empty set. Then, since $\mathfrak{N}_1$ and $\mathfrak{N}_2$ are equivalent, the set $\mathfrak{N}_2$ is α'-succeeded ($\lambda(s_i, \alpha')$-succeeded) by a nonempty set $\mathfrak{N}_4$ but $\alpha' a_j$-succeeded ($\lambda(s_i, \alpha' a_j)$-succeeded) by the empty set. Similar arguments hold if $\mathfrak{N}_1$ and $\mathfrak{N}_2$ are interchanged. Hence it follows that for any word α the sets $\mathfrak{N}_1$ and $\mathfrak{N}_2$ are α-succeeded ($\lambda(s_i, \alpha)$-succeeded) by sets $\mathfrak{N}_3$ and $\mathfrak{N}_4$, respectively, which are either both nonempty or both empty. But then it follows from the definition of A_1 and A_2 that $\lambda_k((s_i, \mathfrak{N}_1), \alpha)$ and $\lambda_k((s_i, \mathfrak{N}_2), \alpha)$ are either both defined or both undefined.

Theorem 102. The collection of classes $\mathfrak{U}_{11}, \ldots, \mathfrak{U}_{1N_1}$ ($\mathfrak{U}_{21}, \ldots, \mathfrak{U}_{2N_2}$) is a system of invariant classes of states for the automaton A_1 (A_2).

Proof. Condition 1 for such systems [see p. 4] is satisfied by the construction of the classes $\mathfrak{U}_{k_1}, \ldots, \mathfrak{U}_{kN_k}$. That condition 2 holds was verified in Lemma 26.

Consider two states $(s_i, \mathfrak{N}_1)$ and $(s_i, \mathfrak{N}_2)$ in the same class $\mathfrak{U}_{kj}$. It follows from Lemma 26 that for any letter a_l the values $\lambda_k((s_i, \mathfrak{N}_1), a_l)$ and $\lambda_k((s_i, \mathfrak{N}_2), a_l)$ are either both defined or both undefined. If both are defined, then $\delta_k((s_i, \mathfrak{N}_1), a_l) = (\delta(s_i, a_l), \mathfrak{N}_3)$ and $\delta_k((s_i, \mathfrak{N}_2), a_l) = (\delta(s_i, a_l), \mathfrak{N}_4)$, where the sets

* It is easy to see that there is actually no need to label the arcs of the graph $G(R_1, R_2)$; their sole purpose is to facilitate the proof of Theorem 101.

$\mathfrak{N}_3$ and $\mathfrak{N}_4$ a_l-succeed ($\lambda(s_i, a_l)$ -succeed) the sets $\mathfrak{N}_1$ and $\mathfrak{N}_2$, respectively. Since $\mathfrak{N}_1$ and $\mathfrak{N}_2$ are equivalent, so are $\mathfrak{N}_3$ and $\mathfrak{N}_4$ (Lemma 25), and the states $(\delta(s_i, a_l), \mathfrak{N}_3)$ and $(\delta(s_i, a_l), \mathfrak{N}_4)$ are in the same class $\mathfrak{U}_{km}$. Thus condition 3 for invariant classes is also fulfilled. Q. E. D.

Two states s'_i and s''_j of automata A' and A'' are said to be equivalent if for any word α the values $\lambda'(s'_i, \alpha)$ and $\lambda''(s''_j, \alpha)$ are either both defined or both undefined, and in the former case $\lambda'(s'_i, \alpha) = \lambda''(s''_j, \alpha)$. (The automata A' and A'' may coincide.)

By Theorem 102, we can construct automata A_3 and A_4 as follows. Their states will be the classes $\mathfrak{U}_{11}, \ldots, \mathfrak{U}_{1N_1}$ $(\mathfrak{U}_{21}, \ldots, \mathfrak{U}_{2N_2})$. Denote the class $\mathfrak{U}_{kj} = \{(s_i, \mathfrak{N}_1), \ldots, (s_i, \mathfrak{N}_N)\}$ by $(s_i; \mathfrak{N}_1, \ldots, \mathfrak{N}_N)$. We then define the output and next-state functions for a state $(s_i; \mathfrak{N}_1, \ldots, \mathfrak{N}_N) = \mathfrak{U}_{kj}$ and letter a_r by

$$\lambda_{k+2}(\mathfrak{U}_{kj}, a_r) = \lambda_k((s_i, \mathfrak{N}_1), a_r), \quad \delta_{k+2}(\mathfrak{U}_{kj}, a_r) = \mathfrak{U}_{k\sigma},$$

where $\mathfrak{U}_{k\sigma}$ is the class such that $\delta_k((s_i, \mathfrak{U}_1), a_r) \in \mathfrak{U}_{k\sigma}$ $(k=1, 2)$. If A_k has an initial state s_{ki_0}, then the class $\mathfrak{U}_{kl_0}$ such that $s_{ki_0} \in \mathfrak{U}_{kl_0}$ is the corresponding initial state for the automaton A_{k+2} $(k=1,2)$.

Definition 62. We shall say that sets of states $\mathfrak{S}'$ and $\mathfrak{S}''$ of automata A' and A'' are isomorphic if there is a function φ which maps $\mathfrak{S}''$ in one-to-one fashion onto $\mathfrak{S}'$, so that $\lambda'(\varphi(s''_j), a_r) = \lambda''(s''_j, a_r)$ and $\varphi(\delta''(s''_j, a_r)) = \delta'(\varphi(s''_j), a_r)$ for any state $s_j \in \mathfrak{S}''$ and any letter a_r.*

Theorem 103. Let $R'(\mathfrak{A})$ and $R''(\mathfrak{A})$ $(R'(\mathfrak{B})$ and $R''(\mathfrak{B}))$ be two sources defining the same regular event $\mathfrak{R}(\mathfrak{A})$ $(\mathfrak{R}(\mathfrak{B}))$. Then the sets of all states of A'_3 and A''_3 $(A'_4$ and $A''_4)$ are isomorphic.

Proof. Set $\varphi(s''_{3j}) = (s_k; \mathfrak{N}'_1, \ldots, \mathfrak{N}'_{M_1})$, where $s''_{3j} = (s_k; \mathfrak{N}''_1, \ldots, \mathfrak{N}''_{M_2})$ is an arbitrary state of A''_3 and the sets $\mathfrak{N}'_\rho$ $(\rho=1, \ldots, M_1)$ and $\mathfrak{N}''_\sigma$ $(\sigma=1, \ldots, M_2)$ are equivalent. It follows from the construction of A'_3 and A''_3 that these automata have no states $(s_k; \mathfrak{N}_{11}, \ldots, \mathfrak{N}_{1P})$ and $(s_k; \mathfrak{N}_{21}, \ldots, \mathfrak{N}_{2R})$ where $\mathfrak{N}_{1i}$ and $\mathfrak{N}_{2j}$ are equivalent. Thus the mapping φ is one-to-one, provided the automaton A'_3 has a state $(s_k; \mathfrak{N}'_1, \ldots, \mathfrak{N}'_{M_1})$. The state s_k and set $\mathfrak{N}''_1$ are combinable, and so there exist a word α and an initial state s_{i_0} of A such that $\lambda(s_{i_0}, \alpha) = s_k$ and the set $\mathfrak{N}''_1$ α-succeeds the set $\mathfrak{N}''_0$. Since the source $R'(\mathfrak{A})$ defines the same regular event as $R''(\mathfrak{A})$, the set $\mathfrak{N}'_0$ is α-succeeded by some nonempty set $\mathfrak{N}'_1$ of vertices of $R'(\mathfrak{A})$, the state s_k and set $\mathfrak{N}'_1$ are combinable, the automaton A'_1 has a state $(s_k, \mathfrak{N}'_1)$ and the automaton A'_3 a state $(s_k; \mathfrak{N}'_1, \ldots, \mathfrak{N}'_{M_1})$. Thus the mapping φ is well-defined.

It remains to show that φ is an isomorphism.

For any letter a_r, the values $\lambda'_3((s_k; \mathfrak{N}'_1, \ldots, \mathfrak{N}'_{M_1}), a_r)$ and $\lambda''_3((s_k; \mathfrak{N}''_1, \ldots, \mathfrak{N}''_{M_2}), a_r)$ are defined if and only if $\lambda(s_k, a_r)$ is defined and the sets $\mathfrak{N}'_\rho$ $(\rho=1, \ldots, M_1)$ and $\mathfrak{N}''_\sigma$ $(\sigma=1, \ldots, M_2)$, respectively, generate the word a_r. Since these sets are equivalent, the values of λ'_3 and λ''_3 for any letter a_r are either both defined or both undefined. By the construction of A_1 and A_3, if both values are defined they coincide.

Now,

$$\delta'_3(\varphi(s''_{3j}), a_r) = (\delta(s_k, a_r); \; \mathfrak{N}'_{11}, \ldots, \mathfrak{N}'_{1N_1}),$$
$$\delta''_3(s''_{3j}, a_r) = (\delta(s_k, a_r); \; \mathfrak{N}''_{11}, \ldots, \mathfrak{N}''_{1N_2}).$$

* A similar definition holds for isomorphism in automata B' and B''. In the sequel, whenever different sources are used to construct various automata the notation for the latter and for all their components will follow that used for the sources (as regards subscripts, primes, etc.).

Here each of the sets $\mathfrak{N}'_{1\varkappa}$ a_r-succeeds one of the sets $\mathfrak{N}'_\rho$, and each of the sets $\mathfrak{N}''_{1\lambda}$ a_r-succeeds some set $\mathfrak{N}''_\sigma$. By Lemma 25, the sets $\mathfrak{N}'_{1\varkappa}$ $(\varkappa=1,\ldots,N_1)$ and $\mathfrak{N}''_{1\lambda}$ $(\lambda=1,\ldots,N_2)$ are equivalent, whence it follows that

$$\delta'_3(\varphi(s''_{3j}),a_r)=\varphi(\delta''_3(s''_{3j},a_r)).$$

This proves the theorem for A'_3 and A''_3; the proof for the automata A'_4 and A''_4 is analogous.

Lemma 27. Let A_1 be an ILS-I-N automaton and suppose that the principal part of the standard inverse B of A_1 with delay N contains states $((s_i,\mathfrak{N}_j),\beta)=t_{i_j}$ $(j=1,2)$. If the sets of vertices $\mathfrak{N}_1$ and $\mathfrak{N}_2$ are equivalent, the states t_{i_1} and t_{i_2} are also equivalent.

Proof. Let α_1 and α_2 be two arbitrary words of length N such that $\lambda_1((s_i,\mathfrak{N}_1),\alpha_k)=\beta$ $(k=1,2)$. Since $\mathfrak{N}_1$ and $\mathfrak{N}_2$ are equivalent, the states $(s_i,\mathfrak{N}_1)$ and $(s_i,\mathfrak{N}_2)$ are also equivalent and $\lambda_1((s_i,\mathfrak{N}_2),\alpha_k)=\beta$ $(k=1,2)$.

Suppose that the first different letters of α_1 and α_2 are at the M-th position from the beginning of each word. Each state of the automaton is compatible with itself, and so by Theorem 10_{I} the states $\delta_1((s_i,\mathfrak{N}_1),\alpha_1)$ and $\delta_1((s_i,\mathfrak{N}_1),\alpha_2)$ are disjoint of order M. Since the states $(s_i,\mathfrak{N}_1)$ and $(s_i,\mathfrak{N}_2)$ are equivalent, so are the states $\delta_1((s_i,\mathfrak{N}_1),\alpha_k)$ and $\delta_1((s_i,\mathfrak{N}_2),\alpha_k)$ $(k=1,2)$, whence it follows that the states $\delta_1((s_i,\mathfrak{N}_1),\alpha_1)$ and $\delta_1((s_i,\mathfrak{N}_2),\alpha_2)$ are also disjoint of order M.

Since A_1 is ILS-I-N, it follows that the state $\delta_1((s_i,\mathfrak{N}_1),\alpha_1)$ is consistent with itself, with delay N. But then, as before, the states $\delta_1((s_i,\mathfrak{N}_1),\alpha_1)$ and $\delta_1((s_i,\mathfrak{N}_2),\alpha_1)$ are also consistent with delay N.

By virtue of Theorem 10_{I}, this implies that the states $((s_i,\mathfrak{N}_1),\beta)$ and $((s_i,\mathfrak{N}_2),\beta)$ are compatible.

Suppose that for some word β' both values of $\mu(t_{i_j},\beta')$ are defined, and furthermore that $\mu(t_{i_1},\beta' b_r)$ is also defined. By the construction of the standard inverse, this may be true only if the automaton A_1 in state $(s_i,\mathfrak{N}_1)$ has a possible response $\beta' b_r$. Then there is a word α such that $\lambda(s_i,\alpha)=$ $=\lambda_1((s_i,\mathfrak{N}_1),\alpha)=\beta\beta' b_r$, and the set $\mathfrak{N}_1$ is α-succeeded by some nonempty set of vertices. Since $\mathfrak{N}_1$ and $\mathfrak{N}_2$ are equivalent, the set $\mathfrak{N}_2$ is also α-succeeded by some nonempty set of vertices, and so $\lambda_1((s_i,\mathfrak{N}_2),\alpha)=\beta\beta' b_r$ and the value $\mu(t_{i_2},\beta' b_r)$ is also defined.

Thus the states t_{i_1} and t_{i_2} are equivalent.

Now let B be a generalized inverse with delay N for the automaton A_2, constructed as described in §1 of this chapter. We may assume that the construction of B observed the following additional condition: for any equivalent sets $\mathfrak{N}_1$ and $\mathfrak{N}_2$ of the source, state s_i, word β of length N and letter b_j,

$$\mu(((s_i,\mathfrak{N}_1),\beta),b_j)=\mu(((s_i,\mathfrak{N}_2),\beta),b_j).$$

Let $s_{2i_1}=(s_i,\mathfrak{N}_1)$, $s_{2i_2}=(s_i,\mathfrak{N}_2)$ and suppose that β is a type I-i_1-l-i_3 characteristic word for A_2. Then $\delta(s_i,a_r)=s_j$ and $\lambda(s_i,a_r)=b_l$ for some letter a_r, the state s_j may yield the response $\beta\beta'$, and the set $\mathfrak{N}_3$ is $\beta\beta'$-succeeded by a nonempty set of vertices, provided s_i may yield the response $b_l\beta\beta'$ and the set $\mathfrak{N}_1$ is $b_l\beta\beta'$-succeeded by a nonempty set. Consider the states $s_{2i_2}=(s_i,\mathfrak{N}_2)$ and $s_{2i_4}=(s_j,\mathfrak{N}_4)$, where $\mathfrak{N}_4$ b_l-succeeds $\mathfrak{N}_2$. Since the sets $\mathfrak{N}_1$ and $\mathfrak{N}_2$ are equivalent, it follows from Lemma 25 that $\mathfrak{N}_3$ and $\mathfrak{N}_4$ are also equivalent. But then β is also type I-i_2-l-i_4 characteristic for A_2. Thus the additional condition does not restrict the class of automata A_2 for which generalized inverses may be constructed as in §1.

Lemma 28. Let B be a generalized inverse with delay N for A_2, whose principal part contains states $t_{i_k}=((s_i,\mathfrak{N}_k),\beta)$ $(k=1,2)$. If $\mathfrak{N}_1$ and $\mathfrak{N}_2$ are equivalent, then so are the states t_{i_1} and t_{i_2}.

The proof is obvious in view of the additional condition introduced above.

Just as in the case of the automata A_3 and A_4, the state set of the principal part of the standard inverse B_1 (B_2) may be partitioned into classes $\mathfrak{B}_{11},\ldots,\mathfrak{B}_{1N_1}$ ($\mathfrak{B}_{21},\ldots,\mathfrak{B}_{2N_2}$) in such a way that each class contains all states $((s_i,\mathfrak{N}_j),\beta)$ $(j=1,\ldots,n)$ for which the sets $\mathfrak{N}_j$ are equivalent.

Lemma 29. The collection of classes $\mathfrak{B}_{11},\ldots,\mathfrak{B}_{1N_1}$ ($\mathfrak{B}_{21},\ldots,\mathfrak{B}_{2N_2}$), together with all states of B_1 (B_2) not in the principal part of the inverse, forms a system of invariant classes of states of B_1 (B_2).

Proof. By Lemmas 27 and 28, states contained in the same class satisfy condition 2 for invariant classes.

Condition 1 holds by virtue of the definition of $\mathfrak{B}_{1j}$ ($\mathfrak{B}_{2j}$).

Now let $((s_i,\mathfrak{N}_1),\beta)$ and $((s_i,\mathfrak{N}_2),\beta)$ be states in the same class $\mathfrak{B}_{1j}$ ($\mathfrak{B}_{2j}$). Considerations of equivalence show that

$$\mu_k(((s_i,\mathfrak{N}_1),\beta),b_j)=\mu_k(((s_i,\mathfrak{N}_2),\beta),b_j)=a_r \quad (k=1,2)$$

for any letter b_j such that both values are defined. Then

$$\varepsilon_k(((s_i,\mathfrak{N}_1),\beta),b_j)=((\delta(s_i,a_r),\mathfrak{N}_3),\beta' b_j)=t_{kj_1},$$
$$\varepsilon_k(((s_i,\mathfrak{N}_2),\beta),b_j)=((\delta(s_i,a_r),\mathfrak{N}_4),\beta' b_j)=t_{kj_2} \quad (k=1,2),$$

where β' is a suffix of length $N-1$ of the word β, and in the case of B_1 the set $\mathfrak{N}_{\rho+2}$ a_r-succeeds the set $\mathfrak{N}_\rho$ $(\rho=1,2)$. By Lemma 25, the sets $\mathfrak{N}_3$ and $\mathfrak{N}_4$ are equivalent and the states t_{1j_1} and t_{1j_2} belong to the same class $\mathfrak{B}_{1\lambda}$. Since the states of the initial part of B_1 are not combined with other states, condition 3 for systems of invariant classes is satisfied for all the classes $\mathfrak{B}_{11},\ldots,\mathfrak{B}_{1N_1}$ and the states of the initial part, so that the lemma is proved for B_1.

The only modification to be made for the automaton B_2 is that the set $\mathfrak{N}_{\rho+2}$ $\lambda(s_i,a_r)$-succeeds the set $\mathfrak{N}_\rho$ $(\rho=1,2)$.

By Lemma 29, we can construct automata B_3 and B_4, imitating the construction of A_3 and A_4.

The states of B_3 (B_4) will be all states of the initial part of B_1 (B_2) and the classes $\mathfrak{B}_{11},\ldots,\mathfrak{B}_{1N_1}$ ($\mathfrak{B}_{21},\ldots,\mathfrak{B}_{2N_2}$). The definitions of the functions μ_3 and ε_3 (μ_4 and ε_4) for classes $\mathfrak{B}_{1j}$ ($\mathfrak{B}_{2j}$) are analogous to those of λ_3 and δ_3 (λ_4 and δ_4). Suppose that t_{1i} (t_{2i}) is a state not in the principal part of B_1 (B_2), such that for some letter b_l the states $\delta_k(t_{ki},b_l)$ are also not in the principal part. Then we set

$$\mu_{k+2}(t_{ki},b_l)=\mu_k(t_{ki},b_l)$$

and

$$\varepsilon_{k+2}(t_{ki}, b_l) = \varepsilon_k(t_{ki}, b_l) \quad (k=1, 2).$$

The same notation is used here for corresponding states of B_k and B_{k+2}. On the other hand, if $\varepsilon_k(t_{ki}, b_l) \in \mathfrak{B}_{k\nu}$ for some class $\mathfrak{B}_{1\nu}$ ($\mathfrak{B}_{2\nu}$), we put

$$\varepsilon_{k+2}(t_{ki}, b_l) = \mathfrak{B}_{k\nu}, \ \mu_{k+2}(t_{ki}, b_l) = \mu_k(t_{ki}, b_l) \ (k=1,2).$$

If the automaton B_k has initial state t_{ki_0} and there is a class $\mathfrak{B}_{k\nu_0}$ such that $t_{ki_0} \in \mathfrak{B}_{k\nu_0}$, then $\mathfrak{B}_{k\nu_0}$ is the initial state of B_{k+2}. If there is no such class $\mathfrak{B}_{k\nu_0}$, the initial state is t_{ki_0} $(k=1,2)$ itself.

Automata B_3 and B_4 derived from the standard automata B_1 and B_2 as described will also be called standard. The principal parts of B_3 and B_4 are of course the subautomata containing the states $\mathfrak{B}_{1\nu}$ $(\nu=1,\dots,N_1)$ and $\mathfrak{B}_{2\rho}$ $(\rho=1,\dots,N_2)$, respectively.

Theorem 104. *Let $R'(\mathfrak{A})$ and $R''(\mathfrak{A})$ be two sources defining the same regular event $\mathfrak{R}(\mathfrak{A})$. Then the principal parts of the automaton B'_3 and B''_4 are isomorphic.*

Proof. As before, we denote the class $\mathfrak{B}_{1j} = \{((s_i, \mathfrak{R}_1), \beta), \dots, ((s_i, \mathfrak{R}_M), \beta)\}$ by $((s_i; \mathfrak{R}_1, \dots, \mathfrak{R}_M), \beta)$.

Let $t''_{3j} = ((s_k; \mathfrak{R}''_1, \dots, \mathfrak{R}''_{M_2}), \beta)$. Set

$$\varphi(t''_{3j}) = ((s_k; \mathfrak{R}'_1, \dots, \mathfrak{R}'_{M_1}), \beta) = t'_{3k},$$

where the sets $\mathfrak{R}'_\rho$ $(\rho=1,\dots,M_1)$ and $\mathfrak{R}''_\sigma$ $(\sigma=1,\dots,M_2)$ are equivalent. The automaton B'_3 has a state t'_{3k}, since A'_3 has a state $(s_k; \mathfrak{R}'_1, \dots, \mathfrak{R}'_{M_1})$, and so the mapping φ is well-defined. Since A'_3 does not have two states of the form $(s_k; \mathfrak{R}'_{11}, \dots, \mathfrak{R}'_{1N_1})$ and $(s_k; \mathfrak{R}'_{21}, \dots, \mathfrak{R}'_{2N_2})$, where the sets $\mathfrak{R}'_{1\rho}$ $(\rho=1,\dots,N_1)$ and $\mathfrak{R}'_{2\sigma}$ $(\sigma=1,\dots,N_2)$ are equivalent, it follows that φ is one-to-one.

For any two states $((s_k, \mathfrak{R}''_\rho), \beta)$ and $((s_k, \mathfrak{R}'_\sigma), \beta)$ and any letter b_j, the values $\mu'_1(((s_k, \mathfrak{R}'_\sigma), \beta), b_j)$ and $\mu''_1(((s_k, \mathfrak{R}''_\rho), \beta), b_j)$ are defined if and only if there is a word $a_r\alpha$ such that $\lambda(s_k, a_r\alpha) = \beta b_j$ and the sets $\mathfrak{R}'_\sigma$ and $\mathfrak{R}''_\rho$ are a_r-succeeded by nonempty sets of vertices of the sources $R'(\mathfrak{A})$ and $R''(\mathfrak{A})$, respectively. Since $\mathfrak{R}'_\sigma$ and $\mathfrak{R}''_\rho$ are equivalent, this condition will hold for every word $a_r\alpha$ either for both sources or for neither. Hence it follows that for any letter b_j the above values of μ'_1 and μ''_1 are either both defined or both undefined, and in the former case they are equal. Since the states of the automata B'_1 and B''_1 in one class are equivalent, we have $\mu'_3(t'_{3k}, b_j) = \mu''_3(t''_{3j}, b_j)$.

Let $\mu''_3(t''_{3j}, b_j) = \mu'_3(t'_{3k}, b_j) = a_r$. Then

$$\varepsilon''_3(t''_{3j}, b_j) = ((\delta(s_k, a_r); \ \mathfrak{R}''_{11}, \dots, \mathfrak{R}''_{1P_2}), \beta' b_j),$$

where each of the sets $\mathfrak{R}''_{1\rho}$ $(\rho=1,\dots,P_2)$ a_r-succeeds one of the sets $\mathfrak{R}''_\sigma$ $(\sigma=1,\dots, M_2)$, $\varepsilon'_3(t'_{3k}, b_j) = ((\delta(s_k, a_r); \ \mathfrak{R}'_{11}, \dots, \mathfrak{R}'_{1P_1}), \beta' b_j)$, and each of the sets $\mathfrak{R}'_{1\varkappa}$ $(\varkappa=1,\dots,P_1)$ a_r-succeeds one of the sets $\mathfrak{R}'_\mu$ $(\mu= 1,\dots,M_1)$. Since the sets $\mathfrak{R}''_\sigma$ $(\sigma=1,\dots,M_2)$ and $\mathfrak{R}'_\mu$ $(\mu=1,\dots,M_1)$ are equivalent, it follows from Lemma 25 that the sets $\mathfrak{R}'_{1\varkappa}$ $(\varkappa=1,\dots,P_1)$ and $\mathfrak{R}''_{1\rho}$ $(\rho=1,\dots,P_2)$ are also equivalent. Hence it follows that

$$\varphi(\varepsilon''_3(t''_{3j}, b_j)) = \varepsilon'_3(\varphi(t''_{3j}), b_j).$$

This completes the proof.

To establish an analogous property for generalized inverses B'_4 and B''_4 based on two different sources $R'(\mathfrak{B})$ and $R''(\mathfrak{B})$ defining the event $\mathfrak{R}(\mathfrak{B})$, we use B'_2 to construct a new automaton B''_5, as follows.

Step 0. For any initial state s_{i_0} of the automaton A and any word β such that the principal part of B'_2 contains a state $t'_{2j_0} = ((s_{i_0}, \mathfrak{R}'_0), \beta)$, we let $t''_{5k_0} = ((s_{i_0}, \mathfrak{R}''_0), \beta)$ be a state of the automaton B''_5, corresponding to the state t'_{2j_0}.

Step $n+1$. We order the set of states of B''_5 introduced at Step n once and for all and use this order throughout. Suppose that one of these states, say $t''_{5k} = ((s_i, \mathfrak{R}''), b_r\beta)$, corresponds to a state $t'_{2l} = ((s_i, \mathfrak{R}'), b_r\beta)$, and the values $\mu''_5(t''_{5k}, b_j)$ and $\varepsilon''_5(t''_{5k}, b_j)$ have not been defined. Consider the state t''_{5k} in conjunction with each letter b_j such that $\mu'_2(t'_{2l}, b_j)$ is defined, and define $\mu''_5(t''_{5k}, b_j) = \mu'_2(t'_{2l}, b_j)$. If there is as yet no state $t''_{5p} = ((\delta(s_i, \mu'_2(t'_{2l}, b_j)), \mathfrak{R}''_1), \beta b_j)$, where $\mathfrak{R}''_1$ b_r-succeeds the set $\mathfrak{R}''$, we add the state t''_{5p} to the automaton, making it correspond to the state $\varepsilon'_2(t'_{2l}, b_j)$, and define $\varepsilon''_5(t''_{5k}, b_j) = t''_{5p}$.

Since the state set of the automaton A is finite, as are the alphabet $\mathfrak{B}$ and the vertex set of the source $R'(\mathfrak{B})$, there will be some step of this construction at which no new states are introduced and the construction will end.

Lemma 30. Let the states $t''_{5i_j} = ((s_i, \mathfrak{R}''_j), \beta)$ of the automaton B''_5 correspond to states $((s_i, \mathfrak{R}'_j), \beta)$ $(j=1,2)$. If the sets $\mathfrak{R}''_1$ and $\mathfrak{R}''_2$ are equivalent, then $\mu''_5(t''_{5i_1}, b_l) = \mu''_5(t''_{5i_2}, b_l)$ for any letter b_l.

Proof. By the assumptions of the lemma, for any letter b_l,

$$\mu'_2(((s_i, \mathfrak{R}'_1), \beta), b_l) = \mu'_2(((s_i, \mathfrak{R}'_2), \beta), b_l).$$

The lemma now follows from the definition of μ''_5.

Lemma 31. For any initial state s_{i_0} of the automaton A, any word β_0 of length N for which there exists a state $((s_{i_0}, \mathfrak{R}'_0), \beta_0)$ of B_2, and any word $\beta = b_{i_1} \ldots b_{i_M}$,

$$\mu'_2(((s_{i_0}, \mathfrak{R}'_0), \beta_0), \beta) = \mu''_5(((s_{i_0}, \mathfrak{R}''_0), \beta_0), \beta).$$

Proof. Set

$$((s_{i_0}, \mathfrak{R}'_0), \beta_0) = t'_{2k_0}, \ \varepsilon'_2(t'_{2k_{n-1}}, b_{i_n}) = t'_{2k_n},$$

$$((s_{i_0}, \mathfrak{R}''_0), \beta_0) = t''_{5j_0}, \quad \varepsilon''_5(t''_{5j_{n-1}}, b_{i_n}) = t''_{5j_n} \quad (n=1, \ldots, M).$$

By the definition of B''_5, the states $t'_{2k_n} = ((s_{\lambda_n}, \mathfrak{R}'_n), \beta'_n)$, $t''_{5j_n} = ((s_{\varkappa_n}, \mathfrak{R}''_n), \beta''_n)$ satisfy the conditions $\beta'_n = \beta''_n$, $s_{\lambda n} = s_{\varkappa n} = \delta(s_{i_0}, \mu'_2(t'_{2k_0}, b_{i_1} \ldots b_{in}))$, and the sets $\mathfrak{R}'_n$ and $\mathfrak{R}''_n$ $\beta_0 b_{i_1} \ldots b_{i\,n-N}$-follow the sets $\mathfrak{R}'_0$ and $\mathfrak{R}''_0$ $(n=1, \ldots, M)$. *

But then the state t''_{5j_n} corresponds to the state t'_{2k_n} and by the definition of μ''_5 we have

* If $n<N$, the word $\beta_0 b_{i_1} \ldots b_{i_{n-N}}$ is understood as the prefix of length n of the word β_0.

$$\mu''_5(t''_{5j_n}, b_l) = \mu'_2(t'_{2k_n}, b_l)$$

for any letter b_l, whence the lemma follows.

Lemma 32. For any state s_i, word β of length N, letter b_j and equivalent sets $\mathfrak{N}'$ and $\mathfrak{N}''$ of vertices of the sources $R'(\mathfrak{B})$ and $R''(\mathfrak{B})$,

$$\mu'_2(((s_i, \mathfrak{N}'), \beta), b_j) = \mu''_5(((s_i, \mathfrak{N}''), \beta), b_j).$$

Proof. If the automaton B''_5 has a state $((s_i, \mathfrak{N}''), \beta)$, this state corresponds to some state $((s_i, \mathfrak{N}'_1), \beta)$ such that the sets $\mathfrak{N}''$ and $\mathfrak{N}'_1$ are equivalent (see the proof of Lemma 31). Then

$$\mu'_2(((s_i, \mathfrak{N}'_1), \beta), b_j) = \mu''_5(((s_i, \mathfrak{N}''), \beta), b_j)$$

for any letter b_j, and a reference to Lemma 30 finishes the proof.

Theorem 105. Let $R'(\mathfrak{B})$ and $R''(\mathfrak{B})$ be two sources defining the same regular event $\mathfrak{R}(\mathfrak{B})$. For any standard automaton B'_4, there exists a standard automaton B''_4 such that the principal parts of the two automata are isomorphic.

Proof. Construct the automaton B''_5 for the standard automaton B'_2 underlying the construction of B'_4. It is clear that using B''_5 we can construct a system of successors which, via the method of §1 in this chapter, yields an automaton B''_2 whose principal part has the same state set as the automaton B''_5, such that for any state $((s_i, \mathfrak{N}''), \beta)$ and any letter b_j

$$\mu''_2(((s_i, \mathfrak{N}''), \beta), b_j) = \mu''_5(((s_i, \mathfrak{N}''), \beta), b_j),$$

$$\delta''_2(((s_i, \mathfrak{N}''), \beta), b_j) = \delta''_5(((s_i, \mathfrak{N}''), \beta), b_j).$$

(The last equality is meaningful only if both values of δ''_2 and δ''_5 are defined.)

Construct automata B'_4 and B''_4 for B'_2 and B''_2, respectively.

Let $t''_{4j} = ((s_k; \mathfrak{N}''_1, \ldots, \mathfrak{N}''_{M_2}), \beta)$. Set $\varphi(t''_{4j}) = t'_{4l} = ((s_k; \mathfrak{N}'_1, \ldots, \mathfrak{N}'_{M_1}), \beta)$, where the sets $\mathfrak{N}'_\rho$ $(\rho = 1, \ldots, M_1)$ and $\mathfrak{N}''_\sigma$ $(\sigma = 1, \ldots, M_2)$ are equivalent. The automaton A'_2 has a state $(s_k, \mathfrak{N}'_1)$, where $\mathfrak{N}'_1$ is equivalent to the sets $\mathfrak{N}''_\sigma$. For some word α and some initial state s_{i_0}, we have $\delta(s_{i_0}, \alpha) = s_k$ and the set $\mathfrak{N}''_1$ $\lambda(s_{i_0}, \alpha)$-succeeds the set $\mathfrak{N}''_0$. In that case, the set $\mathfrak{N}'_0$ is $\lambda(s_{i_0}, \alpha)$-succeeded by some nonempty set $\mathfrak{N}'_1$ and the state s_k and set $\mathfrak{N}'_1$ are combinable. Then the state $(s_k, \mathfrak{N}'_1)$ of the automaton A'_2 may yield the response β, provided the state $(s_k, \mathfrak{N}''_\sigma)$ of A''_2 may yield the same response, and the automaton B'_2 has a state $((s_k, \mathfrak{N}'_1), \beta)$ if B''_2 has a state $((s_k, \mathfrak{N}''_\sigma), \beta)$. Hence it follows that there exists a state t'_{4l} with the required properties, and the mapping φ is well-defined.

That the mapping is one-to-one follows from the fact that B'_4 cannot have two states of the form $((s_k; \mathfrak{N}'_{11}, \ldots, \mathfrak{N}'_{1N_1}), \beta)$ and $((s_k, \mathfrak{N}'_{21}, \ldots, \mathfrak{N}'_{2N_2}), \beta)$, where $\mathfrak{N}'_{1\rho}$ $(\rho = 1, \ldots, N_1)$ and $\mathfrak{N}'_{2\sigma}$ $(\sigma = 1, \ldots, N_2)$ are equivalent sets. By Lemma 32 and the equivalence of the states of B'_2 or B''_2 in the same class (i. e., in the same state of B'_4 or B''_4),

$$\mu'_4(\varphi((s_k; \mathfrak{N}''_1, \ldots, \mathfrak{N}''_{M_2}), \beta), b_j) = \mu''_4(((s_k; \mathfrak{N}''_1, \ldots, \mathfrak{N}''_{M_2}), \beta), b_j)$$

for any letter b_j. Furthermore, for any letter b_j,

$$\varepsilon''_4(((s_k; \mathfrak{N}''_1, \ldots, \mathfrak{N}''_{M_2}), \beta), b_j) =$$
$$= ((\delta''_2(s_k, \mu''_2(((s_k; \mathfrak{N}''_1, \ldots, \mathfrak{N}''_{M_2}), \beta), b_j));$$
$$\mathfrak{N}''_{11}, \ldots, \mathfrak{N}''_{1N_2}), \beta' b_j), \varepsilon'_4(((s_k; \mathfrak{N}'_1, \ldots, \mathfrak{N}'_{M_1}), \beta), b_j) =$$
$$= ((\delta'_2(s_k, \mu'_2(((s_k; \mathfrak{N}'_1, \ldots, \mathfrak{N}'_{M_1}), \beta), b_j)); \mathfrak{N}'_{11}, \ldots, \mathfrak{N}'_{1N_1}), \beta' b_j),$$

where $\beta = b_r \beta'$ and each of the sets $\mathfrak{N}'_{1\rho}$ $(\rho = 1, \ldots, N_1)$ and $\mathfrak{N}''_{1\sigma}$ $(\sigma = 1, \ldots, N_2)$ b_r-succeeds one of the sets $\mathfrak{N}'_\varkappa$ or $\mathfrak{N}''_\nu$, respectively. By Lemma 25, the sets $\mathfrak{N}'_{1\rho}$ and $\mathfrak{N}''_{1\sigma}$ are equivalent. By the definition of the functions μ''_5 and μ''_2 in terms of values of μ'_2,

$$\mu'_2(((s_k; \mathfrak{N}'_1, \ldots, \mathfrak{N}'_{M_1}), \beta), b_j) = \mu''_2(((s_k; \mathfrak{N}''_1, \ldots, \mathfrak{N}''_{M_2}), \beta), b_j).$$

Hence

$$\varphi(\varepsilon''_4(((s_k; \mathfrak{N}''_1, \ldots, \mathfrak{N}''_{M_2}), \beta), b_j)) = \varepsilon'_4(((s_k; \mathfrak{N}'_1, \ldots, \mathfrak{N}'_{M_1}), \beta), b_j).$$

This completes the proof.

The main conclusions of this section were published in /16/.

BIBLIOGRAPHY

1. Huffman, D.A. Canonical forms for information-lossless finite-state logical machines. — IRE Trans. Circuit Theory CT-6 (Special Supplement) (1959), 41—59.
2. Huffman, D.A. Notes on information-lossless finite-state automata. — Nuovo Cimento Suppl. 13 (1959), 397—405.
3. Even, S. On information-lossless automata of finite order. — In: Theory of Finite and Probabilistic Automata (Proceedings of International Symposium on the Theory of Relay Devices and Finite Automata), 269—279. Moscow, Nauka, 1965. (Russian)
4. Even, S. On information-lossless automata of finite order. — IEEE Trans. Electronic Computers EC-14, No.4 (1965), 561—569.
5. Kurmit, A.A. Finding the initial internal states of the inverse automaton by examining the operation of the original automaton. — In: Automatic Control (ed. E. Kh. Khermanis), 47—51. Riga, Zinatne, 1967. (Russian) [English translation: Jerusalem, Israel Program for Scientific Translations, 1969.]
6. Kurmit, A.A. Detecting compatible internal states of an inverse automaton by studying the operation of the original automaton. — In: Teoriya diskretnykh avtomatov, 179—189. Riga, Zinatne, 1967. (Russian)
7. Kurmit, A.A. Determining the initial and compatible internal states of the inverse automaton of class II by analyzing the operation of the original automaton. — In: Automatic Control (ed. E.Kh.Khermanis), 39—45. Riga, Zinatne, 1967. (Russian) [English translation: Jerusalem, Israel Program for Scientific Translations, 1969]
8. Kurmit, A.A. Investigation of the structure of information-lossless automata of finite order. — Avtomatika i Vychisl. Tekhn., No.3, (1968), 4—12. (Russian)
9. Kurmit, A.A. Types of states in strongly connected complete information-lossless automata of finite order. — Avtomatika i Vychisl. Tekhn., No.4 (1968), 19—26. (Russian)
10. Ginsburg, S. On the reduction of superfluous states in a sequential machine. — J. Assoc. Comput. Mach. 6, No.2 (1959), 259—282.
11. Kurmit, A.A. Self-adjusting inverse automata. — Avtomatika i Vychisl. Tekhn., No.3 (1970), 1—9. (Russian)
12. Kurmit, A.A. Solution of some problems in the theory of abstract finite automata with the help of graph theory. — Avtomatika i Vychisl. Tekhn., No.1 (1967), 10—17. (Russian)
13. Berge, C. Théorie des graphes et ses applications. — Paris, Dunod, 1959.
14. Zhuravlev, Yu.I. Set-theoretic methods in the algebra of logic. — Problemy Kibernetiki, No.8 (1962), 5—44. (Russian)
15. Kurmit, A.A. Generalized inverse automata. — Avtomatika i Vychisl. Tekhn., No.3 (1967), 5—12. (Russian)
16. Kurmit, A.A. Inversion of automata relative to a regular event. — Avtomatika i Vychisl. Tekhn., No.4 (1967), 9—16. (Russian)
17. Nelson, R.J. Introduction to Automata. — New York, Wiley, 1968.
18. Tutte, W.T. Connectivity in Graphs. — University of Toronto Press and London, Oxford University Press. 1966.

SUBJECT INDEX